LOSING IT ALL

SIMON POTTER

T-O-P

2020

"Losing it all" is a revised, modernised version of the hardback "The Fate of Glassingall", originally published by Harrap (Olive Press / Impact Books) in 1991. This paperback was published in Great Britain in 2020 by **TRANS-OCEANIC-PRESS**.

www.simonpotterauthor.com

Simon Potter has asserted his right under the Copyright, Designs and Patents Act, 1988, to be identified as the author of this work.

ISBN No: 978-1-9164295-2-9

Line drawings by Michael Potter

Cover design by Nick England

Printed and bound by Witley Press, Hunstanton, Norfolk, PE36 6AD

For all the schoolboys who've said to me over a half-century: "Tell us a story, Sir."

CONTENTS

THE END

I sat in the 1970s Vauxhall Cresta on the drive leading to the A9 under its dim roof light with a biro in my hand, writing. The car was facing south-west towards Dunblane. Peter had left the car to take a nervy slash behind a bush. Ridiculous – we had come only a few hundred yards, but the shock of what we'd done had been too much for him.

As for me, I was calm – although I had no idea what I was going to do in the future. The short Scottish night in the autumn of that last year was over. Less than twelve hours ago, my last visitors had been walking round Glenturret, entranced, and, even though the great axe was, even then, hanging over my head, I was at peace. It seemed as though I could still hear my visitors' voices: "Look at that Bush radio! Aunt Florence had one just like it at The Elms."."Will you just look at that! It's a Humber Super Snipe! My uncle had one of those." "I smoked Kensitas cigarettes for ages!" "Can we go on the train again?"

I stared over the bonnet towards the A9 trunk road, headed for England, with a pile of paper on my lap, and Peter's bladder was slowing us up when I was anxious to get as far from the scene of our crime as possible.

I think my visitors used to feel that sadness which I have lived with for thirty years; that odd sensation that doors have kept on closing and shutting you out on the wrong side of the past. That's why they came to Glenturret; they knew that though they could not return bodily, their spirits would be refreshed. The only holiday you will fully enjoy is the one that takes you back and lets you range among the trivial, precious objects from the lost world of yesterday. I used to go up to my visitors and tell them that here time stands suspended. I would sometimes murmur, "What was your best year?" Some of them probably thought I was a bit touched, but then I was the guv'nor who owned the house, so they always answered me, coming clean, as one might as well do to a madman: "1958. I was seventeen and in love." "Oh, the best year was 1946. I was twelve and Dad had just come home." "When we bought the Triumph Stag – like your one – that was a great year: 1979."

As I waited for Peter to get back to the car, I reflected that, at the end of the last century, I used to imagine that time was stoppable – at Glenturret, if nowhere else.

Somewhere in the museum's visitors' brochure is my once-held absurd conviction that my house was a metaphor for Britain itself. Peter had helped me to write the blurb, and it went something like this:

*Great Britain and Glenturret have followed the same
winding, downhill-trending path from private,
raucous individuality, through decent, ordered
institutionalism into a flurrying flirtation with
fashion and commerce, and thence to long
retirement as a monument to a huge, joyous past.*

I think I made the point that there's precious little
difference between glass cabinets of early Dinky
Toys and Changing the Guard at Buckingham
Palace. Glenturret, like Great Britain, we had
written, was peculiarly adept at being a museum.

After what has happened, I can no longer feel
there's a mysterious synergy between House and
Nation. Glenturret is clearly not going to share 21st
century Britain's destiny, whatever else the rest of
the twenty-first century brings.

What led to my loss? Class hatred? The tide of
history? Revenge? The will of the Gods? The
blindness of those of us who lived at Glenturret? I
just do not know.

Peter was coming back, so I stopped scribbling
final thoughts on my lapful of paper. I suppose I was
still in a state of shock, but I felt that I ought to say
at the beginning of what has now grown into the
length of a book that my whole world-view had
changed since I first began to write. How ironic the
first stories about our boyhood acquaintance, Hector,
seemed by hindsight; how full of foreboding my

childish terror in Glenturret's haunted corridor.

Peter fumbled at the door. Silly twit! He hadn't done his zip up.

So what are these scribblings about? They are about the house of our childhood – and about paths meeting, about change, love, bad decisions and growing up; but they also touch on several *very* peculiar happenings I still do not understand, and they reflect, as you may have discovered in your own lives, that most ancient of themes. Euripides penned the core of it by the Aegean long ago: "*The Gods bring the unexpected to be – as here we see.*"

But I am going to leave my opening just as I first wrote it, because it starts where it should, with Grandpa, who began my obsession by bringing his house into our lives.

THE GRANITE CITY LINE

Our grandfather travelled every day of his working life from Pangbourne in Berks to Paddington, sitting bolt upright in a first-class compartment on the Western's smooth tracks, well protected from draught. What he liked best of all surroundings was a cold fug, whether on a train or at home.

During the Second World War he amassed a fortune – I don't know how – by being either a bear or a bull at Bradley and Knights on the Stock Exchange. I am still ignorant of the distinction between those fearsome animals that used to haunt Throgmorton Street; I just know that they scooped in a lot of cash.

He seldom went abroad, although he had been forced to take the odd trip to Dinard or Le Touquet by our grandmother. He preferred Frinton, where it was forbidden to hang out washing, or The Grand at Eastbourne. I discovered, when I knew him better, he had never learnt to laugh at foreigners, but simply found them irritating. His whole attitude was nicely summed up by that famous newspaper heading: "Dense Fog in Channel – Continent Cut Off."

His general tendency towards bigotry became extremely pronounced towards the end of his life.

Forced in old age to sell Glenturret in the late 'sixties, he had settled into a large flat at Prince's Gate overlooking Hyde Park in London – a flat in which he complained constantly that he was "always bumping into the servants". His uncertain temper was provoked by a liverish and ever falling blood pressure and, when he got into his eighties, his doctor, the famous Sir Walter Blunt, recommended daily doses of all the things he disliked in order that this blood pressure be kept at a better and higher level. As the people, ideas and objects he detested were practically innumerable, my grandmother did not find it difficult to carry out Sir Walter's wishes. Her greatest success was the use of "*Top of the Pops*", Grandpa's most hated of the many television programmes that he loathed. Wheeled in his portable chair to a distance near enough to the screen for the pictures and sound to be inescapable, but not so near that he could smash the set with his walking-stick, he would sit, convulsively clutching a dry Martini, while the veins in his forehead throbbed like garden hoses. And when The Hollies, David Bowie or T-Rex appeared, he would cry in agony to my grandmother,

'Jane! Jane! It's those homosexual wastrels again! Gah! Get your hair cut!'

Up would shoot his pressure to the required level as he hooted at the TV,

'Go out and get a proper job! Gad, that one's wearing *ear-rings*!'

My brother Mike and I thought it amusing that he should be so old-fashioned, but he was a man of his generation, of course, and not untypical. He had been born in 1889.

I had always sensed that the happiest time of his life had lain between the frigid discipline of Pangbourne and the last surreal incarceration at Prince's Gate – the nine years of his stewardship of Glenturret.

He had bought the house on his quite late retirement from the Stock Exchange in 1960, seven years after I appeared in the world.

'Guy! Guy! You're MAD!' had cried his old friends, according to my grandmother. 'Why *Scotland,* of all places?'

Glenturret is reached by a fine tarmac and gravel drive running through a conifer wood and then meadows up to a great bank of rhododendrons. A curve brings the drive round to the south face of the house and into view of what used to be the dining-room, gun-room, hall, morning-room and ballroom. There is a mock Gothic portico and, amidst incult tangles of creeping vine, lancet windows point up and up, layer upon layer, to the steep roof-line. The style is Scots baronial of the mid-19th century, fake maybe, but undeniably impressive – a *nouveau-riche* gentleman's paradise.

'You're a lucky man, Guy!' said friends who had motored up to see him settled.

The house has (or, I should say, *had*; it's absurd to keep on using the present tense) thirty-seven chimneys and each featured a column of brick lifting the cowl fifteen feet or more off a skyline made by a dozen or more sharp, dipping roofs. The Ochil hills are blue in the distance and the house was never less than ship-like as it floated on its lawns.

Such was the pile which Grandpa so decisively brought into the family fifteen years after the war, and the preservation of which had possessed me like a fever since I was a young man.

Before Christmas day, 1963, I was dimly aware of my grandfather's existence – a distant figure seen briefly now and then at night before we went to bed.

He leapt into the foreground of my mind on that wet, dull day in Maida Vale at the precise moment when Dad, Ma, Mike (aged four) and I snuggled round a hotly glowing gas fire and began the sacred ceremony of opening the presents.

Outside, up Clifton Gardens and down the Edgware Road, traffic had practically ceased. The sky was heavy and stone-grey, but very cosy, as London sky can be when under it a red bus with orange-yellow windows heaves its way down to

Marble Arch.

We had just eaten the Peek Frean pudding with brandy custard and had pulled crackers, and Ma and I were sharing a Fry's chocolate cream in nibbles when Dad passed presents round from under the tree. He hauled out a really big parcel, causing the flames of the clip-on candles to leap.

'Here you are, chaps. Anthony! Don't grab at it, you fool of a boy! It's from your grandfather, and I know what it is, so open it carefully.'

I whipped off the red string, hardly bothering to read the little card attached, and already forgetful of the Corgi and Matchbox toys parked in a neat row. As Grandpa's thick, stylish green and gold paper shredded onto the floor, and was pushed out across the lino which bordered the warm zone of the carpet, three large boxes were revealed.

On the front of the flattest one was a green diesel locomotive hauling maroon coaches. "*The Royal Scot*" was emblazoned across the lid. On the squarer box was printed a picture of a cream coloured station and on the smallest was depicted a grey 12 volt DC "Marshall" controller.

Could it be true?

I stared at Dad with a wild surmise, silent on the carpet. I strongly remember a feeling closer to religious revelation than any I have experienced since. Grandpa had granted my only wish. He had made materialise from the vast horde of his mysterious wealth a Hornby-Dublo train set!

I extended trembling fingers towards those perfect replicas nestling in their cardboard stays. My father balanced the locomotive in his hands. I craned to see its name. It was called *"Crepello"*, D1092. Even then, I knew that it was a model of the then famous English Electric "Deltic" class of diesel engines named after race horses which (at that time the most powerful in the world) were replacing steam haulage on the East Coast route up to Scotland.

'Yes, it's a good weight,' said Dad, nodding approval at the die-cast body.

The tin-plate coaches were very shiny and almost edibly delightful in their maroon livery. Their interiors had brown seating. Mike put one on the carpet and started to push it.

'Watch it, you clodpoll!' I cried, seizing the carriage. 'You'll get fluff in the wheels.'

'Now then, *voila!*' said Dad, producing a big black plug. In a few moments, during the course of which I jiggled up and down flapping my fingers with impatience, the controller was ready to be plugged in.

The table was cleared, the cloth removed and the plastic-sleepered track laid in a satisfyingly symmetrical oval. The station, slotted together and fastened by some brass nuts and bolts by Dad's big fingers, was pushed up against the rails. The knob on the controller was edged round a little and, after a false start in which the engine reversed over my brother's fingers and derailed, *"Crepello"* began that endless, whizzing journey which came to its end so many years later at the start of a new century.

It was the first of hundreds of models which ended up on display at Glenturret and it is still shiny, still confidently powerful looking in its grey and green, unaware that all it stood for has long since vanished.

Few could believe today the fanatical hold that model railways had on schoolboys during the twenty odd years after the war. I came a little late to the party, perhaps, for the height of national fever was in the late '50s. By the end of the '60s it was over – and kids' interests centred elsewhere. My brother Mike, for example, far preferred Scalextric slot-car racing to trains. But, although I had no train set before Christmas 1963, I knew the lore: I had been with Dad to Berkeley Square to see a Hornby-Dublo *"Deltic"* Co-Co pulling, non-stop, between 1st and the 5th October 1961, 51 wagons over a real 100 miles in Meccano Ltd's showrooms. Now I actually possessed one!

That Christmas brought two things into my life which guided existence into the cul-de-sac in which I ended up: trains and Grandpa's riches.

A letter had been tucked into the old man's Christmas card to Ma and it suggested that the following July we all spend the summer holidays at Glenturret. I remember Dad looking thoughtful when this was read out, but whatever his wishes were in the matter, from 1964 onwards until the house was sold in '69, each summer was spent there – the height of the year for me (less so for Mike – too young and becoming too urban a child) and the plague of the year for our parents.

I realise now that Grandpa's glamour, as it seemed to me, was a burden for my poor father. Nearly fifty as he was, I think he was always made to feel an inadequate boy in our grandfather's presence. Grandpa was always fascinatingly dictatorial at all times. If lunch was at one o'clock, it was at one o'clock. We never could have a meal out in the countryside; it was insisted that Glenturret should not be treated "like a hotel". Such ebullitions did not seem to me the vagaries of an irritable, bored, elderly buffer with wonky digestion and too much money. No, they had rather the fine unpredictable grandeur of a thunderstorm, and each manifestation of unreasonableness added a new line to the mythic saga which grew in mine and Mike's minds as each summer passed.

In spite of being enormously rich, Grandpa was astonishingly mean about certain things. By the dining-room, for example, was a splendid old lavatory, constructed like a sarcophagus with a great oaken case surrounding the decorative bowl. It had a china handle with "Adamsez, Scotswood-on-Tyne" printed on it in flowing calligraphy which stuck up by the side of the pan. When you pulled it out the whole edifice roared like a truck changing gear. Mike and I liked using it, of course, and as I always seemed to be bursting just before mealtimes, we were regular customers. Above it, in the lightless room in which it lived, was a tiny, dim, 15 watt bulb, and I always forgot to turn it off after we had flushed the monster. Grandpa's rages at this criminal waste of electricity had to be seen to be believed. He developed a habit of inspecting the loo before each and every meal, and nearly always he stamped, purple, into the dining-room to tick Dad off for our fecklessness.

'Bill! Bill! Cannot you make your children understand that I am not *made* of money!'

I once left a model train running round and round on its track in the old ballroom during lunch. It was doing the two-hour Glasgow to Aberdeen run, and I liked realism in these matters. The result of this prodigal expenditure of current was like Nagasaki – and Dad was the one who got it hot and strong.

'Really, Bill, the hooliganism of these children!'

'But, Guy.....'

'Bill, cannot you restrain your eldest son from this thoughtless stupidity?'

'It's only a twelve volt transformer.......'

'If this boy ends up in prison, Bill, it will be *your* doing!'

Our father spent 98% of the first holiday at Glenturret grinding his teeth almost to powder, and after 1965 took only to popping up for one or two weekends on the pretext of being unable to spend longer because of the pressure of work.

Yet what diverted Grandpa's chilly rage direct on to *my* head instead of Ma's or Dad's was the Kinbuck business – the business of the Granite City Line.

I suppose I was demented as far as trains were concerned by the time I was eleven – probably, I think, quite close to requiring mental treatment at the hands of a good shrink. I had a fellow maniac in the shape of Peter Buchan – about whom I have much to say later – and Hector McAird, Grandpa's long-term chauffeur's son. There was a physicality about mid-century rail travel, in contrast to the uninvolving silence of a high-speed train of today, which made strong impressions on children. Hardly anyone went anywhere in the mid-'60s; by the 1990s every suburban brat had been "up the Costa", or, keeping it less precise, "up Spain". Now it's "up Phuket". I was told recently by a woman friend in teaching about the occasion she had asked a girl who had been to Miami to tell her class about it. "Tell everyone where Miami is," my friend had said. "I dunno," said the wretched girl, "it's where you get off the plane."

We had been nowhere at all, unless you count a spin round the Kingston by-pass or to Whipsnade zoo in Dad's old Packard. Children weren't given costly vacations. When I was ten, Ma and Dad went to quiet, unspoilt Sorrento and they made sure that Mike and I stayed behind with the most bizarre of our aunts. It didn't worry them that they had left their offspring with a lunatic who glued a black wig on her unshaven head and then sprinkled it with talc to make it look grey and greeted us at the door with the words: "Hoy! Sniff me! Do I smell odd?" To which we replied, "Why?" and received the answer that the Sanilav powder was next to the talcum in the bathroom and that she had chucked the wrong one on her head by mistake. It worried them even less that we missed seeing Sorrento on its scented, jewel-like promontory above the dark ocean. Damp Putney was much more suitable.

So, in Mike's and my untravelled world, the railway journey to Scotland remained a yearly cathartic ecstasy of which I never grew tired. Perhaps back then children had the gift of making a little go a long way. We expected less, so were nearly always satisfied and frequently delighted, and we travelled slowly enough and seldom enough to relish each new sight. I wonder if I sound as annoyingly pernickety as Grandpa if I point out that it's only since the restless '90s that we Brits have become a spoilt and sated people whose kids have too much, too cheap, too often and too young. (Those last words make me come over as Mr Nasty 'Daily Mail' reader, which I'm not – but.…...)

Our dear grandfather himself, fortunately, did not have occasion to travel up to Scotland in our company on either the first trip, or on any of the subsequent ones. This was just as well as he suffered all his life from pronounced train fever and, when forced to go anywhere at all, passed uncounted hours at Stirling or Euston stations, arriving half a day before the express was due to depart. Our father, in sharp contradistinction, was one of those lucky people who make things by the skin of their teeth and with no sign of flurry or haste, and on the day of our first departure for Glenturret he got us to Euston with no time whatever to spare. Luggage, our bikes, the train set, Mike's favourite teddy bears – the Buggles – and a picnic hamper and tons of books and magazines for the journey were placed aboard just as the coaches were about to slip from the station. Like Miss Brodie, Dad was always able to say that he was never late and never early. This attitude to train travel infuriated Grandpa.

Because of Dad's penchant for the last minute, I seldom had a chance to nip up and gaze at the locomotive that was to power us north – often a huge Class 40, as BR's dieselisation took hold – but had to be content, as I strained my neck out of the window, with glimpsing its green bulk in the distance as it rumbled up that fiendish incline out of Euston.

The maroon coaches of the Midland Region of BR were a revelation to one who had travelled only by tube on the Bakerloo line, and then not even as far as Stanmore. The wooden corridors of the ex-Stanier design, marked at their ends with plaques describing the type of wood used such as "Oiled Afromosia" or "English Elm", led round angular corners into a frightening void of rubber, steam (for the diesel locos were fitted with Spanner boilers to heat the carriages) and sliding steel plates where gangway met gangway. At speed, these short, dark corridors were overpowering to the senses. The chill gale, the squealing grind of couplings and buffers and the fearful suspicion that they might part in two any second, kept me hovering outside the lavatories at the end of carriages on every journey north we made.

Returning to the first-class compartment (paid for by Grandpa) was like entering that magical world of nursery, study and womb which we all long for in dreams. The shaded lights, plump antimacassar-covered seatbacks and rich wood, the neat folding table and the light-spangled panorama of those square windows drew us back from the banging corridors again and again until we got tired of Dad crying,

'For land's sake, make up your minds, you pests! In or out? And shut the door!'

Then we would sally out along all fourteen coaches, beyond hostile, shuttered compartments, past smoky evil dens, past the hot, gravy-smelling kitchen and beefy, sweating cook at his range hurling dishes across to the brilliantined stewards ballet-dancing among the heavy plates and sharp-edged tablecloths. Past even the freezing, booming hold of the forward luggage van where bicycles jigged against rope lashings and the guard crouched over his pale green wheel, and eventually we would come up against a plain dark door beyond which the great locomotive battled on below huge ejaculations of exhaust. In ecstasy we would breathe, 'Whizzoh!' with shining eyes in the gloom.

At Shap we used to slow; sometimes we were banked by another engine, on two occasions by a steam engine, a Class 5; traversing that incline was a drama – the red carriages went gliding, just above running pace, through the wiry grass and past bouldery walls. Nowadays, the tilting electrics don't even slacken pace – marvellous, of course, but the sense of effort, spectacle and theatre has all but gone.

We found satisfaction in the place names over the border (as long as you didn't look too closely at the places themselves): Coatbridge, Kilmarnock, Larbert, Motherwell. Magical names! And, finally, after many hours, the train would stop for us alone at Glenturret halt. Imagine that! It was extraordinary, for so many stations had been axed by that time, but old agreements settled before the formation of the nationalised British Railways stood for a while on The Granite City line from Stirling to beyond Gleneagles. Up front, under Scottish skies, the locomotive would wait, with slow, deep-chested rumbling, while we clambered down a pair of trestle steps, handing across luggage, and Dad slipped a ten shilling note to the guard after he had assisted Mum to ground level.

'The train, I regret to see, is late,' would be my grandfather's first comment. He and McAird would be standing by the Bentley, and around us would be nothing but moor and hill and the plume of diesel exhaust at the head of the vanishing train. I had strange mixtures of feeling as the dark sealed corridor connection and red lamp swayed out of sight. I felt I had lived on the train for many months, so that bidding it goodbye was a wrench. Mike was always neurotically convinced that we had left something in our compartment. Both of us sensed a link with home had been broken.

'I am sure you would not wish to keep Cook waiting any longer,' Grandpa would say. His life was entirely subject to the imaginary tyranny of the servants' punctuality. My father sighed on that first summer arrival – the first of many sighs.

And so, back to the point, and the incident on The Granite City line in our railway-crazed summer holiday of 1964, when the vials of wrath were so plentifully emptied upon my guilty head. Almost the first thing that McAird's son had done, after we had been introduced: ("Young gentlemen, this is ma son, Hector, a guid wee boy") was to take us down the road to the disused and derelict station of Kinbuck.

'But are we *allowed* to go down on the – the platform?' I had asked – regretting doing so a moment later, because it seemed weedy.

'Aye. Where's the harm?'

'But is it safe? I'm only five,' squealed Mike, even more weedily.

'Here we go,' had sneered Hector, gazing at the sky. 'The two wee toffs are skeered. I thought this would happen.'

Mike and I had looked fixedly at Hector. He had a small pointy head and his top lip was curled in scorn.

'Right!' I had cried, making up Mike's mind for him. 'Down we go.'

The station consisted of two short platforms straddling the twin-road main line via a girder pedestrian bridge. Off the up line was a point leading to a little siding in which there was one ancient seven-plank wagon. Three hundred yards beyond this, on the other side of the track, was a neat wooden signal-box with geraniums in tubs.

Within ten minutes of our arrival a fast train ran through, shaking the frosted glass windows and dog-toothed canopy. The waiting-room was empty except for an old electric fire and a dusty table.

'Bet ye can no hae the spunk to stand on the track,' suggested Hector.

After the shortest of pauses, during which it was quite clear to me that Hector was preparing another of his taunts, I leapt down – quite a long way down, for the fall jarred my ankle – on to the line. The twin parallels seemed very far apart now, a lot more so than their four foot eight and a half inches, and the platform extremely far up and awkward to re-ascend. Mike peered down, flipping his fingers.

'If ye lay your ear to the track ye'll see if a train's coming,' said Hector.

He and I bent our ears to the line. This involved lying on the sharp granite chippings. I toyed with the idea of correcting Hector's choice of second verb, and then thought better of it.

'Well?'

Sure enough there was an extraordinary vibrating roar from the shiny rail. I made a convulsive scramble back to the platform.

'Custard!' sneered Hector. To my fury he lay back on the track, folding his arms behind his head and whistling a jaunty air. 'Are ye all custards where ye come from?' jeered Hector. 'Why dinna ye run back to your mammy an' ask her to change yer nap.....?'

Round the eastern bend came a belch of smoke.

Hector was suddenly a blur and next to us on the platform. With a wonderful sensation of continued acceleration a Gresley A4 Pacific shot round the bend with a fast-fitted freight and clattered by the narrow platform deafeningly, the last parcels van causing a rush of air which sucked at us as we crouched in the doorway of the ladies' waiting-room. 1962 to 1964 were the last Indian summer years of those glorious streamlined steam engines (one of which, *"Mallard"*, holds to this day the world's fastest steam record, attained on the East Coast main line in the '30s), BR having allocated them to the Granite City line to serve out their days.

From this time onward it became a point of honour to take on Hector in ever more hair-raising dares. I often lay in bed desperately thinking of adequate replies to his cutting jibes. Unfortunately I never thought of them on the spot. Clearly, the path of avoidance lay in proving my courage to him.

Thus it was, as that first summer of 1964 at Glenturret wore on, that we stood on the track until the engine's smoke could be seen above the trees at the eastern bend. When this grew tame we stood on the track until the loco reached the end of the platform. Eventually, we would stand, poised and with hearts thumping, until the smoke burst through the girders of the footbridge – getting up just in time and glimpsing the agonised face of the fireman peering down from the cab as the train shot past at 80 mph. Sometimes the engine let out a shrill, yelping whistle – especially on those occasions when we dared to stand right out on the very edge of the platform, clinging to each other with Mike between us to avoid the wind of a racing express sucking us off the station like three crisp bags.

'Not off with Hector again, boys?' Dad would say. 'Wouldn't you like to come with us into Stirling?'

The moment breakfast was over, I'd lead Mike round to the cottage next to the garage and whistle. Out would pop Hector, his sharp head gleaming in the sunlight, and down the drive to Kinbuck we would go.

'I know what I'd like tae do today, but I doubt

you two would hae the spunk,' Hector would begin.

'How those boys love trainspotting,' Dad would say to Ma.

It was something of a miracle, therefore, when the hols came to an end and the three of us were still alive.

The following year, 1965, featured once more our trysts with Hector – even though we were a year older, and even though I had made all sorts of firm resolutions at home in London not to get involved in stupid games of dare. Somehow, upon meeting up with Hector once more, and faced with the alternative of sitting quietly in the corner of the library while Grandpa read "*The Times*", or going shopping with Ma to Dunblane, the adventures at the little station at Kinbuck retained their appeal.

On the best of the '65 "dare days" – when we had grown courageous enough to stand in the middle of the track until the engine's smoke had reached the canopy itself – we heard a sort of keening, wailing roar, like the breakers on some stern rocky cliff or a carriage wheel jammed on at speed.

These sound effects came, we discovered, from the signalman, screaming Scots obscenities at us from the neat wooden box. In the summer before, we had not realised that the box had an occupant; perhaps it had been unmanned in July and August of that year. Now, however, a sliding window was open and a grey-haired man leant out, gesticulating with purple face and rolled-up shirt-sleeves. On that first occasion when we were made aware of his existence, we ran for the road – Hector leading the way. But we were not pursued. And so we learnt a valuable lesson for would-be railway vandals: that a signalman, no matter how purple and enraged, cannot leave his post.

Now began our period of greatest endeavour at Kinbuck. We put pennies on the line and peeled them off six times the size after a train had bashed over them. Mike once scrambled down and put on a half-crown to see if it worked with silver – he was always rash with cash. The result remains among my souvenirs: George VI looks like something from among the distorting mirrors at the end of the pier. We placed wood, china, metal Meccano strips and once a Dinky model of a Hudson sedan (we had two) on the line. A milk jug exploded with satisfying violence. Hector suggested putting the massive and ancient electric fire from the waiting-room down there, but some lingering shreds of common-sense made me dissuade him forcibly.

'Suppose the train derailed?' I asked.

'Yer wee custards!' howled Hector. He was as inordinately fond of that disagreeable word in '65 as he had been in '64, and usually its appellation galvanised us into action. But Mike, at six showing a mature grasp of both language and psychology, was a match for him.

'You are only a chauffeur's son, so you must do what we tell you. You are a servant. Just like your father being our Grandpa's servant. You are not as good as us, and you speak in a funny, common way.'

I nodded, forgetting for a moment that we habitually lived, not among servants in a grandiloquently named Scots baronial hall, but in an apartment in Maida Vale, W9, near Dad's office, in which our only servant, indeed, was Mum.

Mike's words had a most satisfying effect on Hector, though. He went quite pale with mortification and struggled for words, but none came.

'You ought,' I continued, capitalising on the effect, 'to remember that my brother and I are your *betters*.'

Hector remained silent – grimly so, as I recall. The dusty electric fire remained in the waiting-room. Perhaps the signalman would have been gratified had he known that snobbery had prevented a severe crash on his stretch of line.

From this time on I realised that I had a powerful weapon and I used it as mercilessly as Hector used his taunts. I often spoke over his head to Mike, using words I knew were not in his vocabulary, or Latin tags, and making sophisticated comments about his accent. We were aided in our campaign by Grandpa himself, who overheard McAird addressing Mike by his Christian name.

'McAird!' Grandpa had rapped. 'I think it more fitting that you address my grandson as *Master* Michael.' These words were spoken in Hector's hearing, and we often said to Hector afterwards,

'*Master* Michael, if you please, Hector.'

Meanwhile the adventures at Kinbuck went on. The point, or switch, at the end of the down platform fascinated us like a snake. It had a large rusty turnover handle, so could clearly over-ride wires from the signal-box, even if it had ever been remotely operated.

We all agreed that, between trains, it would be sensible to see if this point worked. After all, it would do no harm – it was a trailing point, as I remember explaining to Hector and Mike at the time, and would snap back the right way if a train ran over it by mistake before we could shut it. What drew us as powerfully as the operation of the point itself was the wagon – that very old sad wagon in the siding beyond it, which had evidently not moved an inch since the previous year. Surely, we argued, it would be a legitimate experiment to see if the wagon could still roll?

We darted through thistle and spiky grass to the hidden end of the wagon. "Return to Perth" was dimly printed on its sides; obviously someone had forgotten to do so. Up and over from one wheel to the other was a long rusting crank secured in a holed bracket by a thin flaking pin. We pulled the pin out. The long crank easily shifted, and down against the orange wheels we could see that the brake shoes had been sprung back.

'Shove!' I cried, and how easily, how delightfully, the wagon creaked a few inches from off rest. Above the chaunting of its dry axle boxes came the familiar keening sound of a signalman hurling reproductive and excretory messages across the abyss of the Glasgow to Aberdeen main line.

Next day Mike and I went back to the station alone. We were relieved of the dour company of Hector, who had had to 'visit on ma gawky cousin Keith at Bridge of Allan.' His parting sneer to us had been,

'Ye'll no do nothin' at that station wi'out me there tae put spunk in you. Ye're a pair o' skeered custards.'

In spite of the fact that we had convinced ourselves of our enormous social superiority over this mere chauffeur's son, his words, as ever, rankled, and I determined to have done something to report to him when he returned.

The wagon's brakes were still off, just as we had left them the previous day, and, after a determined heave, I found that the wheels still rotated a little. Sitting on a pile of tarry sleepers, I conceived a plan which proved too irresistibly right to ignore or denigrate. I announced to Mike,

'Look. I'm going to turn the point and we're going to push the wagon out on to the main line. Then we can see the next train pick it up on the buffers as it passes. '

'Scoop! Whoosh!' laughed Mike. He indicated the process with both hands. 'And then it'll go back to Perth like what it says on the side?'

'Yes. It'll be something to tell Hector when he gets back.'

'Whizzoh!'

Hector would have pooh-poohed the wheeze had he been there, precisely because he hadn't thought of it, but to my mind it was a perfect plan. After all, we had demonstrated that this sort of scooping up could be achieved in 00 gauge – so why not in real life?

Gravity works in the same way irrespective of scale – as I now understand, of course – so that "*The Flying Scotsman*", falling from a model Forth Bridge in 00 scale, takes an absurd fraction of time to plummet its 21 inches to the water. It travels at the same speed as the real engine falling from the real Forth Bridge. But the orders of mass are so different (look how a toy train can whisk round a hairpin curve without falling over at scale 250 mph speeds, or stop dead without crushing itself) that modellers never have a realistic sense of the vast and implacable forces of nature. So it was that Mike and I did not stop to reflect on the consequences of a real locomotive smiting a real stationary wagon. We began the task - Mike able only to reach an axle box, and my shoulder against a buffer, and helped by the slight downhill gradient - of violently shoving the sad old wagon towards its apotheosis.

The harsh clanging of a police bell broke in upon our ecstasy. A black Austin Cambridge scattered the gravel in the station yard, and flat Scots coppers' hats bobbed above the stinging nettles. A second later we were grabbed. It dawned upon me that this part of the story would have to be entitled: "The Signalman's Revenge".

Whistling shrilly, a "*Brittania*" class Pacific clattered past with a long maroon train on the main line, and steamed on towards Aberdeen without ever proving whether or not it could scoop up a wagon on its buffers and, propelling it before itself, return it to Perth. The curious faces in the coaches which turned to watch two small boys being swept off their feet by burly policemen didn't realise what a lucky escape they had had from being one of the "Fifty Killed and Many Injured in Child Vandal Railway Crash Horror".

So – Home, James! in the police Austin

Cambridge.

I have always found something frightening in glimpses of pale faces seen through dark windows – faces with intense, unwinking eyes. An aunt of ours (not the one with the wig) working with the WVS in London after the war, had occasion to visit an elderly man who lived in a first-floor flat in Ebury Street. On the afternoon she arrived, she saw the old boy standing at his window. Just behind him was a tall, very pale gentleman whose face was nearly resting on the old chap's shoulder. My aunt, when she got upstairs, said, 'Well, you don't really need a visit from me today as you've got a friend with you.' To which the old boy replied, 'Eh? I haven't seen anyone all week, except the postman.'

It was with something of what must have been my aunt's emotions, therefore, that I saw the basilisk, the thing from the pit, my grandfather's face, glaring from the gun-room as the police car scrunched up the gravel and parked by the rhododendrons.

My brother, sobbing, was led off to bed by Goddard, the parlour-maid, supperless and frightened. I suffered the fate of the eldest and was whopped by Dad with one of those Pirelli slippers made of check brown wool; and, although a cane hurts more, let no one underestimate the power of the slipper when propelled by a really exasperated son-in-law.

So our days at Kinbuck station came to an end, and although, not long ago, revisiting past glories, I stopped on the road-bridge and looked down on to the platform and the roof of the waiting-room (now a private house), I had no desire to try to recapture the magic of those earliest attempts to become a public menace. The siding has gone, the heather pushes up and overwhelms the few sleepers and bits of ballast which are left. The footbridge upon which we three stood to let the huge blast of steam locomotives lift us as we straddled the missing planks, has gone. Over the line is a square of untidy stones with grass growing around some wooden stanchions where the signal-box stood – gone too, and the whole line run by computer from Glasgow.

After my thrashing ("hurts me more than it....") I too was sent to bed, supperless, but not, I'm glad to record, sobbing.

Next morning Mike and I stood trial in the library. The court consisted of:

JUDGE: Grandpa.

PROSECUTION: Grandpa.

JURY: Grandpa.

PROSECUTION WITNESS: Hector "Judas" McAird.

HALF-HEARTED DEFENCE COUNSEL: Dad.

The proceedings went something like this:

PROSECUTION: And do I believe my ears when

I hear that these young ruffians, my grandchildren, *insisted* upon committing acts of vandalism actually within the railway premises over a long period of time prior to the outrage?

WITNESS: Aye, Sir. I didna want tae go near the wee station, but Master Anthony said I was a servant an' had tae do what I was told, an' they made me put wee bits on the line, an' stand on the track wi' a train coming.

PROSECUTION: And am I to understand that my grandsons actually *endangered* your lives by their folly and hooliganism?

WITNESS: Aye, Sir, they made me do it – they said I was "custard" if I didna.

(Suffocated yelps from the defendants)

PROSECUTION: May I remind you, Bill, that after repeated warnings from Mr Turnbull... [the signalman's name, apparently]....after *repeated* warnings from Mr Turnbull to leave railway property alone, these sons of yours so endangered the safety of the track, and so blatantly and *wickedly* tampered with property not their own, that the County Police had *actually* to be called in to prevent an act of criminal insanity being perpetrated.

DEFENCE COUNSEL: Oh, dear.....

(Breakdown and abandonment of Defence's well-reasoned case that we had never done anything like this before and would never do it again.)

JURY: GUILTY.

JUDGE: With your permission, Bill, of course, I suggest that Anthony be sent to bed every evening at six with bread and milk until the end of the holidays, that the picnic drive to Loch Eal be cancelled, that neither boy sees television – especially not "*Top of the Pops*" – for the remainder of this visit.....

(Gasps from the prisoners, for whom doses of "*Top of the Pops*" were a narcotic craze)

....and that they write letters apologising to the signalman and to the police station. Most important of all, they must apologise *here and now* to poor Hector, for making him a party to their insensate, childish and dangerous games.

CONE, PARROT AND DEMON

I have passed out from over-eating only twice. The first time was the result of unwisely entering a sausage-eating contest between "Bunter" Malone and "Beast" Hegarty at university and claiming that I could beat them both with no preparation other than lining the colonic passage with Milk of Magnesia the morning before. Twenty-five plump, greasy pork sausages later I was finding out what a stomach-pump was like at close quarters.

The second (and last) time was in Tuscany in '76, two years after I'd graduated, when, following Dad's death and Ma's emigration to an Italian villa near Montecatini Terme, I ran over my brother's neck before the familiar sensation of losing consciousness swept over me.

I record this because, looking back with regret, I seemed, by the time I was twenty-three, to have made a life's work of accidentally damaging poor Mike. Running over his neck marked the end of a decade of fraternal torture which began at Glenturret with the invention of The Cone.

Before relating this, I'll touch on the over-eating bit first.

Our mother had grown friendly with Alberto Buonamici, her nearest Italian neighbour, and we were all staying at his villa while Ma's place was nearing completion of its re-decoration. It was getting close to Christmas and it had been suggested that we spend the great day together after the ice had broken. The ice needed to be broken, incidentally, because Mike and I had put our feet in it up to the groin when Alberto, on Ma's invitation, had visited London in the autumn to meet some aunts and cousins. He spoke little English (Ma had excellent self-taught Italian) and was more or less confined to "Hello", "Goodbye" and the expression "Cheeri-ho!" when he took his drinks. For some reason, Mike, by then a snooty seventeen, took great exception to this.

'Good heavens! That's the sort of man Ma is getting friendly with over there. "*Cheeri-Ho!*" Oh, it's dreadful, dreadful.'

He tried to make Alberto aware of his appalling solecism. 'Look, Alberto, in this country we just don't say that. It's so – so *maleducato.*'

Alberto, no doubt nettled at being thought ill-educated and common, asked us what people did say, and I'm afraid I simply couldn't resist telling him that the favoured phrase among the best sort of people was: "Whoops! I'm going to throw up!"

Mike gazed at me, feeling I'd gone too far, I'm sure, but Alberto seemed to accept the suggestion.

'*Grazie. Bene, bene. Grazie tante, giovanotti.*'

He practised once or twice, getting the unfamiliar toast round his tongue; I gave Mike a vaunting look; he raised his eyes ceiling-wards and we then forgot all about it.

Two days later the gathering of aunts and cousins was assembled in the lounge of the Piccadilly Hotel, London, where Alberto was staying, and drinks had been served. Ma cried,

'Now, darlings, I want you to drink to my new life in Italy!'

Amid mumbles of '....new life....' Alberto stood up and, mustering his new-found English and gulping a little over the olive he'd just eaten, raised his glass and shouted theatrically,

'A-whoopsa! Ah'm-a gonna zrow-a UP-A!' and caused the aunts to go into a general stampede.

As I've said then, the ice needed thawing. Mike, keen to make amends, came up with an idea to restore international good-fellowship.

'It is jolly *bene*, Alberto, *molto, molto bene* spending Christmas together, but wouldn't it be *buono* if we had an Italian *and* an English Christmas feast at the same time? Your type of dinner, and our type of dinner, at the same meal?'

'At the same meal?' laughed Ma.

'Well, why not? You translate, Mum, and say we could have a sample of each of the traditional seasonal foods. It would be fun!'

Ma laid down the plan, explaining that we would provide the British parts of the Christmas meal, bringing them over (for it was difficult then to find the delicacies of the various European countries in anything other than specialist shops in the capital cities; procuring a dozen mince pies in Tuscany would have presented a severe challenge).

Alberto possessed an ancient cook, a whiskered lady in black called Carla Pellegrini. She had only two front teeth, placed where Dracula kept his. She suffered from the delusion that she was ministering to the needy in some African famine region, and cooked as if for the starving millions. We have often sat down to meals at which she has hovered with a pan and serving-spoon, jamming more pasta, more meat, more sauce on the plates if she saw any slackening of ingestion.

Mike and I had turned up at the villa on one of our early summer Italian visits and found her preparing lunch for Ma and ourselves.

'What....we....going....to....eat....*oggi*?' we had asked, becoming aware, as we spoke, of a rat-like rustling in the kitchen.

'*E la!*' cried the harridan, gesticulating towards a corner where a brown paper bag was twitching. She had darted to the bag, opened it, and drawn out a live thrush with rubber bands round its beak and wings.

'*Certo,*' she had cackled, beginning to talk about the weather, '*il tempo non e buono oggi.*' And snap! went the little bones as she took the wretched bird and twisted its head round to break its neck. '*Ma fa meno caldo, si?*' she croaked, as she poked the long nail of her little fingers into the bird's eyeballs to hook out the tiny bright jellies. '*La mamma – e OK? Sta bene, si?*' she mumbled, as she began to pluck out feathers before cutting it in half, ripping out its guts on the end of her knife and tossing it into flour, pepper and oregano. *'E voi? Fame?* 'Ungry, *giovanotti?*' She reached for another rubber-banded victim and went on until eight small bodies lay in flour before us and the paper bag was still. The nearest I liked to get to nature back then was a fish finger, so I found it the snack a little unappetising.

It was this Mengele of the kitchen, then, who was to prepare our twin Christmas dinners when we all had agreed that Mike's idea had smacked of the best traditions of the EEC, as the EU was then known.

The day arrived, as Christmas day often does, in a rush, almost as a surprise, and, after just a roll or two for breakfast in the part-decorated house next door, Ma, Mike and I presented ourselves at the villa, complete with carrier bags bulging with presents, just after twelve.

'*Buon Natale, carissimi!*' cried Alberto behind his dark glasses. He was not tall but impressive, as rich, elderly Italian gentlemen can be. I thought there might be a hint of steel behind his urbane manner. He owned a large hotel in Florence which I gathered he had bought cheap after the war – yet I'd have said he had income from other sources; he kept a silent, grizzled driver and a black Lancia, and he travelled everywhere first class. If something didn't please him, he made it known. I have seen him in Florentine restaurants, on finding that the mineral water wasn't fizzy enough, pour his glass on to the floor. He always dealt directly with the manager – and they all fawned on him. I know he was visited on many occasions by the proprietors of bakeries, garages and wine cooperatives – everyone's idea of a Godfather.

'An 'appy Chreestmas to you,' he beamed, kissing us with a strong whiff of *Guerlain.* Also present were his daughter, her husband Silvio, their two daughters and a cousin and her son. We sat down, ten in all, at 12.45, and were glued to that table until after four.

We started with Parma ham and figs, and attacked the salty meat with gusto, fig juice running over our chins. We went on to a rich lasagne, and, as our plates emptied, old Pellegrini heaved further slabs in front of us until we were chewing the meat-filled strips with difficulty. Alberto waved a bejewelled hand and Pellegrini cleared the plates.

'*Molto buono,*' grunted Renato, opening his waistcoat. In came a fish fettucini bathed in cream, butter and *basilico*. Following this were pigs' trotters in brine. The gristly knuckles parted easily and aromatic flesh was revealed between hoof and ankle. Brine dribbled down Alberto's cousin's face. Alberto gave a genteel belch and swigged a beaker of *vino rosso*. Ma Pellegrini plonked two capons in the centre of the table, and Alberto graciously held the knife to me. I cut the one at our end open to find it was stuffed with crystallised fruit. Pellegrini was dismayed to find some of the plump birds left uneaten when she returned from the kitchen.

'You eat!' she wheezed. Mike and I were given a further helping. Silvio mopped up gravy and fruit juice with a piece of bread. In came a pork *arrosto*, succulent with crackling. Potatoes sweated in olive oil accompanied it. And then the main course and centrepiece: a turkey, cooked English-style with Brussels sprouts, cranberry jelly and mash. Mike, revivified by the sight of a familiar Christmas dish, attacked his big portion splendidly, gulping down the breast with chestnut stuffing and raising his glass to cry, 'Merry Christmas!' Some chestnut spattered from his mouth and Alberto's grand-daughters giggled.

By this time I was growing hot, shiny and sticky and had some difficulty breathing. Under the tablecloth I reached for my zip and loosened the top of my trousers. Pellegrini returned again with fresh roast potatoes and a dish of *polenta*. Renato held out his plate and had it piled with the yellow dough. While the turkey was reduced to a gaunt wreck (and I found, with my waistband loose, that I could manage some more dark meat), the crone had brushed the table clear and was laying out new dishes. There was a chocolate wing cake and an almond *torte*, received with cries of pleasure by the girls and by the cousin, and there was a plum pudding, specially brought over from Fortnum's, and a bowl of brandy butter. This was greeted by dark looks of suspicion and wrinkled foreheads. Ma took up a spoon.

'Wait, Mum!' said Mike. 'We must put brandy over it and light it!' When the mince pies arrived, we poured lashings of brandy over them as well. Mike was getting a little hysterical, and although I could not have moved if my chair had been on fire, he whisked round the table with a lighted candle and practically force-fed the girls, who squealed deafeningly as pastry crumbled in their hair.

'*Ragazzi! Per favore…*,' remonstrated Alberto. In came Pellegrini with the *panforte di Siena,* a rich fruit slab encased in rice-paper. It was followed by *panettone,* and those buttery aromatic slices melted in our mouths, washed down by champagne.

Marsala wine appeared next and hard nut cakes: *specialite di Prato*. The pain threshold had been crossed; I felt an airy, unearthly emptiness and hurled myself on them, as I did upon the festive *gelato all'amarena* which followed. The nuts, the chocolates, the tangerines and jellies, and the platters of gorgonzola, *bel paese* and parmesan were surmounted, embraced with an ease and freshness that made me yearn for more, even as perspiration poured down and the table was being cleared.

We gazed at each other over the food-splattered table-linen. Silvio began clapping and belching at the same time.

'Brava!' he cried, wheezily. Like a conductor reappearing on the rostrum at the end of a grand symphonic concert, old Pellegrini came for the last time into the dining-room from her dim, greasy kitchen.

'Brava!' we shouted. I found out afterwards that her own Christmas dinner had consisted of a bowl of vegetable soup, a slice of *panettone* and a cup of weak Lipton's tea. Her whiskered dial bobbed in appreciation like a death's head. Mike rose unsteadily to his feet and gave a horrible gurgle.

'Uuuurgh! I – I must get a little fresh air,' he mumbled, lurching to the door. With a few barely coherent words, interspersed with violent and embarrassing belches, I followed him. We staggered round to the garage. There were our faithful mopeds, bought for us by Ma: The Torpado and the Garelli. We wheeled them to the gate. Mike clambered aboard and free-wheeled down the slope, too spent, I suppose, to pedal. With a sharp blare, like the expiring blast of a stomach burst asunder, the Torpado fired and Mike bounced away on the unmade road that led to the vineyards below the villa.

I managed to start the Garelli on its stand, kicked it back, and followed Mike. The cold wind revived me briefly, but the motion stirred up with a frosty hand the sixteen courses warring with each other in the space between my throat and the bike's saddle. I crashed over the hard ruts and came to the bend. As in a strange, silent dream, I saw a peculiar sight. In front of me, stretched out across the road was Mike. He had passed out and had left his machine as it had taken the curve. His neck seemed, to my capon-blurred eyes, to be about eighteen feet long and as unavoidable as a telegraph pole blown across a three-lane freeway. I drove straight over it, hearing my wheels thudding "bump-a-bump" as they broached the quivering adam's apple. Then I too passed out and, still gripping the handle-bars, ploughed into a thorny bush.

Since that day I have been more prudent about eating. I have completely dropped what used to be my normal measure of having eaten enough: the onset of abdominal cramp and blurred vision, and I now always stop after six courses. Guys born without appestats have to be careful.

We were less than twenty minutes unconscious and, apart from clear Michelin imprints along his shirt collar, and a head that wouldn't turn for some time, Mike seemed none the worse for having been a one-man Lombard rally obstacle.

On arrival back at the villa, we found Alberto & Co gulping tea, and Pellegrini handing round English Christmas cake.

This little incident of upper-vertebra moto-cross stemmed directly from Mike's original idea about having two Christmas dinners, so I could hardly feel that I was to blame for any discomfort he might have felt (and his neck was sore for more than a month). The same cannot be said about the dreadful thing that happened to him as a result of my grotesque invention of The Cone.

As children at Glenturret in the mid-'60s, we had no recourse to amusements other than those which were self-made. Our great delight was to have army-style adventures in a small gang made up of four foundation members and one associated member. In such matters a pecking order is quickly established, and by 1966 ours was as follows:

SELF: *Obersturmfuhrer* (aged 12)

PETER BUCHAN: Keenly combatant 2i/c (aged 12)

HECTOR McAIRD: Sergeant Major (aged 11)

DAVID SHERWIN-LEMOND, known very wittily by us as Sherbert-Lemon: newcomer and unknown quantity, (aged 9, curly-haired, and regarded as a mummy's boy and weirdo, but too tall to victimize)

MIKE: Dogsbody, dupe and sole victim (nearly 8)

'Let's play "he"!' would cry Peter.

'Right. "Tag" it is. You be "it"!' would be my order to Mike.

'Oh, why *me*?' was the complaint.

'All right. Toss you for it,' I would say, and out would come my double-tailed coin – two filed pennies stuck together, face to face. It was known that Mike had a mystic's faith in "heads" and would never call anything else. Up went the coin. Two seconds later Mike was "it".

When the model railway was put on to realistic runs in Grandpa's unused ballroom, and the Trix *"Brittania"* or Hornby-Dublo *"Crepello"* ran sleeper trains all night long from King's Cross to Inverness, there was a fierce debate about who should creep downstairs in the middle of the night to stop the train at York, and change locomotives at Edinburgh. What nowadays would be dealt with by a mini-computer was handled, in that era of full employment, by Mike. Twice a night, at the age of seven or eight, he would be woken by alarm clock and be required, under threat of dire punishment, to thread his way through Glenturret's cold passages and to tiptoe into the ballroom to carry out his duties. This practice ceased, not as a result of workforce revolt, but because the *"Brittania"*, hauling twelve carriages all night long, burnt out its motor, and operations were suspended pending overhaul (which did not occur until 1985, eighteen years after Trix Twin Railways, which had manufactured it, had gone bankrupt.)

Mike was put onto anything which required slavish, unquestioning menial labour. He was promoted to "bicycle maintainer" in '66, but so resented it that I was compelled to thrash him with a Bluemell's bicycle pump (which I broke on him) after he had punctured my tyres with a meat skewer.

'You are a disloyal and snivelling little beast, and I may turn you out of the gang!' I had shouted on that occasion.

'No, no. His loyalty needs testing, that's all,' Peter Buchan had interjected.

'Get lost, freak, while we discuss your fate!' I had screamed, and Peter and I had sat down there and then to think of ways to put an end to outbreaks of independent thought on the part of gang members.

'I can tell you now,' said Peter, 'we need a test of

courage and – and fitness to belong. We should all take it.'

'Perhaps a thrashing – with a bamboo cane?' I asked wistfully. But Peter had other ideas.

'We must have a test of real endurance. Let's go to the cathedral to discuss it.'

The "cathedral" was a faux-Gothic summer-house with croquet mallets in it, which Grandpa never used, but which was our daily meeting-place.

Mike was hanging about, still looking sullen and rebellious.

'You can buzz off out of it, Mike. We'll let you know what we decide.'

It was evident that the Glenturret gang needed a shaking-up to test allegiances. Hector was already far too ready to sneak to his father and to suggest adventures and then back out at the last minute. Mike was generally subservient, but, possibly as a result of long-term impaired sleep, was becoming neurotic and had once actually derailed the Royal Scot after fumbling a point change and had caused our new six-wheel luggage van to scratch its tin-plate sides. The final member, Sherbert, was that new boy whose mettle I did not yet know, and whose pop-eyed, curly-haired looks I did not admire. This freak had joined up with us early in the summer holidays. His father was John Sherwin-Lemond (the rib-tickling pun on his name had been received with bellows of mirth when first suggested by Peter), Conservative agent for the local MP and a neighbour of Grandpa's. Sherbert and Mike had hit it off at once – each sensing, perhaps, the strong likelihood of their becoming increasingly subservient drones.

'Right,' said I, when Peter and I were crouched in the cathedral among the mallets, 'a very severe test for Sherbert, Hector, Mike and you.'

'A very severe test for Sherbert, Hector, Mike, me and *you*, you mean,' said Peter. There was a silence. The croquet equipment gave off a whiff of damp in the mouldy stone folly.

'I mean a test for Sherbert, Hector and Mike, of course,' I murmured. Peter nodded. We shook hands. A Very Severe Test for Three had to be sought.

'Eating seven slugs each?'

'Why seven?'

'Why not?'

Pause for thought.

'Getting them to stuff a worm up their noses?'

'Drinking a whole bottle of syrup of figs?'

'Eating a packet of margarine?'

'Walking naked down to Kinbuck?'

'*Running* naked down to Kinbuck!'

'Why running?'

'Why naked?'

'Eating a tablespoon of cow dung?'

'Sitting in a cow-pat?'

'Sitting NAKED in a cow-pat!'

Pause for uproarious laughter. Really there seemed no task fitting enough to test the moral, intellectual, physical and spiritual calibre of Mike, Hector and Sherbert.

'What about dog's muck? It's easier to carry.'

'Eating it?'

Pause for incredulous reflection.

'No. Perhaps not.' Visions of my grandfather's neat moustache and thin lips mouthing impenetrable threats floated before my inner eye. 'What about something which *nearly* involves eating or sitting in dog's muck or cow-pat?' I suggested.

'Howja mean?'

'I mean,' I cried, striving to recall the western where a white man was buried up to his neck in the desert by redskins and had rattle-snakes writhing near him under the scorching Mojave sun, but uttered no word of appeal to his dusky captors and was accordingly judged a hero and freed. 'I mean a test where it *seems* that something horrible is about to happen to you, and you don't know it isn't going to *really*, but you don't cry out and you have your bravery tested. See?'

Peter gazed thoughtfully out into Grandpa's park.

'You mean *they*,' he said after a long moment. We shook hands again.

'I mean, of course, they.'

Under the tried and tested stimulus of discussion, Peter and I decided the fate of our army of three.

We were to amass a gigantic cone of mixed cow-pat and dog's muck under a tree, throw a rope (from the garage) over a conveniently low branch and tie the end round the victim's ankles. We would then lower him slowly head-first down towards the apex of the cone. If he did not flinch or cry out with horror, he would be adjudged worthy to be a member of the Glenturret gang. Peter and I slapped each other heftily on the shoulder-blades.

'Fab! Outa space!' we cried, mightily pleased that we had engineered a scheme which met the following criteria:

- Presented a testing challenge to the three camp-followers
- Did not involve any real contact, internally or externally, with cow-pats or dog's muck, thus lessening any likelihood of typhus being caught and Grandpa hearing about it, yet
- Involved cow-pats and dog's muck.

It is easier to write about the compilation of a huge pile of turds than undertake it. After a while, Peter and I decided that the three intended candidates should be given the actual collection of the means of their trial. With queasy stomachs, Peter and I watched a monumental cone of pats grow beneath the oak by the iron fencing half way down the drive. Hector was sick on the final morning when, at last, the pyramid was completed.

Such was the magnetism of their great leaders' personalities that at the appointed hour all three stood ready by the pyre of their own making.

'You first, Hector!' I yapped. Hector was bunked up to the branch, tied his end of the rope (which he himself had brought in secrecy from his father's garage, for McAird was stickily possessive about the props he deemed necessary to maintain Grandpa's cars) round his ankles and Peter and I below began paying it out. Hector bobbed face downward until his head was practically touching the evil-smelling cone. Not a word or gesture came from him – perhaps his earlier vomiting had cured him of further revulsion. As the top of his shiny head momentarily brushed the apex of the cone, I ordered,

'That's enough! Hoist him up.'

Up he went, grinning. Peter was probably as disappointed as I was that Hector had got by with flying colours. Safely on the ground again, he bragged,

'Ah'm no custard! Ye didna think I'd squeal, did you?'

Secretly, I was glad not to have gone further than we had done with him, for he would most assuredly have squealed in another sense. We knew how little honour he had.

'Now you, Sherbert!' said Peter, and David Sherwin-Lemond was lowered off the oak and then down over the pile. I jogged the rope deliberately and was rewarded by a sudden, bewildered, pop-eyed look of horror as he plummeted cone-wards before being jerked to a halt just in time. Like Hector, he uttered no word or cry. He too, with disappointment, was released.

'Now you, Mike.' I cried.

'What about you and Peter?' objected Mike sturdily, when he'd clambered up onto the branch.

'Our turns come next,' I lied (for, to tell the truth, we had not seen fit to mention that Peter and I considered ourselves exempt, not only by virtue of seniority, but because of doubts as to whether or not the others might not let the rope slip when one of us was aloft – by accident, of course. Hem, hem!)

'OK, then,' said Mike, with bright, forced merriment. 'Here I go, sailing like a jet fighter above the dreaded poo-poo!' and he plunged like a man from the branch, the rope creaking. Just at that moment, a roar, like that of a rhino in labour, was heard over the damp fields. It came from Barable.

Barable was Grandpa's head-gardener, a grubby man of odd appearance (I had heard one of my grandmother's friends describe him as "Bugs Bunny with syphilis", but hadn't understood what it meant) whose fly-buttons were permanently in an unfastened state. The shirt, poking from his flies, and bobbing like the white tail of a rabbit, was what enabled us to recognise him across five acres of lawn.

Barable crossed our path constantly during the summer holidays. The previous year he had intervened at just the wrong moment when the gang had decided to burn a squaw at the stake, had roped Susan Cairncross to a tree, doused the ground about her with petrol (supplied by Hector from the garage), had run a long trail of it back to the greenhouse and had lit it with Dad's lighter. Barable had sprinted after the flame, his flies gleaming like a talisman, and stamped it out with his ex-army boots before it had reached the squaw. Grandpa weighed in with punishments of a Genghis Khan-esque nature, and we never found out what maidens did and said when being burnt at the stake.

This same annoying Barable, seeing Mike in mid-air, now tore down upon us, waving his trowel like a samurai sword. Hector and David bolted. Peter and I, with one agonised look, dropped the rope and followed them, in momentary expectation of an ex-army boot crashing on our trousers. Behind me I heard the squelching sound and the muffled squeals of a younger brother dropping at speed head-first into a four-foot high cone of assorted shit.

Two peculiar tales came to our ears in the summer of '66, which seem, even now, to have given counterpoint to an even more bizarre occurrence at Glenturret itself – and all three involved the persistence of the paranormal.

The first story was one Mike and I heard from the lips of George Gross, a business partner of our uncle Charles. He and his wife were staying at Glenturret for a long weekend, having just moved from their flat in Belgravia after a peculiar mishap had befallen their pet parrot, Benito.

Ma, Dad (up for a few days – reluctantly), Grandpa, my grandmother, the Grosses and we brats were sitting in the library; the grown-ups having drinks before dinner, and Mike and I swigging Pepsi as a treat before going upstairs to supper. George Gross said:

'Well, I will tell you the full details – the boys might find it interesting.'

We boys doubted we would, such a comment usually preceding some educationally or morally improving sermon about success attending hard work, but we dutifully gave him our attention, if only to postpone the hour of going to bed.

'It's more likely to upset them,' murmured Ma. 'It may give them nightmares.'

'I liked ghost stories when I was a boy,' grunted George Gross. 'Besides, this one's true, and I wish it weren't.'

'Tell us!' squeaked Mike.

'We had,' said George, 'to move after what happened. We couldn't bear to go on living there.' He lay back in his chair and fixed us with his prominent blue eyes. 'Belgravia is supposed to be a badly haunted part of London.'

'Why?' asked Mike.

'Like Gravesend, it was where mass graves were dug for the corpses of the Great Plague. Because few people at the time could be sure whether or not someone was dead, many victims of the plague were buried alive. They went through the various stages of plague sickness; you know the sort of thing – ring o' roses swellings in the armpits, a-tishoo, a-tishoo, then "all fall down" into the coma which came before death. That's what the nursery rhyme is about, see? Without being able to discover whether a person was still alive, they heaved the sufferer out of the window into carts which passed in the night. These wagons were heaped with bodies in different stages of decay, and their drivers, heavily muffled up and calling, "Bring out your dead!" whipped the horses through the narrow lanes to the burial pits, so they themselves could get clear of plague-infested areas. The carts stopped at the pit-brink, the bodies were dropped off and thrown down upon layer after layer of packed corpses. Very likely you came out of your coma when your body thudded down on piled-up cadavers, but then it was too late. Likely enough, several more wagon loads were chucked on top of you, so you came to under a squelching carpet of partially decayed limbs only to hear the earth being shovelled back on top of you as quickly as the gravediggers knew how. In silence your death-agony came while your mouth was pressed right into the swollen face of a plague carcass; and the more you fought to claw your way back to the light the tighter packed the stinking press of bodies came. Is to be wondered that premature burial in such cases caused uneasy spirits to wander still in the vicinity of those graves?'

George Gross took a swig of whisky-and-soda. I looked at Mike. Clearly he hadn't understood most of it. But George had seemed, to me, to be speaking only to *me* – and I understood. No one had told us about this at school. George had warmed to his grim theme with all the panache of the advertising man that he was.

Not all his audience was appreciative.

'I think you may spare us such details,' rasped Grandpa. 'We shall soon be having dinner.'

'Sorry,' said George. 'I'm just filling in the background for these lads here. Now I'll tell you about our horrible experience. We knew that the area had a reputation for being haunted, but paid no heed.

Who really believes in things like that? After all,
Eaton Place *is* Eaton Place, and the flat was a bit of a
snip. There had been W.R.E.N.S in it during the war,
then a little secretarial business, but the tenancy was
still in Lord Clifton's hands. He wanted nothing
more to do with the house and his agents partitioned
it for sale. We had the whole of the third floor;
lovely big rooms with fine mouldings and
convenient for Sloane Street, so Cecily and I jumped
at it. We had the house to ourselves for a month and
then old Mona Grant took the second floor. John
Grant's aunt, you know.'

'What *happened*?' I interjected. I was not keen to
see the story develop into one of those maddening
name-dropping conversations that grown-ups loved.

'You boys never saw Benito, I don't think,'
continued George. 'We bought him on impulse in
Southampton because he was so brightly coloured
and could shriek "*Merde!*" '

'George!' hissed Mum. I didn't know why.

'Oh, ah, yes, of course. Well, we decided to hang
his cage on chains in the middle of the drawing-
room. C. always thought we could teach him to say a
few more words, but we didn't manage to do that
before he died. His cage was shaped like a bell, and
he would come out and perch on a rail in the kitchen
when we were at home. He was a very friendly bird,
but not much of a talker. But after we'd been at

Eaton Place for a week, he became even more silent – not a squawk, not a whistle – and one day, after C. and I had met up at Charles' office, we returned to find him gone.'

'I was astonished,' put in Cecily, who, up to now, had let George do the talking. 'I mean, we opened the flat door, went round the L-shape into the drawing-room, calling "Benito!" and looked up to see that the cage was gone from the ceiling. There was the hook, and nothing else.'

'We hunted round the flat,' said George, taking over again, 'and found him, very cross, in his cage, in the bath! C. thought I must have taken him there to put water in his doo-dah, didn't you? And I thought she'd done it.'

'Neither of us remembered doing so,' Cecily went on, 'because neither of us had. We could think of no other way he could have got there…..'

'….unless he'd started flapping like mad, lifted the chain from the hook, and flown through the flat, gripping his perch with the cage around him! That seemed unlikely as the cage was so heavy. So we shoved him back on the hook and sort of dismissed it from mind – although I privately thought C. had gone ga-ga.'

Mike giggled at the word.

'Silly man,' smiled Cecily, with a mixture of acidity and fondness.

The library clock struck seven-thirty. George caught Grandpa staring at it and resumed hurriedly,

'Yes – er, to cut a long story short, this happened every other day. Back we would come, open the door, go round the L-shape, call "Ben!" and bingo! Gone again! Sometimes the cage was in the kitchen, sometimes in the bathroom. Once it was slap in the middle of our bed – and that was after we knew we had shut all the interior doors of the flat in the morning.'

George lit one of Grandpa's Abdullah cigarettes and blew the smoke into his whisky glass so that it swirled like ectoplasm. 'Then it happened!' he declaimed, picking a fragment of tobacco from his lip. 'Then it happened. C. was still at the WVS and I got back before her. As I came in from the street, old Mona Grant met me downstairs in a terrible twitter. "Thank God you're back!" she cried. "There's been a *frightful* accident! The police have been here." She dragged me into her flat – the one underneath ours. "Look!" She directed my eyes up to her ceiling. Most of the plaster had come down, some of the beams were visible, the ceiling itself had a great bulge in it, and was bowing downwards. She told me that at three o'clock there had been a tremendous bang above her, as if a bomb had gone off upstairs. Seeing her own ceiling partially caved in, she dashed up to see if we were all right – she'd thought that a large piece of furniture had fallen over and that one of us might be injured – but our front door was locked. She then rang the police and they had been unable to open our mortice locks, so they told her to contact them again when one of us returned with the keys.'

'Didn't the police stay with Mona?' asked my grandmother.

'No. They clearly didn't think they could do much until we got back. There was no fire, no smoke and what I smelled when I got in hadn't gone beyond the door,' said George. 'I got back before C. and found the old thing quite hysterical. So up we went and I got the door open. The moment I'd done so, the stench hit me. It was the reek of burnt feather and roast meat. I went round the L-shape hardly knowing what I'd find. What I did see I could hardly believe. The room was *gutted*. The sofa was charred; some charring went up the wallpaper. The floor sloped slightly down to the spot beneath Benito's hook, where there was a black round patch in the carpet. All round the room tiny pieces of light twinkled. I couldn't think what was causing this until I realised that it was metal shards – what had been Benito's cage, torn into fragments of steel as if by a manic hand. Right in the centre of the black circle were the remains of our parrot, ripped to tatters and cooked. We discovered later that his tiny bones had been

64

driven so hard through the carpet, as if by a pile-driver, that they were embedded like nails in the floorboards.'

'Is it really true?' piped Mike.

'I'm afraid it is,' said George, shaking his head and putting his glass down carefully, as if worried that it too might blow up unexpectedly. 'I wouldn't live there again for a million. The police could do nothing. No forced entry had been made. They have several cases like ours on file, you see – poltergeists, see?'

I was about to ask what a poltergeist was, but George intercepted my thought. 'It means "naughty spirit" in German, but Cecily and I think it was one of the plague dead, bitter and enraged, trying to attract our attention, trying to say: "Look what you did! You buried me alive".'

The second tale of the unexplained in that interesting summer was related to us only a couple of days later, after the Grosses had left, by a Catholic priest; a man whom Grandpa might, in other circumstances, have distrusted on principle, but who had impeccable antecedents (Beaumont, the Jesuit boarding school, and then Oxford) and who had been a contemporary of Dad's in the army in Italy during the war.

This Father Cunningham stayed briefly at

Glenturret while coming to the end of a stint as locum in the Catholic parish at Auchterarder, and he proved very pleasant company. His stay, at Dad's persuasive insistence, extended, beyond the Friday and Saturday originally proposed, to a full week – Dad himself postponing his return to London – and by the end Grandpa was eating out of his hand.

The old boy was not, of course, anti-Popery in speech and manner, but I realise now that Catholics had hitherto been bracketed vaguely in his mind with conchies, commies, vegetarians, CND supporters, homosexuals, articulate blacks and the sort of Non-U intellectuals who wore dark-coloured shirts, like George Orwell. Fr James Cunningham was so obviously "pukka" and civilised, and knew so many people whom Grandpa himself knew, that he ceased to get sidelong glances (as if Grandpa feared he might suddenly pick his teeth at table like, as Grandpa might say, 'some awful dago') within twenty-four hours of his successful visit.

It was a blazing afternoon in that array of hot thundery August days which followed damp July in Scotland in the mid to late-'60s, when the family gathered for tea round the dark, slatted table on the terrace under the library windows. Below, down a slope of feathery grass, were cricket stumps on the croquet lawn at which Father Cunningham had been showing Hector and me how to bowl twisters. Mike lay on his front next to Sherbert, peering at daisies through a magnifying glass. Ma looked on through round black sunglasses, Dad nodded in a loosely tied cravat and Grandpa sat upright, persuaded out of doors for once ('Tea taken outside is so inconvenient for the servants') and very pink in heavy tweeds and cloth cap.

'Come and have tea, Father!' called Mum to our priestly coach. We chucked down the bats and flung ourselves on the strip of grass near Dad's feet. Fr Cunningham lay back in a deckchair, squinted up at the sky from under perspiring black brows, and remarked,

'Could be in Italy again, eh, Major Bill?'

My father grunted assent. Mike and I had already heard of the heat and privations which he and Jim Cunningham had endured at Bari and Brindisi during the liberation of Italy. Father C. took tea and went on, 'I remember one particular hot day. I'd been having a game of cricket with some of the chaps in the RASC just before final troop withdrawal in 'forty-six on an afternoon as humid as this, when a squat, dumpy little peasant of a man came rolling up from the Villa Messina asking for the English chaplain. "Here I am," I said. "Good, good," said he, "I want your help with an exorcism. Can you come?" He started flapping his fingers agitatedly. Really I didn't know what to do. It was such a peculiar request – I hadn't thought that exorcism was still practised and, as you know, Bill, I'd been chaplain for less than a year and had no idea what to do at one. *"Andiamo, fratello in Cristo",* said he in Italian, and I realised that he too was a priest. He had no dog-collar on and was dressed in a blue shirt and dirty corduroys, but he was the local padre all right. That made a difference and I said I would help. We went off down to the Villa Messina, and across the town into his house. Do you remember Di Nardo's, Bill? Well, he was based two houses on, and his church was round the corner in Piazza Cavour – that odd church which seemed to have no windows.'

The church's identity was confirmed by nods from Dad. I could see that each of them relished recalling those exciting times in their twenties. Certainly I had always known that Dad had enjoyed the war, and I now realise that he found the peace rather a let-down.

Father Cunningham proceeded with his odd tale. I suppose I remember it so clearly because, during its telling, there were the exciting, far-off rumblings of heavy thunder from a great mass of alpine clouds rolling across south of the Ochils – thunder almost deeper than hearing from a black wall like a tidal wave on the horizon. I have loved the approach of that sort of storm ever since.

A lightning flicker came from the dark mass.

Grandpa waved away wasps and flies from the jam sandwiches, every now and then grunting 'Gar!' or 'Tchah!' and Father Cunningham calmly related in his high, refined voice, the bizarre horror of that immediate post-war exorcism.

It seemed that he and the little priest had dived into the presbytery, and, over a glass of wine, Fr Cunningham had been told that at the hospital of Santa Croce, in a small room far from the soldiers and the open wards, lay a man possessed by a demon. He screamed with horror whenever the sacrament was brought into his room; he foamed and gnashed his teeth, howled obscenities, defecated in his bed and, it was said by the nuns who nursed him, sometimes levitated. His excrement was brilliant green. Yes, clearly a case of demonic possession, thought the little priest of Bari.

Father Cunningham, a public-school man who had played at Lords in the Beaumont v Oratory match, thought this sounded the biggest load of cobblers he had ever heard. Typical Wop hysteria. Man in the bed needed a beaker of Scotch, a couple of aspirins and a good brisk walk. No wonder he'd gone barmy, stuck in solitary with a gaggle of silly nuns and the temperature over a hundred degrees and the windows closed.

His reaction, he gave us to understand, was what

my grandfather's, or any Englishman's at that time, might have been. Bloody foreigners!

However, the little priest was so anxious that Fr C. accompany him on this visit to the patient, so insistent that the ceremony needed two of them, Fr C. found himself agreeing to assist at the exorcism of the demon.

'We went together to the Santa Croce,' continued Father Cunningham, 'and my Italian friend was carrying a shopping bag. "What's in there?" I asked. "The meat," said he, looking surprised. Inside the hospital, we walked down a stone corridor, round a corner into a passage at the end of which was a small white door. From behind it came mumblings. The room was bare, except for an iron bedstead and a table. On the bed, held in by leather thongs, was the patient. A nun was in the room, on her knees in prayer by the bed. The patient looked ghastly. He strained silently, gurgling, at the straps. His eyes were rolled up, his neck sinewy, wet with sweat and with tendons straining. I didn't know what I'd expected to see, but for the first time I realised the affair was not some comic-opera mumbo-jumbo. The man looked on the edge of death. There was something horrifying in the contrast between the nun's calm olive face and the brutal straps pinning the sufferer to the bedstead. I was about to speak, when the man became aware of our presence. He seemed first to shrink into the bed, as though falling through it, then he lunged upwards and outwards towards us. His lips were drawn back, his teeth ground, and from his throat came a baying, like a tortured animal's. I comprehended, as the thick straps creaked, that had he been loose he would have tried to kill all three of us. I glanced at the nun's face with respect. "Leave us, Sister," said my fellow priest. I could see now why two of us would be needed. I would not have stayed alone in the room for a fortune.'

Father Cunningham paused. I was filled with his story, if it can be put that way. I didn't look at Grandpa, or Ma, or Dad; I was aware that Mike – too young to concentrate for so long – had picked up the magnifying glass again. Sherbert lay on his back near him, gazing at the sky. Hector was eating a slice of cake. I sensed that Fr C. had decided that I was his audience, for his eyes rested on mine as he went on.

'Spit spattered on us from the bed. Italian obscenities, guttural laughter and choking came in quick succession. "Now you help me," said the priest. He took from his shopping-bag a dinner-plate and placed it on the table. He lifted out a paper-wrapped packet, opened it, and revealed a large chunk of fresh liver – dark red. "What on earth's that for?" I asked. "Listen,' said he, "when we exorcise this demon, it will leave the body of this poor man for a second or two. It must then immediately go into flesh, and there is only you and me and this meat in the room. We will resist it, but the meat cannot. Understand?" He sloshed the liver on to the plate. I stood, astounded. All my disbelief came flooding back; this is ridiculous, I thought. The patient's clearly a loony, not possessed. How could he be?

'I was passed a stole and put it about my neck. "Help me lift him," said the little priest. "He will break his back if he is lying down as the demon leaves him." I can't describe with what reluctance I approached the man. Disgust swept over me as his smell came squeezing into my nostrils: excrement and sweat. The sacrament was taken from its box. I was handed a thin, black book of the Church's Exorcism Rite. I'd never known that such a thing existed. We'd heard nothing about this at the seminary at Wonersh. I was directed to intone the proper responses. Holy water was brought out, incongruously, in a hip flask. The plate of meat – that red, bloody liver – was placed near the patient's head, and we began.'

Perhaps it was only I who found that the thin, cultured voice relating these oddities over tea on the terrace at Glenturret made the tale more believable, rather than the opposite. I felt the strangest mixture of sensations in that jumpy, disappearing sunlight, under which thunder boomed from afar. How effective the pathetic fallacy is, where Nature mirrors the mood of Man. Dracula biting throats in Tesco's on a Tuesday morning in June near the fishcake freezer wouldn't work. As thunder rolled, Fr C. continued,

'We cried together, "*In nomine Patris et Filii et Spiritu sancti*" in shaky voices, and commanded the demon return to Hell. The patient levitated, as it seemed, against his straps and a stream of bile dribbled from his chattering mouth. In spite of what we had done to prop him up, he slid down into a lying position again, arching his back. Then his mouth opened so widely that two cracks appeared at the corners and blood dropped in tiny puddles on the startling white of his pillow. He screamed as the sacrament was held over him – screamed like a foghorn, like an air-raid siren, like an animal in a cage of hot iron, and the room was filled with an appalling stench. He flopped back on the bed. I looked round the room, rather wildly I dare say, for there was a sense of a presence for a fleeting moment. An instant later, my eye was riveted with a bang upon the plate, there on the table by the head of the patient. Gone was the obscenely bright liver, glistening with unwholesome bloodiness in that white room. Gone! In its place, was a running sore of grey-green slime. The meat had putrefied utterly.'

Father Cunningham paused and wiped his mouth, then his forehead. Young as I was, I could see how the re-telling of this event had moved him with bewilderment, even after twenty years. 'Oh, dear, you will not believe what I say next, and I myself might not absolutely swear to it under oath, but, as I gaped at that plate of slime, I thought I saw it writhing – just for an instant, you know.

'The little priest from Bari was calm. He said, "Now you come with me." He picked up the disgusting plate and led me with it to the hospital boiler-room. There we cast the liver, plate and all, into the furnace – and, as it burnt, there seemed to me a short, complete silence, after which the noises of the world rushed back again. I am sure you will not be surprised to hear that the patient was calm on our return. The nuns had taken the straps off him. The priest showed little interest. Back in his house off the Piazza Cavour, he gave me some wine and thanked me without emotion for my help. It had not been a strange day for him, you see. But I think that day saved my faith, for the war had secularised me more than I had thought. And the patient? Well, he was a simple chap, really, until his troubles, and when our unit left Bari I made the effort to find out what he was doing. He was back in his old job with the *Commune* as a gardener. He took his temporary misfortune phlegmatically, as in the course of things. Now it was over, he pragmatically forgot all about it. I was the one, it seems, who never forgot.'

Father Cunningham stopped, with a wry smile and a short laugh. The tea in the big pot was cold. The thunder storm was nearly upon us. His story made an impact on all of us, I think. Mike told me he had a nightmare about it a day or two later, some of the tale's horror having got through to his little brain. I found it gratifying that the word "excrement" had actually been mentioned at tea-time without a murmur from Grandpa.

There was one further effect, not really savoured at the time, but growing with the years. George Gross and Father Cunningham had established in my youthful mind a natural association between Glenturret and the unexplained.

THE COLD SPOT

Glenturret is not an old house. The Perth architect William McConnell received the commission for its construction in 1858 and by 1863 it was complete – a house nurtured in the bosom of Gothic revivalism and of a type seen all over the British colonies wherever Scots Baronial is admired, and the spirit of Walter Scott alive. Its first owner had been a publisher whose fortune had been made by a fiction weekly called "*Fireside Gems*".

There is no reason, therefore, why it should have the remotest claim to be haunted. When Peter and I had our visitors, of course, I pushed the notion that some dreadful fiend was treading stealthily behind them; it was good for business, and the house's museum guidebook devoted a half-page to the sinister affair of The Cold Spot, although not the tiniest trace of chill remained after the 1960s.

In 1969 it was otherwise, and it started when Grandpa decided he must restore some unused, shabby rooms on the third floor. We boys didn't know it, but he had been persuaded, at last, by our grandmother to put the house on the market, and this was to be our very last summer there.

Museum customers never went beyond the door marked "Private" – beyond it was our old estate office. It was next to a big cabinet full of cigarette packets from the past. I'm sure that our visitors (gazing at the *Craven 'A'*, *Abdullah*, *Churchman's No 1*, *Olivier, Sweet Afton*, *Passing Cloud* and *De Reske* boxes, and mentally comparing them unfavourably to the cheapo, glossy modern packs, with those grim "Smoking Kills" logos on the cartons) would have noticed that the corridor took a slight curve beyond the cabinet, so that the door marked "Private" was only partially seen.

Now this curve seemed to me, at the age of fourteen, the most perturbing feature in the whole of Glenturret. I would walk up to the beginning of that curve and see half of the door, a large door with the upper panels frosted in Victorian decorative glass, and have an insane desire to run back to the safety of the upper landing. The combination of glass you couldn't quite see through, and a door you couldn't quite see whole, seemed to open up all sorts of possibilities about the unknown. And to cap it all, the curve was so very surprising in a house which made a virtue and a science of angularity and the perpendicular.

Thus, of all Glenturret's inhabitants in that summer of '69, I was the least surprised that work on re-decoration was soon halted by fearful complaints from the workmen that "there was somethin' verra weird aboot yon upper passage".

Back in 1961, Grandpa had divided the original, enormous room into three smaller ones connected by a corridor running along the window side. The suite thus formed was for the accommodation of Darby, my grandmother's lady's maid, and a sewing and ironing room. In the early years after Grandpa had bought Glenturret, Darby had been situated in a guest room on the first floor, and had to sew and iron in the same room in which she slept. Only a domestic servant born in the 1890s would have accepted such an arrangement, and Darby would no doubt have remained crammed in with her sewing machine and ironing board, but that my grandmother was anxious to return the fine, airy first-floor room to use by house-guests (of which there was a never-ending stream) and that Grandpa was such a considerate employer.

Darby had retired to Boscombe in '63, and even at Glenturret it was becoming less fashionable (and less necessary) to have a lady's maid, so what had been her three rooms slipped out of use for six years until it was time to spruce the house up for sale.

The corridor partitioning came down in July – about the time we were invading for the final time. By the end of that month, the men from Dougal's of Stirling had fitted new wainscoting and re-wired the lights, and the house resounded to bangs and crashes from above. Then one day came a tap on the library door after lunch. Mike and I were lying on the floor reading a Marvel comic and *"The Thirty-Nine Steps"* respectively, with Grandpa's eye glaring more or less balefully over the topmost edge of *"The Financial Times"* (he preferred people to sit on the furniture provided, not sprawl on the carpet like Bedouins); Ma was riffling through the summer edition of *"The Scots Magazine"*, and our grandmother, for once not in her letter-writing room, was smoking one of her Sullivan and Powell Turkish cigarettes in the window bay. The tap came again on the door.

'Go to the door, my boy,' said Grandpa to me, and I put down Richard Hannay just as he had glimpsed the aeroplane pursuing him over the moors.

At the door stood Mackechnie, Lord High Priest of the decorating team – a gnome-like and brilliantined man with thick pebble glasses, whom Mike admired because he drove the bright red Leyland lorry and trailer which scrunched up the gravel every morning at breakfast time. Mike had once asked him to have lunch in the dining-room, a *faux pas* which Mackechnie had not compounded by accepting.

'May Ah have a wee worrrd, sir?' murmured Mackechnie.

'Pray step in,' replied Grandpa, laying the paper on his knee.

'It's aboot yon room,' said the gnome, gesturing upwards. 'Ah dinna know how to tell you, but the men are fair gripin' aboot the job at the present time.'

'Griping?' barked Grandpa. 'What do you mean by "griping"?'

'Weel, they say the cold up there is getting awfu' bad.'

'The cold?' snapped Grandpa. 'Why man, it's late July! How can it be cold? It isn't cold. It's warm.' Admittedly, Grandpa regarded any temperature above 15 degrees centigrade as warm – a point of view felicitous in one who chose to live at Glenturret all the year round – but, in point of fact, the weather was warmish at the time; not sunny, of course – after all we were on the Perthshire/Stirlingshire border – but muggy and not at all chilly.

'It's no cold doon here, I admit,' replied Mackechnie, 'but it's like the arctic up in yon room, and it's been steadily getting worse these last twa days.'

'Tchah! Absurd!' snorted Grandpa, heaving himself to his feet. 'I will see for myself, Mackechnie.' He waited for Mackechnie to go back out of the library, waving an impatient hand as a signal for the High Priest to proceed.

Grandpa followed him, amid cries of, 'Can we come?' from Mike and me.

'You boys may come, if you do not interrupt,' said Grandpa.

We went up the main staircase, up beyond the guest-room landings to the third floor, and were soon standing facing the curve. The frosted door was open and, in the doorway – this side of it, were Mackechnie's three storm-troopers: two burly chaps and a long-haired youth who looked like Pete Townsend of The Who used to in the '70s. They had a guilty hang-dog air, and clearly they had been waiting for their leader's return with a sullen determination not to continue with their work until something had been done about "the awfu' cold".

'Well, what's this nonsense?' grunted Grandpa.

The three stooges said nothing, but gazed pointedly at Mackechnie.

'It's half-way doon the room, sir. It's verra cold, and there's a nasty feeling in the air. The men say they feel something's watching them. They keep wanting tae turn their heads to see if something's behind them.'

The three "men" nodded vigorously.

'Can I go in and see?' squeaked Mike, and he darted round the workmen from Dougal's and went into the room. 'It's true, it's really cold!' he piped from beyond the door.

'Let me pass, if you please,' said Grandpa, as least as frostily as the purported cold spot.

I followed him into the room, and the change in temperature was startling. It was like stepping into a walk-in fridge. And there was more. What I had always felt about the upper passage seemed to crystallise into an understanding that there was something extremely wrong about it. The chill had, overlaying it, an acid feeling of unease, and my predominant impulse, as I remember it, was to get back again to the safe end of the curved corridor.

'Stop fidgeting, boy,' snapped Grandpa, and he paced right to the end of the long cream-coloured room and then turned and paced back.

'I'll look into this, Mackechnie,' he said eventually. 'I expect that there is a draught coming up through the boards; it cannot be rising damp at this height. Be ready to start work again in the morning.'

I remember peering up at his little moustache and irritable mouth and feeling astonished that he showed no sign of perturbation. Could it be possible that he felt no eeriness lying deep within the penetrating chill?

The next morning, of course, brought no perceptible diminution in the cold of the room. Why should it have done? Grandpa's "looking into it" meant nothing more than one more visit to the third floor before going to bed and snorting, 'Tchah!' (Mike and I had heard his footsteps and his snort quite clearly from our rooms near the stairs on the floor below.) Mackechnie and his troops carried out their threatened suspension of work, impervious to Grandpa's most acid comments – and so several days passed. Grandpa ordered Nichol up from the farm to put light bulbs in the sockets of the newly installed wall-lamps, for the work had been abandoned at the stage where the empty fixtures with power going to them were bulb-less. When the lights were switched on, the two near the corridor end burnt as normal, but the four further into the room in the area of most intense cold – there were three on each wall – immediately blew. Nichol replaced the blown bulbs and tried again, with Mike and me watching, fingers pressed into ears as, phut! they went once more. After a third attempt, Nichol reported to the library that "the vicious wee chill has bugger't the lichts".

The same day brought a report from Barable that the creeper up on the outside of the third-floor wall immediately adjacent to the room's windows had died, leaving a brown circle of withered leaves in the midst of bright green.

By that evening we heard from McAird (who had probably contributed to it) that the phenomenon was the talk of the district.

I was thrilled, and Peter Buchan was a practically permanent visitor, arriving on his bicycle soon after breakfast and going home with great reluctance before supper after anxious telephone calls from his mother. I think that the word "thrilled" does not express fully the extraordinary range of emotions one experiences when living in a house generally agreed to be badly haunted. We were thrilled in the joyful sense during the daytime when, cycling down to Kinbuck to buy a tin of Cremola Foam or a shilling's worth of flying saucers, we could give to the shopkeepers the latest news and embroider to our hearts' content. We were thrilled when, with Peter, Hector and Sherbert, we crouched in the Gothic folly where the croquet mallets lived, swigging Tizer to assist the downward passage of slabs of Devona toffee or Coulter's Candy, planning our midnight foray into the haunted room, armed with garlic, crucifixes and the exorcism rite of the Church of England (if we'd known where to obtain it).

But we were thrilled in a different and less pleasurable sense when evening came, and Peter, Hector and Sherbert were safe in their own un-haunted homes, and Mike and I were alone on the second floor.

Grandpa was of the old-fashioned, splendid belief that children should not inflict their presence upon their betters in the evening, so Mike and I had supper in our dressing-gowns upstairs while dinner was in progress downstairs. Normally we looked

forward to this cosy arrangement, and after our
scrambled eggs or ham sandwiches we would lay a
long line of Trix railway track from our bedroom
along the dark green carpet to the stair-head. A box
of 00 gauge track was, in fact, kept in my room at
Glenturret specifically for this purpose.

Back in 1968, I was just beginning to find my
fanatical interest in model trains ebbing slightly in
favour of rock music, especially that of the Beatles,
The Doors, and the Hollies. However, on most
summer evenings during that last holiday at
Glenturret, we had my recent Christmas present, a
Triang-Hornby *"Brittania"* with 'Synchrosmoke'
(ie: it puffed burning oil as it moved) and three
Pullman coaches ready to run. We would crouch at
each end of the long track, my old Hammant and
Morgan controller plugged in to the mains, and
would send engines hurtling back and forth at scale
speeds of 200mph. When we laid twin tracks we
could race my birthday present of '64, a Trix
"Warship", against *"Crepello"* and other engines,
and I once built a top-heavy flier out of Meccano –
just a clockwork motor and a mass of gearing on a
frame – which beat the lot of them.

As London children used to a small flat in W9, we
had an enthusiastic fondness for long corridors, and
the distance from my room to the stair-head used up
every piece of track. The timespan of the adults'

dinner was enough for our game to be inventive and inspiring, but short enough for it never to become boring. Always, as we were about to set the engines off for the fastest run of the night, Mum would appear at the turn of the stairs, calling,

'Nine thirty! Bed, you two!'

Up would come the track and the corridor would be deserted when she returned for coffee in the library.

The peculiarity of the haunted room, however, put paid to these railway operations completely. Just ONE floor up the stairs was the beginning of the passage into it, with its sinister curve and frosted door – and which of us wanted to be out of his room, squatting at the end of the line with his back to the dark stairwell?

The dimness for which we had once liked our bedroom corridor seemed oppressive under such conditions, and the mystery of length became an awesome gulf separating us from the warm chatter and opening doors of downstairs.

'You boys not getting silly ideas?' Dad had asked on his flying weekend, after the haunting had become a *cause celebre*.

'No. Fine, Dad,' we twittered. What liars we had become. The nights of early August that year were the most disturbed I had ever spent. I suppose it hadn't helped that, by one of those quirks of perversity, I had been irresistibly drawn to read *"Dracula"* – an early Stoker edition which I had found in the library, and only too well illustrated, particularly on that dreadful page where Harker, hearing shrieks in the night, opens his window and sees the evil count, aching for babies' blood, crawl downwards into the moonlit castle yard with cloak spread out behind him on the rough wall, like a huge, obscene, clinging bat. Paralysed with terror, I sat up, night after night, reading on beneath the Cold Spot, leaping like a chamois every few minutes as my toes fancied something creeping about in the bed with them, or my eyes imagined movements in the room's corners.

And all the while the Cold Spot grew colder.

'Guy, why don't you ring the Society for Psychical Research?' asked Diana Steele, a visitor to the house one tea-time. 'Just tell them what's wrong and they'll send someone to look into it. That's what my brother-in-law did in Sussex, and it worked. It's rather exciting, isn't it?' With that sentiment few of us concurred any more. Grandpa loosed off a snort like a Boeing 707 crash-landing. His conventional High Anglican Toryism simply couldn't swallow the idea of a haunting in the house. Obviously he believed that Michael, Gabriel and the Archangels administered things in Heaven, that Noah built an ark, that Jesus had risen from the dead, that Peter and Paul had founded an everlasting true church, that Protestantism was its correct expression and that the monarch was divinely appointed, but nothing was going to make him admit to the supernatural in the servant quarters of his mid-Victorian chunk of stockbroker Gothic; and as for some hysterical London ghost society – Tchah!

It was with some surprise, therefore, that I learnt at breakfast that "A Man from London" was coming to stay for two nights to look into the Cold Spot. The surprise was mitigated, said Dad ironically, by the reflection that for Grandpa there was a greater god than God – viz: money. Worn down by the hideous spectre of having to pay Mackechnie and Co to do nothing all day, theological niceties had taken back seat to economic reality (as always seems to be the case, I have since realised) and the Society for Psychical Research had been telephoned, with reckless disregard of long-distance expenses, and instructed to unleash its most redoubtable sleuth.

We three boys, Peter Buchan, Mike and me, went – all of us agog – with McAird in the Bentley to Glenturret halt to meet the train from the south. From it emerged an extremely fat and perspiring man with red sideburns and a bright checked suit. The guard handed him down a small tan suitcase covered in railway stickers, which he seized in plump fingers before McAird could get at it.

'Glenturret mystery?' he enquired of us. We nodded. 'Carboy's the name. Glad you kids came to meet me; it'd be a bugger to get a cab round here, wouldn't it?' He squeezed the immensity of his check-clad buttocks into the front seat of the Bentley, overflowing onto McAird's side.

'I shall drive you straight tae the hoose, sir,' said McAird with dignity, slipping behind the wheel.

'Nice motor,' grunted Mr Carboy. 'I've got a Cortina myself. I don't bugger it out on assignments though. Not if you are paid expenses on the train. Bloody long journey. I was sticking to the seat. Funny, but I've never been to Scotland before. Don't know why. After all, I've been to Trinidad and Romania, but bonny Scotland – no. Mind if I puff, chum?' He ignited a Woodbine with a chrome Ronson. 'Gor! I can't reach the ashtray. I'll flick it out. Comes of liking my ale, kids,' he cried jovially, patting his jutting abdomen and turning to wink at us over a podgy shoulder. 'Bugger me, I couldn't half push one back now.'

There was a one-sidedness to the conversation. The fact is that all four of us were sitting frozen and spellbound in the purring Bentley. McAird, I suspected, was in a state of shock at being addressed as "chum" by one of Grandpa's guests, and seemed unable to remonstrate as ash sprinkled the sacrosanct interior of Grandpa's best car.

But Peter and Mike and I were struck dumb by disillusion and disappointment. It is difficult to say precisely what we had been expecting, but on the way to the halt we had speculated that the ghost hunter would certainly be on the lines of Sherlock Holmes, or even, perhaps, Dracula himself – high cheekbones, pale, set face, tall, veined forehead and eyes locked upon the infinite and full of suffering and mysticism – a sort of mixture of Aztec High priest, the horror-film actor Christopher Lee, and revenant.

Our distinguished guest belched and lit another gasper. 'Wind's a right sod,' he said, spraying ash.

After breakfast next day, history not being able to relate how the paranormal expert had gone down with Grandpa at dinner, a procession made its way up to the curved passage. The assembled personnel was: Grandpa (reserved and sceptical), Mr Carboy (wheezing, podgy and with egg on his jumper), me, Mike, and Peter Buchan, who had arrived at the unprecedented hour of 8.45 and had waited out of everyone's sight in the kitchen, scoffing a second brekker until Glenturret was ready to receive him.

'I hardly consider it necessary for you boys to accompany us,' Grandpa had complained, and we could see a firm dismissal coming when Mr Carboy interjected with, 'I don't mind the kids tagging along. Nothing's going to happen. Just keep your traps shut, that's all.'

On arrival at the end of the curved passage a podgy hand shoved open the frosted doors and a breath of arctic and sinister air spun round us.

'Oooh,' squeaked Mike, and I held a finger to my lips as a sign for him to belt up.

'Oh, I say! You've got a good one. I've come upon this many times, you know. The sod of it is finding where the centre is. If you get that right you can usually sort it out. Some places the centre is in the most inaccessible spot. You see, some hauntings go on after a new house has been built over the old one. People say they've seen ghosts walking in mid-air; you know, where the old floors were. Get it? Ten to one the centre of a disturbance is slap in a new loo pan! Ha, ha, ha!'

Mr Carboy's laugh rang out, unfittingly it seemed to me, in the oppressive corridor. Grandpa seemed to be hunting for the *mot juste* in reply to Mr Carboy's pleasantries, but failing, contented himself with a grunt. Mike and Peter gazed wildly around as though expecting to see spectral legs between floor and ceiling.

'There was no house here before this one, I believe,' said Grandpa at last, in a tone which expressed his doubts of Mr Carboy's competence.

Mr Carboy opened a slim leather wallet and his plump fingers extracted from it a cotton reel, a packet of drawing-pins and a dozen glass thermometers.

'Spirit thermometers,' said he. 'Get it? *Spirit* thermometers? Ho, ho! We call it a joke in the trade.' Grandpa stared at them frostily. 'They react quick, you see. Got a ladder?'

He balanced on the steps which I had been sent to fetch from the pantry, and tied tiny knots of cotton round the thermometers which he then suspended from the ceiling at different heights by means of drawing-pins. 'Now we have elevenses,' he wheezed, drawing out his Ronson and lighting up. 'Come back in half an hour.'

This process of temperature measuring took him all day, and again and again he repositioned the thermometers on different lengths of cotton, and retired for a coffee and fag, then lunch, then a snack, and tea, then a drink.

Mike and I began to lose interest. Peter had had to go home. All three of us had expected something more on the lines of "with bell, book and candle" and "Get thee behind me, Satan". Perhaps too, we had expected a spot of incult mutterings in a runic tongue, or even Latin, like "*Veni, Mephistopheli!*" – but, of course, in reverse. It was all very disappointing. Fiddling about with drawing-pins and making a sort of bargain-basement Christmas decoration in different parts of the room was not only unexciting to watch, considered as a spectator sport, but seemed to be having no effect. The area was dreary and chill and ominous, but no more or less so than usual. On this unpromising low spot in Mr Carboy's visit we went to bed.

During the following morning Mr Carboy was unusually active. Clad in his bright check (and the same shirt in which he had arrived) he crouched over the library desk with a propelling-pencil and a long list of figures. Grandpa sat nearby reading *The Times*. Our grandmother was discussing menus with Cook. Ma had taken the estate car to Stirling to put Dad on his train back to London, and then to do some shopping. Normally we would have gone to see Dad off, but the two of us, and Peter, who had arrived mid-morning, kept popping into the library and, meeting Grandpa's eyes over the top of the paper, retiring again. We were anxious to miss nothing, but there didn't seem much to miss.

At twelve, on the umpteenth occasion of our visit to see how Mr Carboy's calculations (whatever they were) were coming along, we were greeted by the following exchange:

'What?'

'A pickaxe.'

'What!'

'Pickaxe.'

'But you are surely aware that I have just had it redecorated.'

'We'll have to break it open.'

'But…..'

'Suit yourself, chum. That's what you've got to do if you want it cleared up.'

Mr Carboy was standing over Grandpa, wiping his plump fingers on his trouser-seat. Grandpa's eyes met mine.

'Ah, Anthony, my boy. Request McAird to bring a – a pickaxe to the upper corridor.'

McAird and I, plus pickaxe and Hector, arrived breathless at the haunted passage, to find Grandpa and Mr Carboy already there. Mr Carboy turned to me.

'Hold that bugger,' said he, and thrust a sheet of paper into my hands. On it was a surprisingly fine drawing of the upper corridor and room in firm pencil. There was a perfect circle on it, the centre of which was at a spot on the outer wall. A further sketch, with another circle, showed the wall upright; the circle's centre was down near the floor. The outer parts of each of the circles enclosed part of the outside wall (where the creeper had died), and part of the upper wall (upon which the lights had blown when switched on).

Sausage-like fingers took the pickaxe from

McAird's grasp and a bright checked jacket was removed. A splash of spit was applied to podgy, pink palms, and Mr Carboy swung the pickaxe round and crashed it into the plaster-work above the wainscot. We boys held our breath with delight. Now something was happening!

Crash! Smash! The plaster gave way, and we immediately saw that the wall was hollow. Down came the axe and the wainscot split noisily.

Grandpa began to say, 'I would be grateful if you would not....' But suddenly we were all aware of a great increase in the cold, and of a very nasty, close dread in the passage. Mr Carboy paused. Mike whispered, 'I want to go downstairs.' I felt a strange creeping on my shoulder-blades and neck.

'Take the kids down, chum,' said Mr Carboy to McAird. 'I've reached the bugger.'

McAird dropped his hand to my crawling shoulder and I nearly yelped with fright. Mike and Hector had already fled, Peter had gone to the frosted door, but before I turned away, I saw, in slow motion almost, Mr Carboy stoop down and pick from inside the wall a tiny skeleton from the lap of a bony shape in cobwebby rags. The shape's head had open jaws stretched in a dental silent scream that seemed to howl: "Don't wall us in alive!"

Mr Carboy had found a girl and a baby at the junction between wall and floor. There was not, at the time, any explanation of their presence. Ma later told us that the pathetic bones had been dated to a time roughly in the mid- to late- 19th century. The Rector, a keen local historian who had written a pamphlet on such matters, visited Glenturret to inform Grandpa that the Celts used to bury unwanted babies in new fortifications, and that they might have done so for the same reasons that the Minoan Greeks used to bury soldiers alive in earth at the bases of pillars in ceremonial buildings – the "watcher at the threshold", whose spirit remained to ward off evil.

But that was, after all, back in the Bronze Age. Why such a thing should have occurred in the 1860s on the third floor of Glenturret, no one could guess. One theory was that the girl had been a local siren got with child by the son of the contractor – but there was no proof. Grandpa's re-building had disturbed something, but we thought it odd that it had not happened earlier when Darby's rooms had been partitioned, nor in the time of previous owners.

The mysterious bones were decently buried, and slowly the Cold Spot warmed up. The Society for Psychical Research charged nothing for their services, beyond expenses, but Grandpa sent them a donation of £100. It was by such sums that they kept going, I guessed.

And that seemed to be that.

Not until the early 1980s did it become clear that the malevolent force in that part of the house was still very much alive – and that there was more to be found than mere skeletons. But by then Grandpa was dead, the house an institution, and a wretched obsessive was seeing out his last days with a terrifying entity – his plaything in the night hours. Such details as are necessary to explain form a piece later in this memoir of my loss, so I shall leave the topic until then, after I have brought things up to date.

SCHOOLING

Looking back over the last ninety-seven pages, I'm sure you're thinking: Is this rambling mass of anecdote going to get into some sort of shape? I'm not sure that it will end up having a plot; real life doesn't have a plot, does it? How often does real life begin with: "Claridge, the silver-haired butler of Harburton Grange, stepped into the hall, shock engraved on every line of his pale, fattish face – for had he not been the first to discover Sir Gerard Armiter-Snipe pinned to the shiny oak floor of the long gallery by the strangely chased oriental dagger which heretofore had adorned the stern old baronet's great desk"?

Read such a question, and you know that a *plot* will unfold, with punctilious attention paid to the diverse lives and multifarious doings of the carefully arranged characters. If you read Brit detective fiction regularly, you are certain to guess before too long that while Haunch, the vile-mannered poacher, and Major Rex Tarrant, once in the Brigade of Guards, now a professional gambler of Mayfair Mansions, *seem* the most likely suspects, it was clearly Ysabel, Sir Gerard's quaint, childlike ward, who had always felt such exquisite pain when contemplating the haughty baronet's unrivalled collection of pinned butterflies, who had done the horrific deed.

Real life, unlike a crime novel, has no plan. It is

like these blank pages on which I scribbled (just for myself as a piece if personal history and then typed up, because I was encouraged to believe that others might find it interesting) and there is comfort in the 2D nature of paper; you can only go up or down. I know that I have already touched lightly on the fact that, in 1969, Glenturret was about to be sold. That needs relating in detail. Yes, anecdotal dysentery must take second place to information.

In late August, 1969, we were coming to the end of our last summer hols at Glenturret, some weeks before my fifteenth birthday. Grandpa had been increasingly grumpy since his prostate operation in '66, was getting arthritic, and travelled round his estate less and less. On shoots at Sherrifmuir, he sat in the back of the Bentley with a plaid rug over his knees while Nichol banged at the snipe, and McAird showed me how to handle a gun, steadying the twelve-bore at the moment of explosion. On the Dunblane Road, Grandpa winced more than he used to as lorries hurtled past, and McAird was instructed to drive more and more slowly. When Grandpa drove himself, he stopped dead whenever a lady pedestrian seemed about to cross the road – even on the A9. This mixture of chivalry and nerves earned many hoots.

Mike and I had successfully played on his

jumpiness the summer before when returning in the estate car from a cattle show at Alloa. We took it in turns to thump on the side of the car surreptitiously, and at each thump Grandpa stopped dead.

'Thee it goes again, Bill!' he had cried to Dad. 'Do you think it safe to proceed?'

'Yes, Guy,' Dad had answered wearily. 'It's just a bump in the road.'

Thump!

The car rolled to a halt.

'Good God! There it is again! Bless my soul. McAird must take a look at it.'

We had taken ages to get home.

I suppose, looking back, it was around this time that Grandpa was growing old; becoming a real "old" person, that is, with the first weaknesses and foibles of advanced years starting to show. This is no doubt why Jane, our grandmother, felt the time was right to begin the steady propaganda war aimed at selling the house and moving back to her beloved London.

'Sell Glenturret!' I recall Grandpa hooting, when our grandmother, informing him that some people called the Newtons had found a buyer for their large hunting lodge at Bridge of Allan and gone to Oxford to be near their son, followed up with one of her hints. 'Never!'

But sold it was in the winter of '69, and Grandpa

exchanged the gun-room with its mahogany cases and copies of *The Scots Magazine*, the cold fug of the lofty dining-room with its silvered food warmers and lacquered portraits under picture-lights, the stone flags of the hall with its grand staircase, the unused ballroom, the cavernous shelved library with its long views across to the Ochils, the rows of bells on springs in the kitchen corridor, the maze-like passages, off which sprung so many lavendery, plump-bedded rooms, the freezing bathrooms and gurgling pipes, the ozone of pines and heather under a twinkling winter sky, for a big smart flat at Prince's Gate, London, SW1.

Mike was impressed by this apartment – more so than I, for I was strangely upset by the loss of the Scottish house – but Grandpa complained bitterly, as I have mentioned already, of "bumping into the servants". My grandmother, who had only to pop through "the hole in the wall" at the end of Ennismore Gardens to get to Harrods, took on a new and vibrant youth, while her uprooted consort dwindled into a peppery figure in a chair, snorting at the news, the pop, and the horrors of satire on BBC2 and the northern accents on ITV (neither of which channels could at that time have been got in mid-Scotland).

Glenturret was not on the market long. I think, from overhearing talk about it between Ma and Dad, that everyone had expected the house and estate to be sold as one unit to a buyer in the Grandpa mould: a successful retired financier or manufacturer who would continue to foster the Edwardian flavour of the place. All were surprised to hear that the dairy farm was bought separately by Grandpa's old farm manager. I now realise that there was a belief among Grandpa's contemporaries that a man of the tenant-farmer class would hardly have the nerve, let alone the money, to set up as a minor landowner on his own. But "Young" Nichol, for long regarded as a comic, bucolic Scots underling, was soon to blossom into a rubicund gentleman-farmer. I did try, after my own re-purchase of the house, to get the dairy farm back under my umbrella, but Nichol was by then too successful to buy out. He made what had been, in the '60s, the Lower Farm into Drummond House and, before he died, was seen bowling to Stirling in his Jaguar, cutting as grand a figure as Grandpa – grander, really, because he was far more purple and bulky.

That sale of the large acreage which made up Nichol's land left a much more compact unit, one less suited to agrarian enterprise. The market was reduced to those who simply wanted a big house and garden (and there weren't many of those around as Harold Wilson's and Heath's governments faced the spectre and then the reality of devaluation of the pound); or those who might require a building to use for an institution.

It was into this unexpected slice of the property market that Glenturret finally fell.

Quite why Frank Costigan believed that an isolated house outside Dunblane was the ideal spot for a boys' school, I never knew, but by the Michaelmas term of 1970, Glenturret Academy was open for business in a modest way and had enrolled seventy-four young men for tuition.

Doctor Costigan had owned a prep school near Kidderminster, but it had not paid. From the proceeds of the sale of this building as offices to a parts supplier of British Leyland Cars, he and two colleagues had raised enough to bid successfully for Glenturret and have money left over to equip it for boarding accommodation and basic teaching needs. The prep school desks and beds were hauled north by Pickfords's, and Matron was persuaded to come too.

In some ways the house was far more suited to institutional use than to private occupation. The squash courts, for example, found themselves used as something other than an avian Buchenwald for the first time since 1960. The large bedrooms made pleasant classrooms for small groups. There were enough smaller rooms left over to be partitioned into senior pupils' study bedrooms. The old drawing-room made a capacious junior dormitory. The dining-room and library retained their original functions, and refectory benches accommodated nearly all the boys at mealtimes, just as Grandpa's many dark-wood shelves were more than adequate for the display of books. The Headmaster himself took over the gun-room, and thus had a good observation post from which to gaze wistfully past the rhododendrons down the drive, as if willing new custom to come crunching up the gravel. Two signs, royal blue with gold lettering, went up on the Kinbuck road, proclaiming the fact that you were passing "GLENTURRET ACADEMY FOR BOYS 13 – 18. Preparation for entry to Oxford and Cambridge and the major universities. Individual tuition. Headmaster: Doctor F N L Costigan, BA (Hons), MA, PhD."

At the time of the sale, and during the six months of re-furbishment, I knew nothing of all this, of course. Mike and I lived on as London children: bicycling in the fog, travelling on the top deck of the cosily-lit No 6 bus to outlandish places like Hackney Wick in search of sci-fi films, wandering round Hamley's or Gamages toy stores like yearning somnambulists, watching "Top of the Pops" and saving for 45s, smoking the odd *"Craven A"* or *"Senior Service"* from Dad's box, and haunting the Science Museum.

Every school day morning we went from Warwick Avenue tube station to West Hampstead (change at Baker Street), and every evening we returned, chewing flying saucers and sucking Barratt's sherbert fountains, while Mike ran his latest Corgi Whizz Wheels car along convenient wall tops, while I imagined that I was in a train, crossing points and mouthing the rhythmic clunking of wheels under my breath. This daily journey lulled the swift months of childhood away. Our year was punctuated by the great regular treats: The Royal Tournament at Earl's Court, Farnborough Air Show, Selfridge's at Christmas, the Zoo, Heathrow Airport (to watch planes), Battersea Funfair, Brighton.

As my fifteenth birthday came into sight during the long corridor of the 1969 Christmas term, my relations with Mike (nearly eleven), grew positively civilised. The variegated tortures to which he had been put as a tiny boy had done their work and smoothed off any tiresome sharp corners with which he might have been left, is how I looked at it in '69. At any rate, I found him quite good company, and blushed to recall how unbrotherly I had been when first he had started going off each day with me to the junior department of our school in West Hampstead.

It amazes me to look back and realise that I was rather a horrid child. Only Grandpa had the power to instil a fear of adulthood. Ma was indulgent and feared sulks, and Dad was too busy to keep me properly in check.

A nervous new kid, Mike had stuck closer to me than the paper on the wall during our first tube journeys together. In fact I had been compelled to tell him to "sod off into another carriage". I had a fear of being thought a cissy, when accompanied by a snivelling younger brother in public.

'Get out of my carriage, creep!' I would cry, and Mike would sorrowfully dismount at Edgware Road and spend the rest of the journey in the adjoining coach, peeking over at me through the end window. At Baker Street, Mike did his "sticking closer than a brother" act again – logically, I suppose, for he had an obsession about getting lost amid the innumerable tunnels and escalators of that station, and might reasonably have expected his big brother to have seen him safely through. This glutinousness on his part gradually led me to realise that some financial gain might be made of his need for guidance. Thus began my demand for his pocket-money in exchange for safe passage and the right platform for West Hampstead. For many months, a shiny half-crown exchanged hands silently on the train. Mike had sneaked to Dad about this pecuniary arrangement, but our saintly father had refused to believe the story, not crediting me with the necessary blackness of soul.

Mike reminds me periodically that, at current rates of sterling value plus compound interest, I owe him over six thousand pounds. There are times when I feel I should dash him off a cheque and hear the last of it.

By 1969, however, all past wrongs were forgiven – even if past extortions not paid back. It seemed a pity, therefore, that our paths were now to diverge following the shock of my expulsion from school.

I imagine, looking back, that I was perhaps a teeny bit naughtier than most of the other boys at Worsley House – that swanky grove of academia in West Hampstead, the prospectus of which had so impressed dear Ma because of its claims to "enlightened methods" and lack of corporal punishment.

By the age of fifteen I should have been boarding at some public school of repute (some rather minor one, perhaps, in view of Dad's straitened financial circumstances), but Ma could never bear the thought of sending either of us away to school. She herself had been dreadfully unhappy at Leatherhead Court during the war, and she believed that a child's place was at his mother's side. Dad had wanted us to follow him to Ardingly in Sussex, but Ma and "enlightened methods" won the day, and off as a day-boy to Worsley House I had gone – first into the preparatory department, and then, from the age of thirteen, into the Upper School. Mike was to soldier on there until 1974 when he too left and went to a big local comprehensive's Sixth Form to do A Levels in Art, Drama and Business Studies – none of which Worsley House offered.

There are advantages to be gained from "enlightened" teaching, but I'm now the first to admit that a spot of severe thrashing might have prevented the ghastly collapse which confronted the family at the end of the school year of '69/70.

My expulsion had been on the cards ever since I had been taught by Mr P. Burgess in Drake C. This beaky, nervy young man's interpretation of the easy-going, psychology-based, child-centred training methods advocated by the Headmaster had gone so far as to insist that we brats call him by his first name (it was Perry – short for Peregrine, we believed) from Day One. This had proved a mistake. Sometimes he forgot to be loving and understanding and, after a particularly exuberant bout of ragging, would seize upon a victim and request that he stand upon a desk and roll up his right trouser-leg. Perry, with a peculiar mixture of vindictiveness and sorrow, would then beat the miscreant's calf with a *six-inch* ruler, the while imploring us never to inform the Headmaster that such a thing had occurred. Partly because I was so often dragged out to receive this chastisement, and partly because I couldn't respect a man who hadn't the common-sense to select at least a *twelve*-inch ruler as his instrument of castigation, I joined the wildest spirits of Drake C, whose mission it was to bring Burgess' hairs in sorrow to his grave.

Perry (known more often as Pee-Wee, a corruption of his initials, PB, I should think) taught (or tried to teach) French. At the time I believed that no true-blue English boy should be expected to master the lingo of so silly a race as the French, and I'm sure that millions of other British youths felt (and feel) the same. This may explain why French lessons have traditionally been the most disorderly of school subjects. Drake C's classroom was on the third floor and, thanks to the jamming together of two buildings of different eras, was approached by a short flight of steps which continued down into the room itself. This room commanded a view of the London tube lines running over-ground towards Stanmore and crossing the Finchley Road through a tunnel. Beneath its windows was the concreted courtyard which was used as the junior boys' playground, and which was reached by the staircase which ran down from our classroom, and by another, thinner flight of stairs round the L-shape of the building.

Pee-Wee would appear at the door of Drake C, a little out of breath from his climb up from the yard, pause, poke his head round the lintel as if to ascertain that all was safe, then scamper in and dart behind the old-fashioned desk on its dais at the other end of the classroom. His passage through the desks would usually be greeted with joyous cries of 'Wotcha, Pee-Wee!' and flying bits of exercise book and inky blobs of blotter. Sometimes a copy of "*The Henriade*" would whizz past him; sometimes he would beat a flying grammar or a heavy Roubaud's French/English dictionary by a short head to the comparative safety of his dais. Very often Roubaud or the grammar would beat him. Once behind his rampart he would bleat,

'Quiet! Quiet, boys! Please be quiet! Quiet, I say! Now today we are really going to work! Quiet! Quiet! Now, turn to page forty-two.'

The rest of the lesson would be drowned out by chit-chat, snatches of "*Old Macdonald had a farm*" ("*....and on that farm was a peregrine, ee-iy-ee-iy-oh! With a 'Pee-Wee' there and a 'Quiet, boys' there, etc.....*") and a periodic squeal from Perry louder than the background racket.

'I *never* had this trouble from the boys at Preston!' he would shriek. Usually a massy book would whizz across the room and thud on or near him. 'Stevens!' he would howl. 'What are you doing? How *dare* you throw that book!'

'Oh, Sir,' Stevens would protest. 'I didn't mean to

throw it. Dombey's just farted, Sir, and I was waving the niff away with my book, and it flew out of my hand.'

And others would chip in with cries of,

'It's true, Sir! Dombey's always farting. He goes to the doctor for it. He's got farto-psychosis, Sir.'

And books would wave away an imaginary smell again, followed by shouts of,

'Whoops! There goes my book now, Sir! Sorry, Sir. It slipped out of my hand like Stevens' book, Sir.'

'Quiet! Oh, *please* be quiet! The Headmaster will hear you!' Pee-Wee would scream.

The six-inch ruler usually followed about ten minutes before the end of the lesson, after which pandemonium would become general. Twice the Headmaster did appear to quell the row, and twice Pee-Wee had burst into tears of rage and hysteria when he left.

In short, Drake C French lessons were among my regular treats of the week.

Pee-Wee fell regularly for every trick we handed out. He really was such a "mong", as we used to say in those days. He even fell for the tarpaulin jape. You place a tarpaulin sheet under the blackboard, in whisks Pee-Wee, you shout: "Careful, Sir! The floorboards are up just there! The caretaker asked me to tell you." Pee-Wee gazes at the tarpaulin, bleats, "Oh dear! I wanted to use the blackboard today," and spends the whole lesson leaning at a dangerous angle across the tarpaulin, overbalancing, dropping his chalk, and trying to write "Page 42: *La visite a la gare*" and attendant work. The twit never thought to pluck up the edge of the tarp to look underneath.

Pee-Wee fell for the alarm-clock wheeze. You get friends to bring nine alarm-clocks in, you place them in the nine large lampshades dotted round the ceiling of your classroom: those proper, scalloped china bowls, so much cosier than fluorescent tubes in the dark afternoons of winter, and you time each clock to go off five minutes after the one before, the *toute ensemble* lasting nicely through a 45 minute French lesson. I recall that our most successful foray into this form of clockwork campanology was the third one. The previous two efforts had not worked quite as we had expected, for two reasons. On the first, Pee-Wee had simply bleated through the ringing, affecting to notice nothing and hoping to win through by bluff, true to his motto of "Peace at any price". On the second, we, his pupils, were making more noise than the nine clocks. On the third and best time, we decided to give the alarms a chance and be silent for once. In dashed Pee-Wee, full of beans, but cautious. We had to give him marks for persistence. After each fiasco he seemed to look forward to the next with undiminished relish. Perhaps he thought that the very next day was going to be the one on which we grew up and showed an interest in his subject. He always put me in mind of a quip we had learned in English: "More frightening than his pessimism is Man's baseless optimism." Who said it, I can't remember – and searching for it on-line comes up with zilch. I often quoted it to Mike – the optimistic brother of us two.

Anyway, in rushed Pee-Wee, amid total and unaccustomed silence from the mob. He cried,

'Right! Page forty-two, boys! Today I want to cover a lot of ground!'

Almost immediately came, "Ting-a-ling-a-ling-ling!" from above his head. I must admit, it was pretty noticeable. The lampshade amplified an already lusty alarm-clock to the decibel level of a dustbin being chucked out of an express in a tunnel. Pee-Wee leapt into the air with wild, staring eyes. I suppose he couldn't believe that "Alarm Clock III" or "Alarm Clock, the sequel" was starting. What an arse the man was! Instead of instantly handing out a detention, to be made more extensive if one of us did not *immediately* remove all clocks, he lost his head, dragged out his high chair from behind its desk, leapt upon it, and tried to fish the clock out from the dust and dead flies. As soon as his fingers groped into the shade, the clock stopped, of course. As the words "I never had this trouble with the boys at Pres.....," were forming on his lips, the second clock went off equally deafeningly. And what did Pee-Wee do? He grabbed up his chair and went to try and field that one too. As the second clock had been halted in mid-ring, there was time for him to descend and begin a squealing tirade before the third started off. This went on for some time, with Pee-Wee trying vainly to anticipate from which of the lampshades the bells would peal, and sobbing with humiliation and exasperation, while Drake C rolled exaggeratedly among the desks in hysterics. The lesson ended, as Pee-Wee's so often did, with his rushing tearfully from the classroom. Wonderful fun!

I think the most complicated trick we played on him – the penultimate one, in fact, before he was taken to hospital and I was expelled – took advantage of our third-floor position. I like to entitle this joke "The Phantom Corpse Wheeze". It provided our classic Pee-Wee story. Whenever two or three Worsley House old boys from the late 'sixties are gathered, and the topic turns to Perry Burgess baiting, there are cries of: "Yes, yes! That was a good one! But surely you remember the Phantom Corpse?"

French, on that star-crossed day, began in utter silence.

Pee-Wee appeared, haltingly, as usual, at the doorway.

'Morning, boys!' he bleated. He was greeted with a dead quiet and then one or two loud sobs. Each of us had powdered a little chalk and smeared it on our faces so that, in the dusky classroom, we looked pale and distraught. The sobbing of one or two boys increased and Pat Stevens buried his face in his hands and rocked to and fro like those women you see on news reports about earthquakes in the Middle East. In short, he was overdoing it, but Pee-Wee didn't notice. He whisked over to his desk.

'Good gracious, boys! What's the matter?'

One of us, looking up with drawn and ghastly visage, sobbed,

'I don't know how it happened, Sir! But he....he....he just fell out!'

An arm was thrown dramatically in the direction of a wide-open window. The windows were large sash types with low sills.

Pee-Wee gasped. Two more boys began crying loudly.

'He was just sitting on the window-sill, Sir, and....and we were talking, and then he just overbalanced and toppled out! And we didn't know what to do!'

'Oh, my God!' shrieked Pee-Wee, rushing across to the window, with saliva streaming back in the wind. He looked out. There, three storeys beneath, spread-eagled in a hideous attitude of death, lay Johnnie Butt, legs twisted, head back, tongue lolling out and curling on his cheek, like a limp party squeaker.

'You were late for class, Sir!' said someone.

'That's why we were *unsupervised*.' I added.

'Oh, my GOD!' screeched Pee-Wee again, and he tore from the room like a banshee, presumably to fetch the Headmaster, an ambulance, the police and so forth.

When he'd gone, we jumped up, wiped the chalk from our faces with our sleeves, leant out and gave Butt a whistle. He cheesed the death pose, got to his feet, darted into the building and nipped across to the back staircase. In a few moments he was sitting in his accustomed place. We lounged back, chairs tilted, hands in pockets, as if awaiting French. Butt had been just in time. There was a firm – a very firm – step in the corridor. The Headmaster had arrived. Behind him hung Pee-Wee, wringing his hands in anguish, and gasping,

'A terrible sight, Headmaster! The poor boy is obviously dead! Look! Look!'

With stately tread the Headmaster descended the steps into our room, crossed it and approached the open window. We stood and, fascinated, watched him. In truth, we hadn't expected him to feature in this jape. John Butt looked rather nervous. A grey scholarly head was poked out. The expression on the Head's face was extraordinary when he turned back to Pee-Wee.

'There is nothing there, Mr Burgess.'

'W-what?' stammered poor Pee-Wee. 'But, Headmaster, Headmaster, when I was here a few moments ago, I....'

It was our cue to barge in.

'Excuse me, Sir,' said Francis Healy to the Head, 'Mr Burgess hasn't been in yet. We have been wondering where he was.'

Pee-Wee gulped, like someone swallowing a chestnut that's too hot.

'But....but....,' he gurgled, 'but, boys, I was here a minute ago!'

'No, you weren't, Sir,' I said.

'Yes, yes, YES! I....I...' Pee-Wee gobbled like a turkey, his voice beginning to rise several octaves. 'I.....they're lying! I.....I....was....was....Why – oh! That's...that's....' He had at last spotted Butt, sitting demurely at his desk with a perfectly judged expression of bewilderment on his face. 'But....you....how did you.....?'

The Headmaster gazed at us, then at him. He took off his spectacles and closed them up with that unpleasant snap which indicates that the wearer is damned annoyed.

'Mr Burgess,' said he at last, in a sub-arctic voice, 'will you have the kindness to come to my office after school?'

Perhaps he thought Pee-Wee was plastered. At any rate, he wisely decided not to penetrate the mystery, scenting the likelihood of defeat at our hands. For the rest of the lesson, Pee-Wee sat in tears at his desk while we enjoyed the joke – bastards that we were.

The long-term Torturing of Pee-Wee culminated in the sad affair which resulted in his needing seven stitches, and my needing to find a new school.

We had never meant the jape to go so wrong, but, as usual, Pee-Wee's ineptitude made things much worse than they might have been.

For some time we had been experimenting with that new and delightful toy: transparent nylon fishing wire. Pretty well every classroom in the British Isles has – or had – hot water pipes going round the edge of the room at floor level. If you tie fishing-wire to your ankle, run it along the floor and under those pipes, and then bring the other end to, say, a statue of St Anthony, or to an oleograph of a coastal scene hanging on the wall, you can, with a single jerk, cause the *objet d'art* (as we say in French) to hurtle to the ground in mid-lesson with gratifying results.

Pee-Wee could actually be standing over you,

saying, "The boys at Preston never gave me this sort of trouble...." And you could be replying, 'Yes, Sir, Mr Burgess, Sir,' while pulling with your foot, and a wall-clock or map would crash down startlingly at the far end of the room.

We had kept this sort of thing up for a few weeks, but the interest was fading, and we needed to try our hands at something larger than mere wall décor.

Pee-Wee's desk, as I have mentioned, was on a dais under the blackboard, and the dais was only just big enough for it and its chair. Before French, on one enjoyable day, this heavy piece of furniture was pushed right to the forward edge of the platform, teetering, you might say, on the brink of the abyss, just in balance. The boys down the centre row – eight in all, sitting side-by-side at the inky double desks of the period – tied fishing-wire to their ankles and linked it, person-to-person, up to the stubby feet on the master's desk. It was known, of course, that Pee-Wee would, as usual, rush for the cover of this rampart, and crouch defensively behind its bulk.

The door opened.

'Morning, boys! Open your books to page forty-two! We are really going to work today!'

Pee-Wee bustled in. A paper aircraft caught him on the neck as he came halfway down the room, and a piece of blotting-paper soaked in black ink followed it just as he reached his desk. There was a lot of general noise, designed to get him quickly behind his defences. He did the last yard or two at an Olympic rush, darted behind his fortress, began squealing something or other about Preston, and leant forward brandishing his French grammar, which he held like a warrior's shield.

As he reposed his weight upon the sloping desk-top, we hissed,

'Now!'

The eight down the centre aisle jerked back their ankles, unseen by Pee-Wee, and the great desk poised for a second on the very edge of the dais. Pee-Wee, feeling it go, reached over to clutch at it. Of course it over-balanced catastrophically, carrying Pee-Wee with it. The boys in the front row immediately ceased operations with fishing-wire from that time onwards. They were painfully buried, crushed by the impact of Pee-Wee, desk, books, board rubbers and all landing on top of them. We roared, while Pee-Wee disentangled himself, gazed wildly around, and ran hysterically from the room, not to appear again that lesson.

I believe that it was after this event that I gave birth to The Grand (but Disastrous) Idea.

I have written already of the short flight of four steps which led down into the Drake C classroom. These were supported by small wooden columns. Pee-Wee, having plucked up courage at the doorway itself, would normally race down these steps, making a beeline for the shelter of his desk. I borrowed a hack-saw, or perhaps it was a fret-saw, from the hobbies room where Loudon was making a model of a seaplane, and I sawed through each of the little columns. I then put the sawn out sections back into place and nylon fishing-wire was tied to them, led round the pipes, and knotted round my ankles. I had this brilliant idea one break, I recall, after a particularly stimulating bout of Pee-Wee baiting the day before, but only put it into practice after being egged on by Stevens, Healy, Butt and Co.

So there I sat, like one of the Fates, the thread of destiny spinning out from my feet of clay to the small sawn-off pillars. There was a sound of squealing from the passage. Pee-Wee had arrived.

He poked his head round the door-jamb, as usual, in order to see if it were safe to proceed.

He began the well-known bleat.

'Morning, b.....'

He dashed on to the steps. I had whisked back my ankle. For a moment the entire cosmos stood still, the stars arrested in their courses.

The short flight of four steps collapsed like one of those minarets made of playing cards, and Pee-Wee, remaining in the air for what seemed like two hours, began his swift descent towards the centre of the earth in illustration of Newton's great law of gravity.

He didn't get as far as that, of course, for the classroom floor stopped him. He tripped over the little pile of collapsed steps and shot along between the rows of desks, ploughing up the wooden flooring with his nose.

Drake C sat, horrified and fascinated. That line: "their furrow oft the stubborn glebe has broke" which we had had in English, went round and round in my mind like a mad refrain as Pee-Wee's boko, Pee-Wee's pointy, economy or family-size schnozzle tore through the sturdy oak like an Antarctic ice-breaker. I had not intended this to happen. After the collapse of the steps, a bemused Pee-Wee was supposed to be left marooned two feet up outside the classroom.

In due course of time, after what seemed nearly a week since I had first pulled back my fateful ankle, Pee-Wee came to rest against my desk. He sat up, gushing gore. Between his fingers, pressed to a lacerated nose, his eyes played like a ray gun around my lower leg and the nylon fishing-wire attached thereunto.

The rest you can guess – indeed know. The rushing to hospital. The painful stitches. The even more painful interview with the Headmaster. The end of my plans for the rest of the O Level year, then Sixth Form at Worsley House. The immediate expulsion of the perpetrator. The long diatribes at home, more in sorrow than in anger. A mother's tears. The need to find me a new school.

It is interesting to record how difficult it was then to procure a place for an expelled boy who had a reputation for "insubordination and hooliganism" and who had assaulted a teacher. Nowadays, in the 21st century, in the era of "ECM" ("Every Child Matters"), schools would be falling over themselves to add such a specimen to the roll, but back then, in an era of NCM ("No Child Matters") they didn't want to know. The only place was a secondary modern in Maida Vale, and firm refusals to consider it were issued by Ma on the grounds that I would be bullied, by Grandpa on the grounds that it wouldn't be suitable for "the son of a gentleman", and by Dad on the grounds that the exam cadre was non-existent and that as I was on the verge of O Levels I must see them through.

So began a twilight time of private coaching, crash lessons (especially in French) at a crammer's in Kensington, and severe moral pressure on me to spend 99.99% of my time in study.

In June 1970, I sat ten O Levels and got nine; (Top grades in English, History, Biology and Religious Studies – if you've got brains, you've got them).

'The boy will go into Bradley and Knights, of course,' said Grandpa. 'It is time he settled into his career. The boy will be sixteen in a few weeks. I have spoken to Geoff Bradley and he will interview the boy gently. The Stock Exchange,' proclaimed Grandpa, sitting upright in his huge wing chair in the new flat at Prince's Gate, 'is the best career for the boy. He is not all bad, by any means.'

The "boy" sat on the tapestry stool and said nothing.

I had as many misgivings about the Stock Exchange at the time as I do now. I had a vague idea that the handling of huge sums of money needed at least some rudimentary mathematical ability. I notice, looking back a few lines, that I have bragged somewhat of my astonishing successes at English, History, Biology and Religious Studies – but honesty compels me to point out that I failed Maths by a margin so vast that it can't have been worth marking the paper at all.

My method of coping with mathematical problems had been structuralist and kinetic, rather than conceptually sound. Given one of those silly sums (popular in the old O Level days) which goes:

A train leaves point A at 30 mph, while a cyclist leaves point B 50 miles away at 10 mph in the opposite direction. How many miles from point B will the train and cyclist meet? (You must show your workings) my immediate reaction had been to reflect a] that trains nearly always run faster than 30 mph, b] cyclists seldom set out on fifty mile spins, and c] was the cyclist on the railway line? My next reaction was to take a pencil sharpener (representing train) and a rubber (representing cyclist), hold them as far apart as my arms would permit – the distance to represent fifty miles – and then move sharpener and rubber towards each other, the sharpener going three times faster than the rubber. I could never show any workings.

Problems about tanks filling through valve A at 3000 gallons per hour, but emptying from tap C at three litres per minute, and how much would be left after two hours, I could not manage at all with sharpener and rubber, I would simply write: "Sorry no time – estimated answer: 4.5 gallons". It was always depressing after tests to hear that everyone else had found it easy and agreed that the answer was 1200 gallons.

This did not prove a recipe for success at O Level Maths.

'Geoff Bradley is delighted at the prospect of taking into the old firm one of my grandsons,' declared Grandpa. 'I may remind you, Bill, that I have built up a not inconsiderable fortune on the Stock Exchange. Anthony may do the same, given an early enough start in the right hands.'

'Sixteen is too young,' said Dad very definitely.
'We both want him to attempt A Levels. His mother

hopes he may consider university in due course.'

'What! University! Humph! Har! Flower Power and homosexuals!' snorted Grandpa.

The last thing on earth Dad wanted me to do, I realised, was to tie my ship of destiny to Grandpa's dockside – backside, he might have put it, having had nearly twenty years of Grandpa's money, Grandpa's influence, Grandpa's punctuality, and Grandpa's ideas shoved down his throat. I understand now how humiliating it was for him to have been poor – even though you would never have guessed it by his manner and deportment. He was very tall and very heavily built, and moved with a deliberate, slow majesty and a downward tilt of leonine hair, winged eyebrows and blue eyes. He gazed down on lesser men, deftly moving his bronzed, manicured hands in the way that rich, leisured people do. Dad was almost the only person I had come across whose sleeve buttons at the wrists of blazers and coats actually undid, enabling him to fold the cuffs back when engaged in the least manual of tasks, such as writing letters. The boys at Worsley House had been impressed by his immaculately polished giant duo-tone 1950s Cadillac 60 sedan. Dad's fingers were so wide and strong that when a newly-lit cigarette was held between them, you could see only the glowing tip on one side and the filter on the other. To watch him handling the great

Cadillac through London traffic, gently rotating the huge cream steering-wheel between fine, outwardly-curved thumbs, was to understand what driving really meant. To see him draw up outside Harrods, and the flunkey leap forward to open the door, was to have that sense which only Royals can know of being a special person – a being set apart. Say what you like, but small men never look rich in the fullest sense of the word. Seeing Grandpa and Dad together, you would not guess that the irritable, clipped-moustached smaller one had made "a not inconsiderable fortune" and that the larger one lived in a mad, topsy-turvy flat in Maida Vale, struggling with free-lance journalism in the cramped, shared office of a minor publishing outfit of hobby books and conscious of having to depend for school fees, summer holidays and large bills on his father-in-law's crusty munificence.

Perhaps, then, it was no surprise that Ma's wish for me to delve more deeply into the ample pages of knowledge was given powerful support by Dad's anxiety lest I become a scion of Grandpa's in Grandpa's old firm. The two of them proved unbeatable, and the promised – and, by me, dreaded – interview with Sir Geoffrey Bradley never came off.

Three cheers! No need to work yet. No need to depend on getting enormous sums right for my living. No need to start on the lowest rung of Bradley and Knight's long ladder. I had no clear idea of what being engaged in "a proper job" entailed, but I was certain it would be disagreeable, and would leave no room for the oceans of whimsy, silliness, self-indulgence and Bohemianism which, at sixteen, I felt sloshing round inside me, waiting to pour out.

With nine O Levels (Top grades in English, History, Biology and Religious Studies) to recommend me to a Sixth Form – provided they could overlook my status as an expelled pupil – it was Hey ho! Hey ho! Off to school we go!

But where?

SNOW WHITE

Well, you don't need to be a NASA rocket propulsion engineer to work out where I ended up.

I can't now remember what put the idea in my mind of nagging and nagging Ma and Dad about going back to Glenturret – but nag I did, as soon as I heard that it had metamorphosed into a school. Peter Buchan had sent me a letter, which probably set the wheels turning; he was leaving Stonyhurst College in Lancashire at last (his mother, being a Catholic, had wanted him educated by the Jesuits) where he had been home-sick, at the end of his O Level year, and his parents had taken him to Glenturret Academy to meet Dr Costigan. It seemed impossibly wonderful that we might in the Sixth Form there together.

The clinchers, I now believe, were Doc Costigan's modest fees, Dad's desire that I should get away from the influence of my irresponsible Worsley House friends, like Butt and Stevens, and go to a school with a tiny Sixth Form where I would be supervised round the clock. Ma, opposed to boarding schools, as I have mentioned already, felt that an exception might be made in the case of a place I had loved as a child.

It is hard to describe the sense of absolute rightness I felt when, at last, after yet another marvellous railway journey north, I nestled down in bed on the second floor in Tennyson dorm, a room that once had been one of Grandpa's many unused guest bedrooms. There were four fairly utilitarian metal-frame beds with curtaining round them, three of which were occupied. I was very excited to learn from the kindly matron, Miss Kickham, that the fourth was ear-marked for Peter Buchan. The Adams washbasin and the single opal-glassed ceiling light were all that were left of the original provenance for guests – those and the yellow and blue wall-paper. Carpet and curtains had gone, as had the fire-basket in the grate; in its place stood a feeble-looking Dimplex oil radiator. The window, uncovered, afforded an immense panorama of stars over my bed, which was just under its sill. I was pleased to have been given this spot in the room – although I was to regret it by November. Dr Costigan never saw fit to curtain any window in the house except those in his own office, and the blast of chill from the lofty black panes and loosely-fitting sashes started off my lifetime habit of wearing socks and vest in bed. Having known Glenturret only in July and August, I was unprepared for the long Scottish winter. We of Tennyson dormitory seldom opened the window. It was as Grandpa would have liked it: an icy fug. Tennyson dorm's occupants were the Lower Sixth. The Upper Sixth had a further half-dozen youths in it for the academic year of '70/'71 – a most select Sixth Form. I quickly got to know and like all of them, and when Peter eventually arrived, on September 26th, having been on holiday in Egypt, of all places, he and I found ourselves established as old-hands, habitués, on account of our long childhood knowledge of the building and its surrounds.

From October's first weeks, I gave all my attention to the writing of a script for the 1970 Christmas Pantomime. Doctor C had given permission for this event to be held just before break-up in what had been Grandpa's unused ballroom – the scene of our model railways of a few years earlier.

The cast was to consist of the whole of the Fifth and Sixth Form – thirty-one boys – and was to be written by a Sixth Form committee of writers and assorted ego-trippers; Peter Buchan and I being prominent for ego-mania, if not for authorial talent. This communist collective method of production produces a peculiar final script: very long, unconnected as regards storyline, featuring many digressions, many clashing shades of humour and style, and giving great prominence to some characters and almost none to others – a bit like TV soaps, which are probably written in the same way.

An old bloke on the staff, Doctor Kettle, was to

blue-pencil our efforts at Costigan's insistence, wielding a censoring pen and keeping it clean. The panto we chose to adapt was *"Snow White"*, my favourite, and, of course, the subject of the greatest film ever made. Old Kettle, or The Boiler, as we called him, was a man of enormous innocence, and quite a lot of our wittier sallies came through unscathed. Some of those which didn't were re-instated impromptu on the night of performance.

The "*Jock Strap Song*" escaped blue-pencilling, and so did the decision to make the Prince gay – or, as we called it back then, queer. The Boiler happily missed this, even though we gave the Prince a fur handbag and a lisp. We did, however, come a cropper over the "*Apple Song*".

Peter and I were responsible for this one and we had put a lot of effort into it. We thought its specific brilliance lay its expected, but undelivered rhymes. I expected The Boiler to jib at rehearsal if he got the drift of them, so I told everyone in the cast not to laugh, but to sing the lines with totally straight faces. The song began:

"When apples are red and ready for plucking/ Sweet Snow White is ready for……."

……..and in comes the chorus (which was about rosy red apples) just in time; and so on for the other verses.

Rehearsals began. The Boiler cried,

'Right! Quiet, please, gentlemen. Nim, nim, nim, nim, nim – er, on you go!"

And we commenced, lustily belting out those fine lyrics:

"On the bright river, with oar in her mitts / Little Snow White is showing her....."

……..and in comes the chorus.

The Boiler was muttering the words and humming to the piano,

'Mmmmm, mmmm, yes, Little Snow White, yes, yes, hmmm, mmmm,' and tapping away with his pencil on the script, his dusty glasses and fluffy remnants of hair bobbing.

"One day when Snow White was sailing her lugger/ Up comes the Prince, the dirty young....."

……..and in comes the chorus.

'Hmmm, mmm, lugger, tum-te-tum, mmm, hmmmm,' hummed The Boiler.

The song came to its glorious end. Peter and I smirked and preened ourselves. We knew we had composed one of the finest stage numbers of all time. There was a silence from the cast. The Boiler began to speak,

'Yes, yes, gentlemen, nim, nim, nim, nim, nim, yes, a very nice number. So perky, I thought, nim, nim, I…..' Across his voice, from the back of the room in the shadows, came,

'Wooah! Haw! Haw! Whoop! Sauce-eee!'

We peered into the gloom, horrified. There by the door was Colman, lights man of the Fifth - the one guy whom I had forgotten to tell not to react. I thought everyone had been fore-warned, Colman hadn't. He gave a prolonged wolf-whistle. The Boiler yapped,

'Colman, nim, nim, Colman! Come here, Colman!'

Colman came up. Behind the Boiler's back we made frantic gestures for him to be silent, running our fingers across our throats. Colman stared dumbly up at us. Of course, as the simple lights were not going to be hired for weeks, he seldom came to song rehearsals.

'Colman! Colman! Why, nim, nim, why are you laughing in that, that, that *disgusting* manner? That, nim, nim, nim, that depraved and, and revolting manner?'

Colman's eyebrows went up, puzzled.

'Well, Sir, it's, it's funny. The song, Sir. That – that song.'

'The song, Colman?' twittered The Boiler. He gazed up at me. 'Come down here, Crepwright,' said he. 'What is so funny about this, er, nim, nim, song?'

I joined Colman.

'I – er, I – well – er – it's not so much, hem, *funny*, as – er – *witty*, Sir,' I muttered.

Still The Boiler had not got it. Dear old boy. He had retired some years before from his lifelong vocation as Ancient History tutor at an Oxford College, and had come to live in Scotland to be nearer his sister, we gathered. A little gentle Classical Studies at Doctor Costigan's small establishment was his way of helping ends meet and giving him an interest. Sophocles, Xenophon, Virgil and Horace presented little or no difficulties to him, but the verse of "*Snow White*" seemed to cause him, like Quintilian of old, to stare and gape!

'Hmmm, mmm, nim, mmmm....and ready for PLUCKING....nim, nim, Snow White ready for.....nim, nim, nim... and in comes the chorus just here....,' murmured The Boiler, scanning the script through dusty lenses. Suddenly his eyes grew wide as the penny, at long last, dropped. The script fluttered in his hands.

'Horrible! *Horrible*!' he cried.

Of course that was the end of "*The Apple Song*", alas.

The rehearsal ended abruptly, The Boiler threatening to close down the whole show. Next morning, at the assembly, Dr C gave a brief address to the rest of the academy, lamenting the "disgusting, obscene, licentious and unworthy activities" of some of the Sixth Form panto writers. I saw puzzled faces from Second, Third and Fourth

Forms turn towards us as we stood at the back. God knows what they thought, as it was not made clear; some misdemeanour with Miss Kickham, the Matron, perhaps?

When The Boiler and I eventually became colleagues, and were attending a literary dinner in Perth some years later, he pounced on me, and, dragging me over in his claws to a group of total strangers, cried, 'You must meet this young man! He writes obscene lyrics, you know.' I expect they thought I made my living penning scenarios for porno movies or was in a punk band. *"The Apple Song"* had clearly made a lasting impact on the old boy.

Pole-axed by the horror of having to continue with the show (for Doctor C had begun to invite local dignitaries and parents, and was anxious that the Academy's first public performance should be a triumph) The Boiler seemed to lose vigilance, rather than increase it, and it was only when letters of complaint came in from the Church of Scotland minister and the Lady Mayoress of Dunblane's office and several of the few parents who unwisely attended the fiasco, that Peter and I fully realised the un-wisdom of making such capital out of the gay Prince Charming's positive refusal, sweetie, to kiss Snow awake, and out of a necrophiliac Jewish dwarf with no such qualms. Almost all of the panto's script offended almost all who came to the performance.

Of my own part, I say little. I created for myself the character of Lucretia D'Arcy-Prune, the Wicked Queen, and gave myself more lines than Hamlet. The fact that I forgot all but a few phrases and had to ad lib the rest, I shan't dwell on. My life passed before my eyes many times that evening on the trestle stage at Glenturret.

Peter and I were, however, proud of one or two West End-ish touches. At one point, three evil characters had to be despatched, and we wanted to have plenty of blood. When sixteen I tended to judge a play's quality by the amount of bloody violence involved.

The other scriptwriters and I were in disagreement about the best method of achieving the acceptable quantity of rich, red gore. The Boiler had blue-pencilled my scene with the disembowelling of the Huntsman, even though I had enquired at a butcher's in Dunblane about the availability and cost of pig's innards and had been on the verge of placing an order. I thought it would look good if the Huntsman had the guts in muslin under his shirt, so that when the muslin was ripped, a mixture of pig's intestines and red ink would come gushing forth. The Boiler's lack of enthusiasm had been unusually marked, so nothing had come of it.

Peter and I were more satisfied by the blood-dagger.

In a twist away from Walt Disney, our plot was to feature the disappointed Wicked Queen having her throat slashed. In the Disney cartoon she slips off a cliff in the rain, if you remember. Tame, we thought.

Peter set to work with parts of a bicycle pump and silvered balsa wood, and after many problems with spring tension and washers, he had a dagger which worked. Of course it had to be tried out, and the occasion on which we tested it proved beyond a doubt Doctor Costigan's capacity for unruffled calm in all situations.

In the open doorway of the old squash court, Peter, with other scriptwriters round him, tried various methods of stabbing the Wicked Queen – me. The dagger's gudgeon (pump cut down to six inches) was filled with Kensington Gore stage blood – a little under a teacupful – and Peter lunged at my chest. The washer stuck and blood gushed onto Peter's sleeve. Someone pointed out that instructions for removing stains from clothing on the Gore bottle were ambivalent, so I thought I'd better take off my shirt.

Peter lunged at me again, the dagger point aimed at my chest. Blood spurted over me.

'Yow! It's dripping on your trousers,' said someone behind me, so I thought I'd better remove those too. I waited, in my pants and socks, for the next assault.

'That hurt!' I said to Peter, rubbing the sore place the dagger's point had made.

'Sorry. Just let me adjust the spring,' muttered the inventor. 'Nearly got it right.' He re-filled the dagger, tightened the end cap, and, with a hideous screech, flew at me again. A teacupful of rich, flowing blood shot out of the nozzles on each side of the blade (Biro refill sections glued on to the top of the pump over small holes) and clung stickily to my neck, chest and arms. The brilliant red in the sunshine was startling.

'God! It works!' cried Peter, lunging at me once more to get the last drop of squidge from the dagger. A shadow fell across the doorway. We heard Doctor Costigan's voice saying,

'And these are our squash courts….'

He was accompanied by a frail, nervous-looking woman – a prospective mother, we supposed. Peter stepped back, an animal snarl frozen on his lips. The panto blokes instinctively moved around me, but not before the nervous mother had glimpsed my gashed throat and blood-smeared near-naked body. Her vulnerable eyes widened to the size of dustbin lids.

'Two matches may be played at the same time,' said Doctor C. 'Now let me show you our kitchen garden. We grow all our own…..' The doorway was empty; his voice faded away. Smoothly done.

If only, on the nights of performance, we had insisted that Nick Orchard had borrowed our dagger, we might not have had our thunder stolen by The Affair of the Tomato Sauce Bottle.

This was the regrettable by-product of producing a panto by committee, and one of the drawbacks of having to cater for a cast of egomaniacs, all of whom expected a large part. Thirty actors greatly outnumber the personnel actually required to stage *"Snow White"*: WQ, a huntsman, a stepfather (optional), SW, seven dwarfs and one Prince. In order to fit everyone in, we had to have many a divergence from the storyline. None was more divergent than the assassination of Julius Caesar.

Anyone might ask what the demise of Caesar (circa 30 BC) has to do with the vacation spent by Snow in some dwarfs' cottage in a wood (circa 1500?). Nick Orchard, studying Shakespeare's play for his retake O Level English, was so taken with the idea of himself as he "who bestrides the narrow world like a Colossus" that he went on and on until we were forced to incorporate the whole of the scene in the Capitol as part of entertainment put on by the dwarfs for Snow's benefit, the night before she learns that the maxim "An apple a day keeps the doctor away" is not to be relied on. All we insisted was that Nick got on with rehearsing it independently with the four dwarfs selected to be

Brutus, Cassius & Co.

What with one thing and another, the Murder of Caesar was never incorporated into rehearsals at all, but, on Nick's assurance that all was well, was left to be slotted in on the night, when Grumpy (Nick) jumps up after a spate of conjuring tricks (performed by Dozy) and cries,

'Well Snow White, that <u>was</u> good fun!

Now you're going to see /"The Death of Caesar" done!'

Nick knew nothing of our invention with the bicycle pump. He was not one of the inner circle of scriptwriters – his father was a chemist in Dundee which, for some reason, went against him. And we in turn knew nothing of his proposed method of ensuring lots of gushing blood at Caesar's death. I reckon we had hoped that by ignoring the Caesar problem it would just go away.

The first intimation I had that Orchard had solved his blood crisis was on the night, when, with the audience moving about restlessly, having had over forty minutes of post-supper "entertainment" in the dwarfs' cottage, he whizzed past me into the "wings" (several pieces of 8' x 4' screwed together with hinges), donned a sheet over his Grumpy costume, pulled out of a paper-bag a large, economy or family-size bottle of tomato sauce, whipped the top off, shoved the bottle under his sheet and tore back on stage.

I was standing in the wing next to The Boiler, who was prompting with a tattered copy of the script. Actually, I liked to be fairly near The Boiler so that I could be fed my lines. I've mentioned that I forgot almost every one as soon as I was on stage, and The Boiler, peering at the blotchy typing with the aid of a torch, had been kept pretty busy. He had become more matey since Time, the great healer, had softened the memory of "the obscene lyrics". Prompted by having to whisper hoarsely almost every Wicked Queen line before I remembered enough to keep going, he had been moved to tell me, during the long dwarfs' conjuring scene, how he had once assisted in the production of "*A Midsummer's Night's Dream*" by the Oxford University Dramatic Society. He had had the job of prompting then too, and during one of the fairy scenes, he had noticed that Puck was still on stage when he should not have been. The Boiler, spotting this, had taken it upon himself to hiss "Puck off! PUCK OFF!" in a deafening whisper and had been puzzled (until a grinning student had explained) that it had brought the house down. The old boy could enjoy a joke against himself.

Anyway, there he was, next to me in the dark, as Orchard flitted back on stage with his sheet and bottle.

'What's happening?' twittered The Boiler, flipping the pages back and forth. Shakespearian dialogue floated to our ears.

'Oh, I think it's Orchard's Caesar scene, Sir,' I whispered.

'What! Nim, nim, nim, nim, *what* Caesar scene? I know of no Caesar scene!' gasped The Boiler, going purple in the gloom, the script dancing like autumn leaves in his hands.

I was about to explain, when an extraordinary commotion came from the stage. After the extraordinary commotion came a bang, a sharp scream, and then general shouting from the audience. The Boiler had crumpled the script and was whispering feverishly – some sort of prayer, I thought.

There are those who would have poked their head round the wing to see what was going on. I did not. Not professional. So I had to wait and hear all about it afterwards.

Apparently, Nick, gripping the tomato sauce bottle to his tummy under his sheet, had unleashed all that stuff about "Wilt thou lift up Olympus?" and Happy (Casca) had cried, "Hands! Speak for me!" and had lunged with his toy plastic dagger at Nick's chest, when Nick had made the discovery of so many purchasers of Heinz ketchup that the sauce never comes out of the bottle when you want it to –

especially when full. He had attempted to shake it under his sheet, and the up and down motions of his hand had elicited a noisy and ribald response from the school-boy audience. The bottle had then slipped from his fingers and exploded like a bomb on the lip of the stage, spraying Doctor Costigan, several parents, the Minister, the Mayoress and Matron with razor-like slivers of glass and many fluid ounces of sauce. The rest coated the floor and Nick had trodden on a splinter and cut his foot. He had then tripped up in the folds of his sheet, screamed, 'BUGGER IT!' and tumbled off the front of the stage onto the front row. That was when the shouting had started.

I reckon, looking back, that the audience had a lucky escape from the rest of the dwarfs' entertainment scene, because Doctor C led a general exodus of guests and staff from the room, and the interval – much longed-for – came early. The Boiler had rushed after him, presumably to explain, apologise and soothe, and some time elapsed before the show re-started. The stage had to be washed and swept.

That is what I mean about Nick Orchard stealing some of our blood-dagger's thunder. By the time Peter's brilliant invention came to be operated, the audience merely gazed on sadly and dumbly. I imagine they'd had enough of fake blood, or found the WQ's death very tame after the incomplete assassination of Caesar.

The Boiler was shirty with Nick afterwards – a pity, because not all his ideas were crap. It was he who came up with a splendid effect for when the Wicked Queen, annoyed with the Huntsman for not bringing her Snow White's heart, clobbers him with her handbag. Nick had suggested that the Huntsman fill his mouth with broken Polo mints and spit them onto the floor as the handbag walloped, as though his teeth had been knocked out. Apart from the rest of us crunching around on wet bits of mint for the rest of the scene, that went down well.

Although it's fun recalling it all now, I did regret all sorts of things about that first panto at Glenturret Academy. I wish that the coffin lid had not slammed shut on top of the Prince's head just as he was reluctantly kissing Snow back to life. It overbalanced him onto her and shut them both inside. There they stayed for what seemed like hours, Snow shrieking, until a couple of dwarfs rushed forward and prised open the lid. Snow was played by our most feminine-looking boy, "Pussy" Lindsay, upon The Boiler's insistence. Peter and I had thought it would have been funnier had the part been taken by Angus Clennan – Glenturret's own tame Upper-Sixth orang-utan and Oliver Reed lookalike. The Prince's entrapment in the coffin brought loud wolf-whistles and shouts of 'Sod 'em and Gomorrah!' and 'Think of England, Pussy!' from a youthful audience already inflamed by Nick Orchard's bottle contortions. (Two letters of complaint.)

I also wished, after it was too late, that the Prophet of Dunblane had not been given such reams of narrative. His task was to act as a chorus-figure, filling in what had happened so far (in case it hadn't been clear) and to provide background plot details. He forgot his lines so completely when about to tell us that the poisoned Snow was now committed to a l-o-n-g, deep sleep, that he stood, with wild, staring orbs fixed upon Matron, saying (with greater clarity of diction than any employed by him thus far), 'Oh, shit! Shit! Shit! Shit! Shit!' over and over again before his eyes had rolled up and he started croaking: 'So vile Lucretia dons disguise/Surely a precaution wise/And packs an apple in her bag/Which she has poisoned, filthy hag', sending the panto back twenty minutes, and forcing Pussy Lindsay to wrench off his pretty "eternal sleep" nightdress and get back into his "Snow in the Woods" gear.

Last of all, I wished that Peter Buchan hadn't got carried away. He played the Northern King (Snow's stepfather) with a good Lancashire accent, picked up from his three years at Stonyhurst College – which is near Blackburn. We thought it would be a *scream* if he had a knotted hanky, carried a brown ale bottle and rolled up his trousers – like a 1950's joke working-class figure at Blackpool. No doubt about it – he had gone down very well with our audience. I guess the great relief of seeing someone on stage who [a] had relatively funny lines, [b] knew them, [c] had a clear, stereotyped comic role, and [d] could act, made the mob long for his re-appearances, as audiences watching *"Henry IV (i)"* yearn for Falstaff after long stretches of political talk from Glendower, Bolingbroke, Hotspur and Co.

It was such a shame that he had to go and overdo it when his fly-buttons blew open.

Their bursting wasn't his fault. He had been grotesquely padded out with blankets, a pillow and two old teddy bears, and few buttons could have been expected to cope. It was the ad-libbing which I censure him for. The 'I've got a surprise oonder here' was greeted with frozen horror; so was 'Wharrer thou peekin' at, tha' randy old slut?' addressed to the Lady Mayoress. He warmed to his theme with several gestures in *very* poor taste, as he tried to stuff the poking-out blanket back into his fly. Luckily The Boiler, hunting in despair with his dimming torch for yet more newly inserted, uncensored lines, missed a lot of it. But the school received five complaints, three of them in the letters about the misfortunes referred to above.

It was a regrettable *debut* for Drama at Glenturret Academy, for which Costigan was inclined to blame me – and I felt most aggrieved at the time. The misunderstood genius – you know.

'Quiet, scum! Shut it, you rabble!' yelled Peter. He waved a ceramic mug in the air. There was a lessening of the hubbub.

'Sssh!'

'Shut up!'

Glenturret Academy was asleep. The panto audience had long gone. The Boiler had retired to bed after being given three cheers and a bottle of Teachers' whisky. (Pupils of every generation have believed themselves to be original in choosing that particular brand of lubricant for their pedants – a fact that will, no doubt, ensure its survival.)

Doctor C had assumed that The Boiler was closing up shop; The Boiler assumed that Doc Costigan was. The result was that there we all were, sitting cross-legged under the trestle stage, costumes still on, having an illicit cast party. In Grandpa's day, the old ballroom was, as I have mentioned before, unused and unloved. Its bright polished floor, carpet-less, stretched away more than eighty feet in length to deep ornamented wainscots, and the sunlight piercing through the shutters of six tall casements made the air dance with a million dusty motes. Sometimes the room had the feel of a bewitched woodland glade, and I loved to lie down in there, gazing up, and imagine what it would be like if the ceiling were the floor, and I could walk among the embossed swags and floral plasters and see the heavy doors and shuttered panels of light far above, beyond my reach.

At the room's end was an embrasure made of two walls of painted wood with polished tops – just the right height for sitting on – and this projected a couple of yards into the dance space, making a bay for whatever long-lost skirling bands of bagpipes or violins first made Victorian slippers tap upon the parquet. In the '60s a gleaming sarcophagus squatted there: a silent old Marconi radiogram of unimaginable tonnage. This monster (never known to have been switched on in our time, although I'd sometimes raised its lid to inspect the chunky 78 disc auto-player within, and the dark glass wireless dial with stations: *Hilversum*, *Home Service* and so forth, picked out in gilt lettering) had clearly been discarded by the time of Grandpa's departure, for in all Glenturret's many crannies I had never come across it again.

It was across the space bounded by these pier-like walls that Doctor Costigan had erected a trestle stage for the purpose of assembly. From the prompt side a short flight of steps ran down to a curtained area where actors could change. On the other side a wing of chipboard gave some off-stage space (the space in which The Boiler had hidden to hiss my innumerable lines). The stage top and wall edges made a large cupboard where Doctor C probably intended to store all those bits and pieces which, in a school, have no home, but at present the shiny floor stretched away under the platform, four hardboard flaps blocking it off from the rest of the ballroom. In this space the entire cast of "*Snow White*" was squashed.

The scriptwriters had made thorough preparations for this cast party – although originally we had aimed to use the squash court. We had gin, whisky, martini, cider, brandy, *crème de menthe* and beer – the latter in those large seven-pint tins which then were called Pipkins. We had Senior Service, Gold Flake and coloured Sobranie cocktail cigarettes, and we had many packets of Lyons' Swiss rolls and Walls' sausage rolls.

It was imperative that the authorities knew nothing of this orgy. We felt fairly safe – the old ballroom was a long way from the nearest master's bedroom, and its doors were thick. The festivities began in a muffled gurgling as the gin and beer circulated. After a while, however, voices began to rise, snatches of "*The Apple Song*" burst forth uncensored, and the atmosphere grew thick and smoky. The cast, costumes coming apart and grease-paint growing greasier, sat elbow to elbow, knee to knee, passing the bottles round, and the hilarity grew more wild and raucous.

'For God's sake, SHUT UP!' hissed Peter.

'What about a story?' asked Pussy, bridling prettily. 'What about a ghost story?'

'A story!'

'Wassesaying?'

'A sexy story!'

'Come on! What about a dirty story!' shouted someone. For some reason faces had turned towards Peter and me – as though they felt that our duties as the co-scripters of "*The Apple Song*" could not be over until this one last act had been performed.

I was feeling as though I had recently parachuted from a noisy, black helicopter, and I think I was trying to convey the sensations of this, and I heard a horrid, camp voice giggling, and I dimly knew it was mine. After many tots of crème de menthe, gin and brandy I was not in the market for telling any story, ghostly, sexy or dirty.

However, the voices shouted on, as if from down a tunnel,

'Oh come on! If you can write *"The Apple song"*, you can tell a story!'

'Get on with it! You wicked queens!'

I racked my brain, but what with dizziness and slight nausea, could not think of a single story to tell at the under-stage cast party.

Peter Buchan, however, was not daunted – probably because he felt himself on a higher moral plane, having been a little more moderate than I had been with the booze. He waved his mug in the air, sloshing a cocktail of beer, *crème de menthe* and Martini over Snow White's pretty frock.

'I,' said he, belching with grace, 'can tell you two stories, one ghostly and one dirty.'

'Sssh!' hissed those round him.

There was silence. Peter belched into it, long and loud.

'Urrrrgh! When I was at Stonyhurst….' He began.

'Warrer he say?'

'What's Stonyhurst?'

'Speak up!'

'When I was at Stonyhurst, my last school, I heard two stories about Jesuit priests, which I will now tell you. Stonyhurst is a huge, rambling place, well known to be haunted, and Father Dixon was staying there in the hols when it was deserted. He and some other priests had spent the evening talking about ghosts, and it wasn't until after midnight that they went back to their rooms. Father Dixon's room was at the end of a long corridor, and he was as far as you can be at Stonyhurst from a bog….'

'Did he say "bog"?'

'Yes, yes,' said Peter. '*Pissoir*, jakes, loo, lavvie, toilet, shithouse, bog! Got it? Well, he lay down in bed, trying to sleep, but sleep wouldn't come, and his thoughts went round and round the tales of the supernatural they had been telling each other, an' he couldn't face going down the dark passage. As he lay in bed, trembling, he found out that he was bursting.'

Peter looked sternly round at us.

'*Bursting*,' he said impressively. 'And you should never let that go on because....' He paused, sloshing cocktail from his mug, '....you can burst.'

He ceased and stared ahead with a strange empty grin.

'Is that it?' someone asked.

'It is not,' declaimed Peter, regally. 'My aunt went hunting for the fox, and she rode all day, bursting more and more, but unable to stop and find a tree, because women can't, you know – and when the hunt arrived back at the pub, she slipped from her stirrups and fell to the ground, and her bladder burst – and – she – died. She is, as a matter of fact, dead.' Peter bit off the words, rather than uttering them. 'That's wharrimean. You must go. Even if you can't.' He giggled hilariously and then stopped, savouring the deep philosophy of his point.

'Hang on. What's a Jesuit?' asked someone.

Peter shook his head from side to side.

'Tsk, tsk, tsk. Fancy not knowing that,' he said pityingly. 'A Jesuit is a member of The Society of Jesus, founded by Saint - erm – Saint Ignatius in the 16th century. They are the soldiers of Christ in the Catholic Church, an' some of them are very, very good fellows, and some are swines….. Depends on who you meet. They run Stonyhurst College, my ole school. But that's wharri'm telling you about, isn't it?' He smiled expansively at us all.

'Oh, get on with the story, if there is one,' yapped Nick Orchard.

'Father Dixon,' Peter went on, 'couldn't bring himself to go out into the haunted corridors, so he decided to ur-y-nate in the room. And there was nothing *in* the room, not a vase, not an ashtray, not a jug. Suddenly his gaze fell on the gaps between the floorboards and, quick as a short-muttered prayer of thanks for the inspiration, he was sending a stream into the hole between two boards, when there was a horrible scuttle and a furious squeal. Up popped a rat, drenched with urine, with dripping ears and whiskers. It glared at Father Dixon who, in his inflamed state, thought it was the devil. Before its head had ducked down again, he had fainted clean away in an old-fashioned swoon.' Peter stopped, and then said, 'He told me that on retreat.'

This information had the force of the revelation of

holy writ and all were silent. In the quiet Peter cried, inspired, 'Have I told you about Father Siebold and the camp-bed?'

'No!' shouted a few voices.

'I don't really want to hear about your Catholic priest friends, Buchan,' growled Nick Orchard. 'I want to hear a good story, so I'm going to tell you about one myself. I bet none of you knows what to do with a rubber johnnie when you're with a girl.'

'Oh, shut up, Orchard. You don't know either.'

'He normally puts it on his nose!' shouted Martin Colman.

'Ssssh!' hissed Pussy. 'Go on, Peter.'

'Father Siebold was a sadist,' resumed Peter, 'so I'm glad to be able to tell you a story about his come-uppance.'

'Yes, yes. Camp-bed?' said Happy.

'This is goin' to be a story about silly, silly schooldays. And we want a damn, damn silly story. A damn stor-y!' It was a few seconds before I realised that this last shouting voice was mine. 'Ssssh!' hissed the dwarfs. Peter swilled some gin into his mug and lit a Cocktail Sobranie. Its smoke twirled round his arched eyebrows and long, pale face.

'Father Siebold,' said Peter, 'was on a walking tour in Southern England at the end of the 'fifties, and was heading, knapsack on his shoulders, for a church in Sussex where a priest-friend was going to put him up. It came on to rain as he was approaching a little village and he realised he was going to get very wet – and he still had several miles before him. "Bless my soul!" murmured Siebold, peering upwards through his pince-nez at the sign by the road: MIDHURST. The name had a familiar ring, so he fished out his diary, standing under a tree, and found what he remembered writing in it. More than a year before, an eager, young Catholic layman whom Siebold had met at the Jesuits' Farm Street Church in Mayfair (where he had been a concelebrant at the young man's wedding) had pressed him sincerely to look him up if he were ever passing through Midhurst. My mother says it is invariably a mistake to offer a casual invitation of this sort to a Catholic priest because he will always take you up on it, sooner or later. Siebold, raising his eyes to Heaven in praise, gave thanks that he had copied this young man's address into his new diary. It was not long before he was standing in front of a small, stone-built house. He rang the bell and the very man whom Siebold remembered opened the door. "Yes? What is it?" asked the young man. "Oh, ah, I don't know if you recall meeting me at Farm Street about a year ago at your delightful wedding," twittered Siebold. "The name's Father Siebold and you assured me that if ever I were passing……"

"Oh, yes! Of course," gasped the young man, running a disturbed hand through his hair. "Ah, of course! Er, do – do come in…."

'As Siebold was stepping into the cottage there was a sudden violent downpour of rain and a clap of thunder. He congratulated himself on his memory and his timing.

'In the small sitting-room he was introduced to a fair, pretty woman who was cradling a baby. "My wife and I have had a child since we met, Father, as you can see," explained the young man. Siebold (who had forgotten what the wife looked like, for Jesuits are always best at remembering men) greeted her with creaking gallantry. "And bless you, my little one," he added, touching the baby's forehead – at which it immediately began to cry. "Won't you stay for supper?" asked the young man, with a gulp. Well, it wasn't the most successful of evenings, for Siebold realised that the wife was not particularly pleased to have him there, but he did his best to twinkle and amuse.

'At about ten o'clock, Siebold began to speak of leaving them, of wondering if there was a bus he could take for those last few miles, and joking about how it was, after all, only rain-water, not nuclear fall-out, ha, ha, and once you were wet through, you couldn't get any wetter after all, ha, ha, ha.

'The young man and his wife exchanged looks.

"Perhaps," said the young man, "you would like to stay the night, Father?" "Oh, no, I couldn't....but yet, well, I must say, it is a very kind and Christian suggestion. If I could just telephone my friend....?"

'Siebold avowed that he could sleep anywhere: on a couple of sofa cushions on the sitting-room floor, but, apologising for the cramped nature of the little cottage, his host suggested the best place would be the baby's room, in which there was a small camp bed, provided Siebold didn't mind sharing with the child. This nursery room led off the parents' bedroom and beyond that was the bathroom, down creaking steps, in which Siebold had quickly washed. The loo had an antique Acme *Silent-Flush* WC which roared like Niagara. The wife had sat grimly on the bed, and the host had stood next to her, awkwardly smiling, when Siebold, his ablutions completed, sidled back past them. "Good night, and my blessings on you both," gibbered Siebold as the ancient floorboards creaked under his feet like exploding mines. "I hope you sleep well, Father," murmured his host. The wife said nothing at all.

'It was past eleven o'clock.

'Siebold lay on the camp-bed listening to the rain. Across the room was the baby's cot. He tried to compose himself for sleep, running over a little of the mandatory Holy Order in his mind. My word, he chuckled to himself, that could have been sticky –

but I'll be off after breakfast.

'At one he woke violently, absolutely *bursting*.

'He sat up in the narrow camp-bed, not sure for a moment where he was. He put a foot out, then another. He unconsciously noted that the rain had stopped. He stood up, and then realised that to get to the loo he would have to blunder past the baby's cot, open the parents' door, traverse their bedroom across the exploding floorboards, open their other door, and descend the creaky steps to the Acme *Silent-Flush*. And he knew he couldn't do it. He was unpopular enough already – and even Jesuits have their share of the finer feelings.

'He pulled back the curtain and gazed around in the moonlight, more like a hunted beast than a middle-aged Catholic clergyman, hoping to find a suitable receptacle. There wasn't a flower-vase, an ornamental bowl full of *pot-pourri*, or even a glass in sight. The window might have been a possibility, but its opening pane was high up, and Siebold was not a tall man and doubted both his aim and his force.

'He cast his eyes heavenward to Him who rules above, and was immediately granted help. His eye fell, in the gloom, on the baby's cot.

'Bing! Of course!

'"If," he reasoned to himself, "if I relieve myself in the cot, they'll think the baby did it. And I won't have to leave the room at all."

'Muttering a brief prayer of thanks to Saint Ignatius for the inspiration, he stood over the sleeping child, about to fumble his pyjamas open. Then it occurred to him that he could hardly spray the tiny infant with gushing urine as if from a fire hose, so, stooping, he gently picked it up. It gave a gurgle. He lowered it with infinite care onto his camp-bed, tore back to the cot and let rip a frothing arc which splashed into the child's bedclothes while he gasped with relief. He returned to the camp-bed, picked up the still sleeping child and carried it back to its cot, where he lowered it into the warm pool of liquid. As it felt the damp, it gave another gurgle. "Bless you, my little one. Sleep. S-l-e-e-e-e-p," crooned Siebold, making a sign of the cross over its tiny head. With a mumble, it stuck its thumb into its mouth and, cradled in the warm wet of its bedding, went into the land of dreams again.

'Siebold whizzed silently back to the camp-bed, gabbling further prayers of thanksgiving and plunged in, only to find........' Peter paused dramatically for the punch-line we could all see coming, '.......that the baby had had the same idea and had pissed mightily in his bed, and that he had landed in a sort of inland lake. So Siebold had a wet night after all!'

Peter's tale had ended. There was a muffled

clapping under the stage.

'Brilliant!' cried Elliott Colston, gazing up at Peter, with vivid eyes full of admiration. Only one voice dissented.

'A right cock and bull story!' sneered Nick Orchard (still a bit sour grapes after the Death of Caesar and the lack of enthusiasm about his tale of derring-do with rubber johnnies).

'A cock story, in any case,' said Peter, and I noticed he gave Orchard a rather ugly look.

'Well, I don't know about you lot, but all that talk about bursting has made me realise that *I'm* bursting!' said Snow White, getting up to a kneeling position under the trestles. 'I'm just popping out to the bog,' he added, picking up his skirts.

'Stop!' hissed Angus Clennan. 'Stop right there! You can't go traipsing round the building in the middle of the night. Costigan, or The Boiler, or Matron might still be up.'

'Yep, we haven't finished here yet,' chimed in Prince Charming. 'Wharrer you think's going to happen to all this drink?'

'Sit down, Pussy,' said Peter. 'He's right. You can't be *that* bursting.'

'I AM bursting!' he cried. 'I was fairly bursting before all that camp-bed stuff; now I'm jolly well going to the bog. Think I want to have a burst bladder? You heard what Buchan said about his

164

grandmother, or whoever she was!'

Most of the cast had gone back to the booze and fags and several had started singing *sotto voce* again, so that few heard the above conversation. One of those few was Martin Colman.

'What about this?' he said, pushing forward an empty Pipkin tin.

'Fantastic!' gasped Pussy, lifting his skirts. In a few seconds the Pipkin tin was receiving his all. Several other members of the cast saw what he was doing.

'Good idea!' they mumbled, and the seven-pint tin was passed from hand to hand. Soon it was practically full with, as Keats puts it: "beaded bubbles winking at the brim".

The last person to use it had been me, and I was preparing to pass it on gingerly, when Nick Orchard's voice could be heard from several feet away querulously demanding,

'Isn't there any more beer?'

Peter Buchan's face was extraordinarily expressionless as he answered,

'Why, yes. There's a full tin here.'

Nick squirmed through the crush. He was three-quarters blotto, of course. He grasped the Pipkin tin in both hands. Fascinated, we stared at him as he raised it to his mouth. He swilled a huge frothing gulp. We waited. The cosmos stood still. And he gurgled,

'Gar! That was good!' and wiped his mouth with his sleeve.

I maintain that nothing would have happened if some idiot hadn't then said to him,

'Do you know what you've just drunk?'

It just shows the truth of Hamlet's observation that "there's nothing good nor bad but thinking makes it so". Happily quenching his thirst a few seconds ago, Nick now turned a creamy white and then exploded with monumental vomiting. I was nearby and was liberally splashed. Shrieks of horror rang out. Soon other half-paralysed members of the *dramatis personae* of the panto began to chuck up – and in a few minutes the party was definitely over. The under-stage area was habitable no longer.

At least I had a lucky escape and did not have to try and tell a follow-up story to "Siebold's camp-bed".

W H E E L S

I sometimes used to imagine soaring above Glenturret in a light aeroplane, about five thousand feet up above what was my pocket of land. The house was in the centre, irregular, but massive and dominating, perched upon a higher rise in the ground than seemed apparent from the drive.

Across the frontage was that broad gravel sweep and, leading off its pebbles to the left, the narrower drive which curved away through trees to the southern lodge. To the west of the house lay the terraced lawns, dropping away to a stream, and to the gothic stone chancel in the centre of radiating paths. That old folly (and place of trysts in mine and Mike's childhoods) was, by Doctor Costigan's day, one of the outposts of empire, for the iron fence beyond it marked the boundary of Nichol's farm. I spent many hours in it revising for my A Levels; it was out of bounds for the junior part of the school (as was the entire frontal area) and most of the other Sixth Form guys didn't see the charm of squatting in the gloom of its mildewed interior.

To the east was the driveway to the back of the house, to its kitchens, back-buildings and Doc C's huts for the lowest forms. From there it snaked off between conifers to re-join the main drive and a transverse road at a little crossroads in the woodland.

Costigan liked delivery vehicles to use it, but by '99 you couldn't get into Glenturret from the gate-house on the Kinbuck road because I'd bricked it over so that there would be only one entrance to the museum, so the drive led to nowhere, and I had let it become overgrown. On each side of Grandpa's old cultivated gardens were the two farms. One, belonging to me, was compact and specialised – a home farm for garden produce and plants to sell in the museum shop. The other was, when I left, called Drummond Upper Estate – another of Nichol's properties. He used it for dairy farming, so that green pasture-land ran down to the main road. From an aircraft, the whole two thousand acres – once all owned by Grandpa – would seem compact, self-contained, a country set apart inside a moat made by the arrow-straight Granite City line to the north and the A9 road to the south. You would look down on a kingdom whole and entire; beyond it, like the stern coast of another continent, were the heather-blue hazes of the Ochil mountains. From the air it would have been the finest vista on earth.

When I was overlord of this kingdom, I had so arranged things that there was almost no trace of the present day. I liked to know, as a certainty, that wherever my visitors looked, whatever shed, barn or outbuilding they might happen to poke into, they would find nothing later than the late 1960s. They would never stumble across a bright orange *Flymo* lawnmower and hundreds of yards of orange flex in one of my potting-sheds. I liked to feel that as the gaze swept the hilly horizon, any of the quarters of the compass could have been sepia-tinted and subtitled 1890, 1910, 1930 or 1955 with equal verisimilitude.

My Sixth-form days at Glenturret Academy were a foreshadowing dream of all this. Luckily, Doctor C never made enough money from his little school to effect great changes to Grandpa's fabric; but then no one was making money during the slump of the early '70s – OPEC and the oil scare, hyper-inflation and the hopelessness of Heath's and Wilson's governments were seeing to that. The Doctor drove a 1962 Vanden Plas Princess and it was the second most modern of the Academy's vehicles. The school van was a mid '50s Trojan, the tractor one of Grandpa's post-war Fordsons. Mr Park, our English master, had a Matchless 500cc motorbike – also elderly. Only Matron bucked the trend with her 1970 Mini.

I guess that a slow liking for cars and motorbikes stole upon me in my Sixth Form days. Before that (and cars never supplanted it) the love of railways had absorbed me entirely. Mike had the real petrol-head mentality; he had, for example, an entrenched loyalty to modern Jaguars all through the years he lived in America – and I've written already of his childhood Scalextric slot-car mania. Unlike me, Mike adored new machines.

Yet I am willing to agree that nothing dates a time like a *road* vehicle. Having absorbed this fact, I made sure that the museum was a home for anything between the dates on which a Fowler traction engine and a Ford Zodiac might have been made (1910 – 1969) – but nothing after these.

Some of these vanished names may mean nothing in the 21st C, but you might like to know that I had a '58 Cadillac series 75 limo – all wings and chrome – on display up until 1997 when I sold it to a collector. It lived in the old Home Farm hay barn with the post-war vehicles. Obviously, there are few people with souls too stunted to enjoy the spectacle of Edwardian traction-engines in steam, but there is an added poignancy to the preservation of, say, a 'fifties Hudson or Caddy or Chevy) because a car like that is the embodiment of two closely connected ideas. Firstly, the artefacts of the late 'fifties were on the very brink of the space and transistor age, and have something in them of the excitement of the growth, after years of war and austerity, of a newly glamorous and luxurious era; that whiff of heady Americana. Secondly, these machines were never intended to survive the passing of the years. There is a fragility and wonder attached to their continued existence. One can never imagine the final decay of a late Victorian road-roller; such iron-clads were made to last until the end of time. An Austin A50 Cambridge, by comparison, is such a delicate confection. Its voluptuous, bulbous monocoque skin is tissue-thin, its thin chrome so easily pitted by rain and time, its white-wall tyres and spindly steering-wheel and sculptured dash so easily scratched by use and its upholstery discoloured by fag smoke and by internal dissolution. When, in the sunshine of a lost weekday in 1954, it rolled from its dark womb in the English Midlands, it was destined, moth-like, through planned obsolescence, for immolation by the scrap-yard in 1962 – a forgotten, faded toy outmanoeuvred by the Ford *Cortinas* and Morris *Minis* which began the making of tomorrow. No surprise then that my visitors traced their fingers on the gleaming paintwork. They loved it for being present against all the odds.

I live now with a peculiar clarity about the circumstances of my great loss: my dreams, ambitions, income, direction and, above all, my vanished house. When I was twenty or so I had no means of understanding the intricate mechanics of loss; no hope, of course, of spotting signs along the way. As late as the summer of 1999 I was not much better at knitting the skeins of influence from early years together to divine my future – but nearly quarter of a century before that I sleep-walked, believing all the time that I was lucky.

Dad died in '74 – the year before I graduated in '75 from King's College, London – and when Mike was at the beginning of his first year in the Sixth form of the London comprehensive to which he had gone after Worsley House. When he too had left school (with modest qualifications) and had persuaded Peter Buchan to give him work experience at EMI's studios, our mother at last plucked up courage to do what she and Dad had planned together before his death: to go and live in Italy. "I'm a bad mum," she would say, "abandoning my poor boys." "Bollocks," we'd reply, "we're nearly twenty-two and eighteen, and starting work. Glad to see the back of you, old girl."

So it was that in the baking heat of the summer of 1976, Mike and I set out, on true-blue British motorcycles, (the very last of their breed, for the home industry had been decimated in the early '70s by Japanese competition) to visit her in Tuscany for the first time. My brother had agreed to join up with some potty expeditionary outfit which was going to photograph the remains of a Carthaginian warship off the coast of Marsala in Sicily.

'You know what?' he had cried one day in the seedy Ealing flat he had recently agreed to share with two oily motor-biking friends, 'I'm going to go by bike!' He beamed, full of enthusiasm, at me. 'Bruvvie, you want to go out to see Ma. I've got to join the photo group. Why go by train? Why don't we go on bikes together? Over the Alps, stop at Ma's, down from Florence through Italy on the *autostrada* and then over with the bikes to Sicily. Wouldn't it be fantastic?' He had struck just the right note. I had bought a 1972 BSA 650 *Lightning* in my last year at King's and was itching to take it on longer treks than to and fro across London from my digs to Peter Buchan's flat, to Queen Mary's where I had done my MA for a year, and from The Gate cinema in Notting Hill to Tooting Bec to buy Indian spices. Fired by Mike's febrile enthusiasm, I booked for two bikes on the Newhaven-Dieppe crossing. I hadn't seen the twit for about six weeks and had no idea what motorcycle he now possessed. He had taken his test (in those days a spin round the block, watched by the examiner, who then steps out and holds his hand up; you stop an inch from his toes, he scribbles a signature on the bottom of a form, and off you go and buy a Norton 750 *Commando*) on one of his pal's machines, but I'd never heard what he had acquired for himself.

'Oh, well, I haven't actually GOT a bike yet,' he admitted, 'but hey, we've got nearly three weeks to look for one.'

Ten days before we were due to depart, he still

had no steed. I was doubtful that the BSA would carry both of us and six weeks' luggage and camping gear. Things were getting desperate.

'What about "*Exchange and Mart*"?' asked Mike, with the air of one who has just discovered some arcane magic formula. No e-bay in those unsophisticated days, of course.

'Haven't you being looking in it already?' I cried.

For anyone buying anything back then, it was the first port of call. So far I had been skimming adverts at the back of the bike mags, but Mike had turned down my suggestions of reliable looking Triumphs, Hondas, BSAs and Royal Enfields in good enough shape to undertake a trans-European run. I had no idea of exactly how much he wanted to spend – and he was being coy about it. At last he seemed to have found the right machine. He came up to me with trembling, nicotine-stained fingers.

'That's the one!' he shouted, jabbing at a tiny advert buried deep in the endless columns of "*Exchange and Mart*". The ad read: *For sale. 1962 Ariel Arrow. 247cc. t/s model. Pressed-steel frame in g/c. N/e. Tyres A1. Rack. £20.*

I gazed at it. It was some moments before speech came.

'Isn't twenty quid rather cheap?' I gurgled.

'Well, it's practically all I've got,' said Mike.

We whizzed down to Morden in South London to

collect it. We would have been wiser to have studied the advert *really* carefully. When looking in a paper or magazine for a motorcycle ten days in advance of a pre-booked continental driving trip, you stumble across one which, in spite of its age, seems remarkable value at £20, look closely at first to see if "n/e" appears somewhere in the specifications. If it does, do not touch it with a barge-pole. "N/e" means: No Engine.

'We can't take it, you dummy!' I hissed in his ear as Mike handed over a couple of ten pound notes to the denizen of Morden in his cluttered garage.

'We told him over the phone we wanted it,' hissed back Mike, equally sibilantly, as the beaming recipient grabbed the cash.

'Now what?' I sighed, out once more in the sunny street, and helping push the Ariel down the road towards my parked *Lightning*.

'You tow me back to Ealing, and we'll fix it up there,' smiled Mike. 'It's a beauty, isn't it?'

The *Arrow* and its more fully faired stable-mate the *Leader* had been cutting-edge designs at the fag-end of the old Brit motorcycle industry, their pressed panels and bold colours cutting a 'sixties dash in a world of mainly staid, post-war designs. And this old bike had worn quite well, its two-tone paint un-faded, its white-wall tyres hard, its saddle un-split, its chrome not too badly pitted. But.........

Back in Ealing (and I pass over the traumas of getting it there at the end of a rope in heavy traffic) the engineless Ariel was established in Mike's lodgings' kitchen, and we bustled about once more, buying every paper we could find in order to search for a 247cc two-stroke "Arrow" engine of 1962 vintage. I never thought such a feat could be accomplished in under, say, a year of constant searching, and, as we sat, surrounded by cast-off papers and magazines, my eye was drawn often to the gaping space beneath the petrol tank of our new acquisition. Would any motor ever nestle there?

By astonishing serendipity (and it shows I should have had faith in my brother's remarkable luck – a luck that was to hold out until the turn of the century) and after hours of hunting and hunting, Mike spotted a promising-looking specimen.

'Oh good! Where is it? And how much?' I asked.

'Welwyn Garden City! Twelve pounds or offer!' cried Mike. 'Let's go!'

Soon, we would have been able to give a further piece of advice to a would-be cut-price touring motorcyclist: Twelve pounds seems a lot less cheap when to it must be added the cost of many periodicals, the return fare for two to Welwyn, and a taxi-drive from King's Cross to Ealing in the rush hour, the main feature of which were the driver's comments about "bleedin' hippies" and "engines drippin' oil over me clean upholstery – I've taken members of the 'ahse of Lords in this cab, mate" – until mollified by quite a big tip.

The engine, which was accompanied by a number of interesting looking spares in its dirty wooden box, turned out to be not quite what the manufacturers had fitted back in '62. We divined this from its inability to mate up with all the lugs to which it had to be attached. Its operation, when turned over manually, was marred by the grit that had got into part of its internals; yet, undeterred, Mike and I and the Neanderthals of the Ealing lodgings, set about rebuilding the machine on the kitchen table in the blazing heat of that hot, hot summer.

A day before we were due at Newhaven, the motor was ready for ignition. Mike jumped on the starting-pedal and, miraculously, the ageing parts choked into life. Mike had not expected animation to spring so readily into those rusty loins, so he had left off the silencers. The decibel level of what was, after all, quite a small engine, running un-muffled on a kitchen table in a small suburban house, was astonishing. Horrified, we shrieked at Mike to turn it off before the police arrived. Panicked by the racket, it seemed, Mike dived into the blanket of dense smoke and tore the high-tension leads off the twin spark plugs with his bare hands. Before the exhaust fumes eddied round him again and he was lost to sight, the Neanderthals and I had one glimpse of a white, agonised face, hair standing on end above it.

On the day of departure, at dawn, the Ariel *Arrow* was chugging on the street. Mike and I had not changed a stitch of clothing for what seemed several years, and there was no time now – the boat was due to sail at noon. We feverishly jammed the camping equipment on to the pillions of the two bikes. Oil-spattered, with yellow fangs gripping soggy roll-ups, the Neanderthals slouched farewell to the Ariel on the pavement. With a wheezing howl, that minion of the last great days of the Brit motorcycle industry clattered off south – to Sicily! We were off! The Alps, the Campagna, the dark blue Mediterranean called us forth!

The first breakdown occurred in Purley in Surrey at the start of the A22, when a puff of smoke and flame darted out of the side of one of Mike's cylinders. We pulled onto the pavement. Mike examined the works.

'Oh, lor,' he muttered. The trouble appeared to be that the right-hand cylinder had no gasket. Clearly this fairly vital part had been one of those many bits and pieces which had remained on the kitchen table at the conclusion of the Ariel's re-building.

'Shouldn't some of these fit somewhere?' I had asked, as I had gazed at the mound of homeless springs, trunnions, screws and bolts.

'Oh, never mind! Don't be a pedantic Big Brother!' Mike had cried, sweeping them into the pedal bin.

Now, in Purley, where a thin drizzle had begun to moisten our camping stuff, Mike seized the largest of our spanners and tightened the cylinder heads down until he was pink in the face. 'That'll do. Let's go!' he shouted above the swish of traffic, and with a rush we clattered off down to Lewes and then on to Newhaven where we made the boat just in time.

In the confines of the car-deck, the rolling volumes of thick blue smoke produced by Mike's elderly two-stroke engine caused supercilious Jag and Citroen drivers to wave their hands ostentatiously in front of their faces. I was about to do the same, but caught Mike's eye and desisted. With noses in the air we left the Ariel roped tight next to the *Lightning* and went aloft.

The modest expenditure upon our means of transport was matched by the extreme poverty of our cash resources, and for some time Mike prowled around the self-service counter – blackened, oily, greasy-haired and hunted-looking – letting out cries of disbelief at the prices. Nervous fellow-passengers gave us a wide berth. One wide-eyed, gentle-looking mother pulled her charges away from our immediate vicinity.

'We'll eat later, dears,' she fluttered, deaf to the

squeals of her ravenous young.

In the end Mike reckoned we could afford a single plate of chips. We shared it in silence, my brother brooding on the missing gasket. After the repast he jammed a roll-up between his teeth and stretched his oily boots out ahead of him. So the long sea-journey wore on. At last we reached Dieppe and made ready to drive the bikes down the ramp.

And, of course, the Ariel would not start. Again and again Mike jumped on the kick-starter pedal but there was nothing – not a spark of life. The smug Jag drivers purred past us, grinning. We looked at each other wildly. Ealing to Newhaven (60 miles) had been no problem – apart from the Purley blip; Dieppe to Marsala (1,800 miles) seemed to have a question mark over it. We wheeled the machines down to the dock; it seemed tactless for me to start up the BSA. Mike leapt on the pedal again. Nothing. With increasing force he jumped.

'Oh START! You vicious, vicious bastard! START!' he screamed. He leapt right into the air, like one of those Russian Olympic pole-vaulters, with a volley of searing expletives which blistered the paint on nearby cars. There was a crack. The kick-starter pedal dangled helplessly. We knelt to look. It had lost grip on the spline, and there was no bolt to hold it on. It was, I imagined, in the kitchen pedal-bin.

I like to look back and remember my brother on that occasion - true blue Brit and proud of it. I'm sure that a neurotic Frenchman or spoiled Italian would simply have broken down and sobbed. Mike, however, reached for the handle-bars, gripped the defunct machine and proceeded to rush up and down Dieppe High Street (or *La Rue Maritime*, as it is called in France) with the bike engaged in second gear – the best one for push-starting.

'Can't you help? Have you died?' he snapped as he passed me for the third time. So both of us pushed the *Arrow* in second gear up and down – and a heavy sweat it was with half a ton of assorted junk strapped on the back. It had not occurred to either of us to unload it first. After six or seven goes I gave up, but Mike, refusing to be beaten, and, by this time, purple, shook the loaded bike like a rat, frothing as he did so.

Eventually his persistence paid off and he got it started again. From this time onwards he would not hear of switching it off, except at night. So when we stopped at roadside cafes for a *sandwich jambon* or a *croque,* sitting at small round tables outside, the Ariel, dripping oil, juddered "Pop! Pop! Chug! Bang! Pop-pop-pop-pop!" and the proprietors and their customers muttered about *cochons d'Anglais* under their breath.

So began a journey which featured thirty-eight

breakdowns, and which took sixteen days and countless *sandwichs jambon* to accomplish. On the third day, on a fast road south of Chartres, with Mike ahead of me riding like the wind with bulging prawn-like eyes and legs splashed with oil, the Ariel's left-hand silencer fell off, clanked past me, and was run over by a lorry. Mike obviously noticed no change in the cacophony under his posterior, and by the time I had caught up and shrieked out the bad news, it was too late to go back. At roadside cafes, the *Arrow* now stood going "Bang! Bang! ROAR! Bang-bang!" and the mutterings about *les fous hippies Anglais* grew louder.

Touching on this business of *sandwichs jambon*, I'd like to point out that it was all we could afford to eat. We had left England with only a few pounds (expecting to rely on Ma when we hit Tuscany) and, in those days, there were no credit cards to fall back on – or rather, if they were just coming in, and I think they had them in the 'States by '76, they hadn't come as far as us. We actually did blow a few francs on a proper meal in the Loire valley, but it wasn't a success. No one had told us not to attempt *andouillettes*, and when I say that after doing so we went back to ham sandwiches with shrieks of delight, you will get some idea of the horrors lying in wait for the incautious *specialite* fancier.

This "proper" meal took place on a rainy evening

when the Ariel and the *Lightning* pulled up, after a long and interesting day of severe breakdowns, outside a *routier* in Nevers.

Unable to face another *jambon,* we tottered to a table and seized the menu card.

Plat du jour: Andouillettes, it read.

I called for a waitress.

'Er, garkon, can vous tellez-moi qu'est ker-say questo andouillettes are, per favor?' I gibbered. (Mike was rather cautious about handling foreign dialogue and left me to speak - on the grounds of my more extensive education at university.)

'*Ah, oui, M'sieu. C'est du porc,*' replied the girl.

'What did she say?' asked Mike. I told him, and for a happy moment visions of pork chops, apple sauce, grilled tomatoes, mash and peas floated before our eyes. A cooked meal with vegetables at last! I think a tear rolled down my brother's cheek.

'Well, or rather, bien, garkon,' I cried. 'Doox andooletties, per favor.' The girl scuttled off. We had ordered, as a starter, some shrimps. They came on a brown ceramic plate. We were joined at the long rectangular table (naturally, for the restaurant was practically empty, they were ushered close to us – so annoying) by two French truck drivers, both of whom seemed to have been maintaining their vehicles' rear axles, for their hands were jet-black. Each had a Gaulois fag hanging from his lower lip.

One had nipped round to the outdoor lavatory before taking his place at table, and clearly his aim had been poor, for he arrived shaking moisture from his blackened fingers. They jabbered frantically at the news of the *plat du jour*.

'*Ah! Andouillettes! C'est bon!*' they shouted, grinning at us. They too ordered shrimps and, unlike Mike and me, who were dissecting them Brit-style with a knife and fork, they began stuffing them in between brown teeth and Gauloises with their fingers.

At length the *specialites* arrived, and Mike and I looked up, beaming, our nostrils dilated and sniffing, our knives and forks to the ready. The waitress shoved the plates in front of us, and Mike's cry of horror was drowned by Gallic bleats of approval from the lorry drivers. United by a fastidious Brit distaste for eating items of sporting gear, we stared at the tennis balls on our plates. We each had a greyish sphere, with a sort of giant staple at two points on the circumference, nestling in a pool of green brine, bordered by some of the soggiest and dispirited chips we had ever seen. Mike took up his fork and prodded his ball, as if suspecting it of animal life. The fork rebounded with a gentle "boing". Ah yes, I had thought at the time, made of rubber; well, why not? We are abroad. Mike jabbed harder and his fork pierced the skin. At once a gaseous farting sound was heard from the orifice and further brine was added to the pool. He sliced open the blob and strips of greyish latex were revealed, scented, none too delicately, with the reek of sewage. He popped a piece into his mouth. I followed suit. We had paid two days' food money for this.

We staggered from the *routier* having eaten every scrap – such were the indignities to which hunger had driven us. Many *sandwichs jambon* and several days later, we could still taste that certain taste. In Tuscany we learned from an English ex-pat that the cooks of the Loire region take the part of a pig of which it has least reason to be proud – the lower colon – and stuff it with other bits of innards, well-flavoured with that which passes through them, snap a metal clip on each end and boil it; fine if you like *haute cuisine*, as Mike said, but not recommended if you are, deep down, a fish-fingers man.

We did not sleep well on our journey either. In the excitement of departure, we had left the tent in Ealing, so we had our nights under the stars, or the clouds, the camp-beds side by side between the bikes. We never dozed off until the traffic stopped, and we woke again covered in clammy dew three hours later with light in the sky. What with that, and the day-long roar and clatter of the bikes, particularly that of the Ariel, and the diet, and the constant mechanical failure, the trip began to take on the quality of an epic nightmare. Mind you, if I had known how very much worse it was going to get, I might have enjoyed the bit before the Alps – even though, with those celebrated peaks slap in front of us, we had a breakdown of a simple but so infuriating a type that at the time I thought we had reached the absolute nadir.

The wretched Ariel, having at last blown the gasket on its other cylinder, owing to the lack of a proper exhaust pipe no doubt, and burning up gallons of two-stroke mix a day, gave a juddering bang just as we were coasting down a long, steep slope in a remote wooded part of the foothills. It came to rest, smoking, in the hollow of a little valley. In front of us, the road rose steeply up towards the mountains; behind us the long incline down which we had come. No traffic passed; we were off the main route and heading for Barcelonnette.

We spent a day and a night in that hellish spot pushing the bike first up one slope and tearing down in gear to start the engine, and then up the other. Remember, we had no starting pedal. At first I had attempted to tow the *Arrow* to the top of the hill, but we had no rope, only knotted towels and things, and the *Lightning* really wasn't up to the job. Its gearing was too high. We stopped when the stench of burning cork made it clear that my clutch was wearing out. The thought of being stranded in that hollow with *two* defunct motorcycles was more than sanity could stand.

So, with the cylinder heads tightened down so hard the spanner practically bent, and with obscenities and threats ringing through the quiet woods, Mike and I took it in turn to tear down the hills at the end of the exhausting half-an-hour climb it took to get the Ariel to the top. Eventually I ceased to take my turn. I had lost faith in the old machine; it seemed to me that it would never be heard spluttering again. Mike, however, true-blue to the end, would not hear of giving up.

'I paid THIRTY-TWO pounds for the sodding thing!' he screamed.

And so, dropping with exhaustion, he would toil up the long, long hill again – usually the one down which we'd come, for it was a little less steep – turn the Ariel around, let it whizz off, leap aboard, jam it into gear, and grind anti-climactically to a halt, with popping shrimp-like eyes, about a foot from where I sat on a log smoking roll-ups.

Once a woodman came and looked on with utter lack of interest and a good measure of Gallic contempt. He shambled away again without offering to help before I had time to think of the French for

188

"AA van".

If that twenty-four hour period was our worse moment of stasis, our worst spot of motion was on the mountain *autostrada* to Savona. Mike had finally started his steed and, as though to atone for its naughtiness, it actually behaved well for many miles. The Alpine crossing seemed to have breathed new life into it. Mike gripped the wounded beast between oil-coated legs and, with veins on his forehead standing out, tore off up the pass to Gap. The cooler air must have reminded the bike's engine of Welwyn Garden City and home, for I had never seen it go so fast and so unfalteringly. In a twinkling, the pale rider of the Apocalypse had vanished round innumerable bends, and I didn't catch up with him for three or four hours. An overloaded *Lightning* 650 with six weeks' luggage and equipment on board, in addition to a rider who had passed out from overeating, (and was to do so again the following Christmas, as I have narrated) takes its time.

At the top, the glimmering landscape was fading. Mike was waiting impatiently.

'Buck up, Speedy Gonzales. We must make Savona before one in the morning.'

'Why?'

'The campsite closes then. I've just been looking it up in the book.'

'We won't do it, will we?'

'If you get out of first, we will.'

'Look, bruv,' I growled, nettled a trifle, 'I could have made Cape Town about three weeks ago if I hadn't been following that geriatric basket-case of yours - with all the gear too.'

'OK. OK. But you have been in first most of the way up, haven't you? Go on, admit it.'

'Well, yes.' I had to come clean. The BSA had that hangdog air of a trusted but overloaded donkey. 'Slow and steady. No slogging of the motor. Keeping revs high enough to circulate oil, but not pushing it. Look at the load on it.'

'Quite! Fatso!' smiled Mike, leaping aboard the *Arrow* once more. 'Well, Savona Ho! And God bless all who sail in her!' He jerked the bike off its stand and clattered off. Suppressing a constipatory twinge I followed him. I had noted the jauntiness of his tone. "See, see, the little victims play, regardless of their fate" seems to be the right poetic quotation.

Around us, in the mountains, the sun swiftly dropped out of the sky. It was time to put our lights on. I reached over to the headlamp casing and twiddled the switch. Mike did the same on the Ariel, but nothing happened. He brought the bike to a halt with a screech.

'What's happened to the lights?' he cried, wrenching the knob backwards and forwards on the

Ariel's rusting headlamp. Nothing. 'Oh, what have I *done* to deserve this?' he raved, clawing at the pitiless sky, as it were.

The lighting system had gone west. In fact, now we thought of it, it might never have worked at all. This had been the first bit of night riding since the Frankenstein job on the Ealing kitchen table. I remembered that quite a lot of faded wiring had been consigned to the pedal-bin at the conclusion of our surgery.

'Perhaps we'd better spend the night here?' I suggested.

Mike stared at me witheringly.

'Where?'

And, looking round, I had to admit that unless we clung like bats to one or other of the twin sheer rock walls, we were unlikely to have much of a night.

'I'm going on, even if I die in the attempt. I'm getting to Savona before one, even if I'm obliterated by a lorry on the next bend!' shouted Mike into the night.

It wasn't the time to discuss prepositional logic, so we made the best bodge-up we could. This involved taking an Opal Fruit (now called Starburst) strawberry wrapper and putting it over the bulb in my reading torch. Mike held this out behind him, steering with one hand, while I drove ahead using the BSA's front headlamp for both of us. In this fashion we darted in and out of the roaring convoys of Fiat lorries on what the Italians laughingly call the mountain *autostrada* – a four-lane wall-of-death patronised exclusively by homicidal Formula 1 drivers trying to do 100 mph and trucks struggling to reach 20 mph. Horns blared, exhausts belched, the Ariel's front tyre bumped again and again into my rear number-plate, and Mike's left arm wavered out behind him with the Opal Fruit wrapper glowing bravely but dimly. This operation seemed to take over a month, but obviously lasted much less, for we made the campsite with sheet-white faces, with hair on end, and with five minutes to spare.

Upon arrival at Ma's, the *Arrow* was practically rebuilt under the auspices of "the walking cheque-book", as Ma was affectionately known, and Benelli and Guzzi parts were machined to fit where Ariel parts should have been. The lights now worked, the silencers worked, the kick-starter pedal worked, and we were ready to set off again – to Sicily!

It was annoying to both of us, therefore, that after so much work, oil, and smoothing down of Ma's alarmed feathers, that everything was put back to square one by what I now think of as The Affair Of The Wasp.

Mention has already been made of my brother's hardihood on the forthcoming Christmas of '76 when I ran over his Adam's apple (on a moped specially bought by Ma to prevent us from going on bringing dangerous motorcycles all the way over from the UK), but if further proof of it were required, the Wasp Incident fits the bill.

We had left Ma's villa after brekker on a boiling morning with few misgivings about the two bikes' abilities to whisk us on a further thousand miles, other than a feeling that we might reap the effects of a pint of holy water sprinkled over the engines on departure, Ma having become more Catholic than the Borgias since her move. But apart from the odd splutter until heat had dried out the works, the bikes were going as sweetly as could be wished. We then roared side by side out of Montecatini en route to the *Autostrada del Sole* and Mike yelled,

'I'm going to let it out, Bruv. If there's anything wrong, there's still time to go back and fix it. Meet me at the end of this stretch.'

With not another word, he twisted the throttle round as far as it would go and rattled away in a dense cloud of blue smoke. I, on the *Lightning*, chugged after him at about 45 mph, the camping gear flapping and clanking behind me. I mused on the fact that wherever we went these days, I travelled like some eastern caravanserai with ground-sheet, camp-beds, kettle, stove, grimy Woolworth carrier bags full of spares, and old cardboard boxes with changes of clothing strapped on to every possible protuberance of the cycle frame (for it had become an unspoken agreement that the frail *Arrow* be now left unencumbered) – so unlike those flash continental tourers from Germany and France who, clad in black leather, rode neatly panniered BMWs armed with nothing more bulky than their wads of travellers' cheques.

After several kilometres, and with the *autostrada* toll booths in sight, I was aware that I seemed to have missed Mike. "At the end of this stretch", he had cried. I reined in my steed, looked back along a hot, empty road, turned and returned, going towards Montecatini again. In twenty minutes I passed the spot where I had last seen him. Very odd. So I went back once more. No sign. I thought he might have gone through the tollbooths and on to the *autostrada* – Ma had provided us with cash for this, so we would not have to confine ourselves to the humblest of cart-tracks, as we had done all through France. So I went on through, getting the usual dead-pan contempt as my junk-shop on wheels passed beneath the haughty Tuscan nostrils of the geezer in the box.

Soon I was rattling along the motorway with the sun in my eyes, keeping to the safe side of the line on the hard shoulder while the Lancias and Alfas screamed past. At the end of an hour's motoring: no Mike. I pulled into the next *servizio* and waited, facing the road. My wait lasted until lunchtime and I really hardly knew what to do next. I wondered whether Mike had said "at the end of this stretch" at all. Gazing at the map, it occurred to me, in what might be described as a blinding flash, that he had probably said "exit for Arezzo" and, what with the helmet and the traffic and the clattering of Brit iron, I'd misheard. Within a trice I was back on the hard shoulder, Woolworth's bags flapping in the *scirocco*, Arezzo-bound.

There is no point in making this tale into a sort of mid-'70s *"Odyssey",* so I'll summarize by saying that he wasn't at the Arezzo turn-off, nor at Orvieto (which could sound like the word "stretch" if misheard above the screaming of a tortured two-stroke). He was not at Orte, and at Rome I spent the night. It being far too late to turn back, I continued the journey, and failed to find him at Anagri, Frosinone, Caserta, Afragola, Salerno, Sala Consilia, Castrovillari, Cosenza, Vibo Valentia or San Giovanni. So I took the ship over to Messina in Sicily and headed across that land of bandits on my own, or *solo*, as they say in those parts. My one comfort was that I had both camp-beds and all the cooking utensils, so that at each stop I enjoyed the contemplation of a careless, hasty brother sleepless and starving on whatever ribbon of black Italian tarmac he found himself.

You will want to know what had happened to

him, I'm sure.

Way back on the road between Montecatini and the *autostrada*, a few miles from Pistoia, my bruv, gripping the Ariel's flapping handlebars with fiendish strength, had been shooting south-east like a meteor, with (as he later admitted) the wild staring eyes of one who is willing his £32 steed to get to Marsala – a mere hundred miles from the African coast – when a wasp lodged itself in between the chin-strap of his helmet and the chin beneath. There it stuck, stinging and stabbing repeatedly. Mike had dabbed frantically at it with his left hand, the other keeping the twist-grip fully open, and the bike had zig-zagged to and fro like a nervous mountain fawn leaping among crags. He told me later that he had not thought of slackening speed and drawing in. There was room in his mind for only one thought: the squashing of the wasp and the saving of his chin from the feeling it was being dipped in hydrochloric acid.

Up to this eighteenth year of his life, he had had merely academic relationships with wasps. He and I, in the dead past, had disapproved of the ingenious wasp-traps set up by Dad at Glenturret; those jars with holes in the lid and dozens of wasps trapped drunkenly in a swamp of honey and cider. Perhaps because of these, Mike had never put to the test what an angry wasp can do, nor had he found out until then that he was allergic to their stings.

With one last frenzied dab, he had passed out, and, with the throttle fully open, had careered across two lanes of traffic and hurtled into a deep ditch, the *Arrow* somersaulting over and crashing on to his back. The hot exhaust pipe had burnt a hole through his jeans, the front fork had twisted slightly, and the newly-fitted silencer had torn from its mountings. A moment later, with the camping stuff flapping, I had whizzed past the tragic scene on the other side of the road, not even scenting the aroma of roasting posterior.

After forty minutes Mike had regained consciousness, discovered that he was pinned in a ditch, and in a rage had banged the bike back on the tarmac and roared on, sadly aware that the Ariel was once again in very much the same state it had been after leaving the kitchen table in Ealing. His thoughts, he told me, were too dark for him to notice that he was careering back the way we had set out. In due course he finished up again at Ma's, and decided to have lunch there and to give first-aid to his machine. He also told me that, until reminded by our maternal relation, he had forgotten my existence. His feelings towards wasps were no longer benevolently scientific.

His chin well doused in TCP, Mike and the *Arrow* set off again, late in the day – for Marsala! With one silencer loose, and the steering very odd, he limited his speed to the low fifties, he told me, and scorched on down the *autostrada* to Rome. Long before he reached halfway, the thought occurred to him that he had no camp-bed, no cooking utensils, no food and too little money to buy any. Our combined possessions were on the BSA, ahead of him by two hundred miles. He took pride, he explained when we met, in reflecting yet again that a lesser being – a foreigner, say – might have given up at this point and blubbed unashamedly. He, knowing that he was made of sterner stuff, swung off the *autostrada* at the very next exit, made up his mind to save all his toll money for the modest ferry crossing to Sicily and travelled south by minor roads only. Furthermore, to save the cost of accommodation and food, he would do without both and complete the journey in one mind-altering zap.

Thus was the Ariel *Arrow* put to its severest test. For sixteen hours solid, with only two petrol stops, Mike tore through blazing, ochre-coloured villages and along the bumpy tree-lined parallels of the *superstrade*. Without food, without water, without a camp-bed, without his brother and without a map, Mike made the great trek and arrived eventually – a gaunt, spiritual wreck – at the ferry crossing. The cost of the passage over the straits, and fifteen litres of petrol and oil mix, denuded him of his final hundred lira piece. He had driven all night and all through the next morning. The sun's heat had provoked a severe and prolonged thunderstorm on the northern Sicilian coast. Through it, soaked, and with lightning playing about his handlebars (so he claimed), he had ridden for a further three hours, until, sometime after we had eaten lunch, he had rattled into Marsala only an hour after my own arrival. When, at last, we were re-united, I thought that his face looked like that bloke's in Munch's painting *The Scream* – hardly human.

I have stressed the Hero-who-rises-above-suffering-and-remorseless-Fate aspect of my brother because *he* had expected the journey to be problem-free and fun. I had dreaded the whole thing, so it was worse for him. Really though, the heroic entity of those Marsalan days was that 1962 Ariel. Marsala, known in Sicily as "the arsehole of the Med", was a baking hot collection of partly finished buildings surrounding a medieval centre – initially fascinating to Mike and me, of course, after Father Cunningham's tale of demonic possession there. It was an axiom of '70s Italian travel that the further south you went the more uncompleted building projects you saw. Local construction firms borrowed huge sums, chucked up what they hoped would be a luxury condo or hi-tech factory on a green-grass site, and then went bankrupt. Undeterred, other optimists started again a few hundred metres away and followed the same path. The result was like one of those dystopian horror movies set in 2146 AD where survivors pick over the rubble after a nuclear holocaust and an oddly bright sun glares down over a deserted landscape of scrub and ruins.

Strangely, this fascinated Mike (as much as it appalled me) and I'm sure that his days in Sicily asking about buildings, land use, borrowing rates, construction methods and sites, helped to spark his affinity with real-estate and led eventually to his stateside real-estate business and considerable wealth.

We had huge expanses of time to fill down there. I had brought many books, wrapped in cling-film in my left-hand pannier. Mike read little and was frustrated by the archaeological organisers' low rate of activity. The British Classical Antiquities Expeditionary Team (grand title for zombie outfit) had its headquarters in a pretty but shabby villa near the sea; but owing to an unforeseen Mafia clamp-down there was no running water, no postal service, no telephone, no church open, no bus running, no garage dispensing fuel, no hotel operating and no food available. Photographing Carthaginian warship remains was a difficult task and a low priority.

Mike, recovered from his epic run, was as dismayed as I was by the squalid boredom in which we found ourselves. He was incensed to discover that one of the legs of his camp-bed had fallen off the BSA *en route*. Nearly a month on, a three-legged bed did little for his spine or temper, although he later told me he got fairly used to it after the first five nights and was quite uncomfortable in a normal bed for a while when we got back.

We lived on Sicilian pizza – a slab of dough two inches thick, with a smear of tomato paste on top, on vanilla ice-cream served in a bun and on water melons. These grew in the villa gardens, and enabled the chronic constipation of our *sandwichs jambon* period to metamorphose gradually into its chronic opposite. We were put in a peasant's cottage, along with three archaeology students. The peasant had a family of thirteen. We slept six to a room and shared the concrete flower trough in the yard which did service as a lavatory. I came to know this trough well, for, although the house was equipped with a WC, the Mafia action against the city (a result of the Commune di Marsala failing to pay its dues, we gathered) had stopped the water supply, unfortunately just after the house's WC had been copiously used. The peasant had shut the door on the effluvia, but weeks later I fancied I could still scent it.

On one memorable morning, Lydia Johnstone, the woman in charge of the dig, rounded us up to go down to the lagoon. We were to travel at last to the warship embedded in the salt-flats. The Mafia's local man, pleased to oblige *i Tommies inglesi*, had arranged the hire of a boat for the team. We Brits all assembled on the harbour-ramp and Miss Johnstone shook hands with a short greying Godfather. Around on the quay were four shiny saloons with black windows, and by each stood a group of *Mafiosi*. They looked, wonderfully, just as they do in films. Here were the dark, shiny suits, black shades, brilliantined heads and bulges under the armpits. The *Capo's* silvery mane gleamed above a jowl like Mussolini's and a nose like Caesar's. He wore a light brown overcoat over his shoulders, even though the temperature was edging 40C.

Twenty of us crowded onto the motor-boat, bobbing in brilliant water so clear that the hull could be clearly seen. The boat was white with a loud red flash along the side, and when, later, we were still, moored over the skeletal wreck only ten feet below us in the salt, this red and white image reproduced itself in the transparent shallows. We grew very low in the water as the archaeologists tramped aboard. Eventually we became absurdly over-loaded for so small a craft. I was the last on, and there were cries of: 'Watch it! It's rocking!' and 'Hey! Why didn't you stay at home?' as my avoirdupois displaced yet more lagoon water. At first I found nowhere to sit, but Mike pointed out a flat section of the raised area in the middle of the deck – a white box with a hole in it. I plumped down, grateful to get a perch, and the swarthy Sicilian, appointed to guide us, started the engine. I then had the extraordinary sensation of having a shovelful of hot coal rammed up my bottom, and leapt up, shrieking, and stumbled over the side with a great splash. The sudden motion caused the overloaded craft to lurch one way then the other, and huge quantities of Mediterranean swamped aboard. The *Mafioso* hooted, '*Pazzo!*' and '*Cretino!*' and '*Furfante!*' *in* chorus with 'Prat!' and 'You steaming great nit!' My cheeks were glowing pretty red as the Sicilian, Mike and Miss Johnstone fished me back over the gunwales. The reason the raised area had been untenanted in spite of the crowd was that everyone else had realised that the round hole was the exhaust pipe – one of the few instances of a motor-boat not having its exhaust fed into the water, and typically bloody Marsalan.

Anyway, to return to the role that Mike's Ariel took on as the Mafia's vendetta brought paralysis to the region. With the Land-Rovers out of diesel, the hotels closed and the entire Expeditionary contingent scattered in cottages far and wide, that brave bike became the only means of transport for thirty Classical Antiquarians. I had set off, on my own, back to Ma's in Montecatini after a stay of less than a week. Mike was booked for the whole month, however, and for all that time the *Arrow* traversed the western tip of Sicily with three aboard, ferrying students and shopping. Mike sat on the petrol tank (kept topped up in dribbles from the motor-boat reserve and from the cans of two-stroke oil he'd bought on the mainland), someone else sat in the middle working the gear lever as Mike, pulling in the clutch, called out, a third sat back on the rack clinging on. With leaking gaskets, a silencer hanging off, dodgy electrics, springs flattened, clutch worn to the metal and tyres bald, that stupendous thirty-two quid bargain, in the brilliant glare of a land far from its grimy birthplace in Birmingham, flew the flag.

Eventually, when every aspect of that Carthaginian warship had been poked at and photographed, and with money for fuel advanced by Lydia Johnstone, Mike clattered it back to northern Italy in a last flat-out run. He would have ridden it on to Ealing had it not been stolen by gypsies (we thought) outside Ma's place. I like to think that somewhere, in the fetid, narrow back-streets of Florence, it ran on for a further thirty years. Peter Buchan and I eventually installed my BSA *Lightning* in Glenturret's museum; I had never brought myself to sell it after its adventures. If only we could have had the Ariel to keep it company.

Looking back after all this time, it amazes me

that, in the careless, easy-going mid-'70s, we sallied forth on our dodgy machines to traverse Europe with no debit or credit cards, just a little stash of grubby francs and lira notes, with no mobile phone, with no sat-nav, no protective clothing and with our gear in carrier bags – and thought nothing of it at all.

ON TRACK

When Glenturret came into my possession years later and my childhood friend, Peter Buchan, joined me in creating its famous museum of 20th century life, it was not on road vehicles that we concentrated our fullest attentions – important though they always are in precisely dating a period, and popular though they may be with the visitors. Our chief focus was on railways, both model and full-size. Peter's fanatical love of railways had matched mine since boyhood; it was our age, of course. If you were a boy in England between 1956 and 1967, those years between the ending of Korean War metal shortages and the apotheosis of The Beatles, you breathed model trains.

In 1994 I was driving through an English town called Godalming and my eye was caught by a dusty shop full of old models. There, back a little from the window-pane, was a grimy cabinet, and in it was a brand-new looking Trix *Meteor.* With feverish fingers I groped for my wallet. A few mins later, the agony of saying goodbye to £250 still bringing perspiration to my brow, I held the handsome red box in my hand – a good weight, as Dad had said about "*Crepello*" at Christmas in 1963 – and I suffused that glow which collectors feel.

Peter knows what a mania for collecting can do to

people. And one of the things it does is make them imagine that everyone knows what a Trix *Meteor* is. The firm of Trix went bust fifty years ago, but it manufactured die-cast locomotives and station buildings and tin-plate coaches and wagons at the scale of 3.5 mm to the foot (for track known in the US as HO gauge and in the UK as 00 gauge). Trix was a left-field choice for boys because the firm was late coming to 12 volt DC, sticking to pre-war 14 volt AC until the late '50s, because its products were considered more toy-like than those of Hornby-Dublo and Triang, its British competitors, and because its range was astonishingly expensive. Although I had plenty of Hornby-Dublo, kick-started by Grandpa's *Royal Scot* train-set, I grew to love Trix models and began a lifetime collection of their "universal" three-rail track, engines and rolling-stock, DC and AC.

Aged ten I wanted a *Meteor* so very badly that I had feverish dreams about it. It was a three coach diesel flyer which appeared originally in red and silver for AC operation and then in blue and silver for DC. Its motor coach was extraordinarily heavy and its corridor connections carried power from the far bogie of the third coach through to the motor bogie at the other end. It had lights that reversed according to direction and the AC version contained a deafening whistle which could be set off anywhere on track. Further centre coaches could be bought to make a longer train. Peter sneered at its design, which, being "freelance" captured the general impression of a fast diesel express, but was not based on any known prototype. I had floated the idea of this model being my birthday present for 1964, but was met with genial guffaws from Dad. The *Meteor* was round about the ordinary weekly wage, then about £15, or £300 in today's money.

Although the model-railway disease may be contracted at any time of life, Peter and I became infected young at Glenturret, in those far-off summers, when, on Grandpa's unused polished drawing-room floor, he and I would lay out Trix "Universal" track to an immense length and lie on our stomachs, heads near the rails, and watch the locomotives (Trix 4-4-0 *"Pytchley", "Warship"* diesel, *Brittania* and WR 0-6-2 tank, Hornby-Dublo *"Crepello", "Silver King"* and Class 4MT 4-6-2 and Triang *"Princess Elizabeth"* – some of them second-hand) whirr past with their loads of rattling tin-plate goods wagons or elegant "blood and custard" and maroon coaches, and gaze at their rear lamps as the train disappeared into the distance.

It did not matter that the trains were small; size, like everything else really, is in the mind. As Wordsworth puts it with his customary insight: the world is something "we half-perceive and half-create".

I often used to hang over the vast 00 gauge layout at Glenturret, when the house was mine and a museum, stepping out of my tiresome six-foot frame and entering that little, perfect world of 4 millimetres to the foot. In that *piccolo mondo antico* there was no death, no vandalism, no threat of war, no disease, no darkness, no hand of time and change wielding their dreadful blows. Every product of Trix, Hornby Dublo and Triang was there – all at last safely found and purchased, ending the "sweet unrest" of boyhood's unfulfilled yearnings. Lorries and cars remained parked to perfection, never rusting, never muddy, never unwanted, crashed or doomed to the scrap-yard. Stations were re-assuring – empty, clean and free from muggers, graffiti and decay, with high, short platforms and buildings embellished with fine cast-aluminium art-deco. The curves that led out of them across bright, solid point-work were traceable by the eye to yet another dumpy, clean station barely seconds down the track. There was no possibility there of heartache, of final farewells in falling rain, of departure on the rusty rails for Auschwitz. Once, near the end of the century – '98, I think – Peter, a grown-up, thin, and greying version of the boy on the polished floor, standing with me as I gazed over the enormous layout when the last visitor had left, suddenly said,

'There IS horror there, too.'

He knew I would disagree. There is nothing dreadful in the unchangeable, and the unchangeable is what I trust awaits us in Paradise: our best selves in our happiest of worlds. For me, that means living forever in hopeful childhood in the decent, optimistic Britain of the mid '60s, before the anxious years of punk and conflict, stagnation, terrorism, national debt and, in more recent times, austerity, food-banks, Brexit madness, immigration fears, the rise of the populist far right and climate change.

'Yes. The horror is there.....as everywhere,' muttered Peter as we both gazed at a quiet model line of track under trees forever green. 'Can't you imagine what it would be like – *living* down there?'

'Yes, I can,' I replied. 'Perfect, predictable, bright. Like being alive for all time on one summer's midday at the age of twelve when you have just received the present you've always wanted.'

'No!' cried Peter. 'For God to enjoy being God, He cannot live upon the world He has made; that way leads to crucifixion, surely? The happiness of being God lies in looking down from such a height that the plan *appears* to be nothing but perfect. Those spacemen were brought to tears and ecstasy by the contemplation of Earth from the moon – so blue and frail and heart-rendingly beautiful. You don't see murderers, laboratory dogs, battery chicken farms, cancer wards and shanty towns from space. Creating the perfect railway layout is akin to God's creation of the world: you who have made it must see it only from outside and from above.

'But I *want* to be less than an inch tall,' I said, gesturing towards a station around which were parked, in small scale, the vehicles of my childhood. 'To be able to live down there would be to live in the best of my past. My past in is miniature all around us!'

Peter draped his bony frame over the rail which prevented the punters from getting too close and poking their fingers where they shouldn't poke.

'All rightee,' he murmured, staring ahead while his pedantic, precise voice grew quieter and quieter and I listened to his version of our vision. 'You are now three-quarters of an inch high and standing on that platform. What surprises you is the clogging string all round your feet. Those wisps of dust are like heavy twine in your new world. They make walking difficult, and as you stir them, they release coin-sized flakes which seem to defy gravity and swirl at chest level. Moving through the twine-thick dust filaments, nearly transparent, are myriads of creatures about the size of large cockroaches. They are skin-mites, blind and milky-white, puffed up by those flakes of skin the size of biscuits. You cannot see the platform surface very clearly, but it does surprise you that it is not all flat. It undulates, and where flecks of paint are chipped off there are inch-deep potholes. Very untidy. The platform worries you because it seems so short, and so high, and you feel unprotected – almost as though you standing on a huge podium.

'You decide to wander out into the station forecourt, and you realise that you can't open any of the doors leading off the platform into the floorless booking-office. The only thing to do is to walk down the ramp and round by the fence. It startles you to find there is a sheer drop of two feet down to the courtyard. Thousands more milky mites scavenge blindly through the high fluff here. You duck under that fence – its railings are at least nine inches deep – and the fluff and the visitors' skin particles emit a shower of dust motes. Some are sharp, and hurt as they knock into your eyes. In the parking lot is a lovely Dinky Toy car – a Hillman Minx saloon. You walk up to it and lean against it. Its paint is lumpen and heavily pocked. Its bulk seems riveted to the ground. In fact, it has nothing of the quality of a car when you examine it. Those scaly, rough rubber tyres would never revolve. It has walls a foot thick, and through glassless windows you peer down into a tangle of dust and sightless mites and cables. Where the engine should be, there crouches a beast the size of a bulldog. The cables run from its belly to the ground, and it shakes wet mandibles at you. You recoil from the Minx and its spidery occupant.

'Above your head, the plastic foam of the model trees looks bilious and horribly unstable. Any moment you expect those ton-weight branches and leaves to crash down upon you. You re-enter the station because your train is due. If it were not for the train coming to take you away, you would feel a sense of panic at re-ascending that scabrous, crooked platform again, and exposing yourself to the malign stare of glassless, useless windows.

'While awaiting the train, you make up your mind to travel, as you have always wanted to do, in the locomotive cab. With palpitating heart you stand ankle-deep in the twine at the end of the platform. Soon your body is jarred by a deep thudding, and, with horrifying speed, but with no swaying on the vicious curves, your engine and coaches arrive and stop instantly. You climb aboard the engine. For a second you feel the guilt you might feel in the real world, and you look quickly over your shoulder. It is more disturbing than being reprimanded to see no eye upon you and to know that no one lives in the station's little town – that the train has stopped for no one.

'Once upon the locomotive footplate, you find that you are much higher off the ground than you thought you would be. Before you have time to register that there is no proper floor within its foot-thick walls, and that you are going to have to balance on the jutting metal plate behind the motor, there is a sickening rush of blood to your head. With gut-wrenching violence, the engine has pulled away – not smoothly, you know, but with a tearing acceleration that nearly throws you onto the massy bar connecting engine to tender. You scramble forward again to your precarious perch, aware of the meshes of that six-foot high gear wheel grinding near your feet. Your trousers are splattered with a dark liquid as heavy as tar. The noise is unendurable. On a shaft ahead of you, running for ten feet or more into the darkness of the heavy boiler, is a huge, rotating mass. From its far end livid electric flashes like the discharge of lightning sear your eyes.

'You cannot see out ahead. For some reason, the slit-like windows in the immense wall are above your head. Beneath your foot-soles, the track tears past. You estimate your speed at 200 mph. There is so little room, and nothing to grip on to. A great bare metal shaft trembles near your head. Your nails are ripped and your shoulder-bone is nearly gouged from you by the wrench of the cornering forces. With no warning you have turned 180 degrees in a fraction of a second and are bumping up and down several inches at every swift revolution of the roller-like, filthy wheels.

'Again you grasp something, anything, staying aboard more by luck than by design, with a steady warm electric wind blowing over you as the motor's coils heat up, and again you have gone through 180 degrees in the blink of an eye. This time you vomit, your sick whipped away to coat the face of the rocking tender. You struggle back to the opening in the loco cab, trying to keep your blinded eyes from the terrifying sparking down the cavity ahead of you. Braced in the doorway, bumping with such violence that your feet leave the die-cast lintel every few seconds, you glimpse the Minx saloon in which the beast lurks in the station courtyard. With an instant's blur you are past where you boarded, and there is no let-up in the mind-numbing racket and liver-cracking rumble of gear, axle, bearing, spinning armature and thundering, juddering wheels.

'Behind the engine, running free, suspension-less, clatters the train of coaches. You decide to board the first coach. It must at least afford more protection than the locomotive's floorless footplate. You hoist yourself up on to the surface of the tender. Easier than you thought, even though the delicately modelled steps are eighteen inches deep and there is no real coal to roll about in. It is such a relief to get away from the screaming roar of the locomotive that you sit for a moment, bruised and bouncing on the modelled coal, but happy to be at a distance from those chewing gears. The wind up here is extraordinarily strong, but you can now see ahead and can brace yourself in time as the train once again hits the savage curve at the end of the layout.

'Spread-eagled on the moulded coal, you survive the battering turns, and the low bars of the signal gantries flashing overhead. On the straight, you make your way down into the corridor connection between the tender and the first coach. Standing just above the huge black couplings which fling their mass to and fro several times a second, you try to open a door which requires a hundred times your strength to shift. A full-size human finger three times your height would do it, but not you. Its hinges rely on the turning of a steel-plate two inches thick in a rough slot. Fortunately, there is no glass in the windows at the coach's end, so you can lever yourself over the sharp tin-plate edges into the carriage.

'At once the coach is familiar. It is *Aries*, one of your most prized named chocolate and cream Pullman cars. The train, perversely, slows the moment you are inside and then, without warning, stops dead from a speed of over 30 mph. You are tossed right off your feet and crack your head on the shiny tin of the door you have just clambered through. You slip into unconsciousness.'

Peter paused at this point, I recall.

'Want me to go on?' he'd asked. I had gazed at him in silence. I knew I had been listening to the words of a visionary. Why did my old school friend never manage to write that great novel, or direct that astonishing movie? Mike, who brought an American girlfriend to the museum at the turn of the century, told me that she had said she had seldom come across a mind as surprising as Peter's – and that was after a mere long weekend.

'Go on! Go on!' I had laughed. I had to know what he thought would happen next in that horrible miniature world which I had fancied was Paradise. I had laughed, but peered with opened eyes at the station we were overlooking, at the Hillman Minx in its forecourt, at the 1959 Trix die-cast model of the 'Britannia' 4-6-2 steam engine with *Aries* at the head of its train of Pullman cars, pulled up at the too-short platform.

'You are now in that coach – there!' Peter had pointed. I followed his eye to the vestibule at the locomotive end of *Aries*. I almost saw myself lying unconscious behind the unglazed tin-plate door.

'You come to your senses,' resumed Peter, 'The train is still stationary. You stagger to your feet and make your way between the dirty white seats and tables. The seats are hard with immense waves in them which simulate upholstery. With a shock, you assimilate that these lumpen, pillared mushrooms on each table are crude representations of lamps. There is the back of a head above one of the seats at the far end of the carriage. The light is not good inside the vehicle – the inch-thick Perspex glazing is smeared and blurry with enormous whirls of oil and twine-like fluff – but you notice that the head is unusually shaped and coloured, that it is dome-like and very big. Although you walk on, you do not really want to pass that head and see the white face which does not turn towards you as you came along between the tables in the utter silence.

'As you approach and draw near, the stale taste of recent vomit rises in your sour mouth. That nose! Those great uneven nostrils! That misshapen, bulging eye so high, and that other puffy slit so low! That jutting Neanderthal forehead! That six-inch long gash of a mouth! And beneath the waist: nothing! Just the thick, encrusted glue which holds the torso to the off-white chair. And that stillness! Look how the banana fingers have grown one into the other! They curl upon themselves like some organic mutation. And the torso is so still! It stares forever at the end wall of the coach. You remember that there are many other *Modelled Miniatures* on the train ("Bring your empty 00 gauge coaching stock to life with our realistic seated passengers!") and you know your sanity depends on your getting off at once.

'You dash past the monstrous figure to the far-end side doors. Fortunately, the smeary, browning cellophane sheeting has torn away from the window, and you can stick your head out. Beneath you is the end of the platform, a long way down. Only tiny susurrations on the surface enable you to make out the skin mites moving in their undergrowth. You are wondering how exactly you are going to descend the mirror-like surface of the flat tin-plate (Trix and Hornby-Dublo coach sides have only painted handles and rails), when there is a fantastic banging and jarring. A double-headed goods train passes at extraordinary speed through the station past the other platform. One after another, the massive, un-sprung die-cast and tin-plate wagons crash past, forty or more of them, each pair of wheels causing the rail joint opposite your vantage point to leap and spark.

'As the racket dies away, your eye is caught by the signal rising. What speed! The heavy cast bar defies gravity, and, in a twinkling, is up, propelled by some strange power. Instantaneously, you are on the move again. You have left it too late to descend.

'If it was terrible in the locomotive, at least unearthly weight and mass kept your vehicle stable over the rail joints. Some of these joints are up to six inches misaligned, others have gaps of nearly a foot between rail-ends. The Trix Pullman, light as gossamer, walls of tin-plate flexing like the lens of a mad eye, and the chassis taking the strains of the terrible pull ahead and the drag of a further four coaches behind, hurls your bruised body up and down like dust. There is nothing still in this yawing world. Sharp edges and uneven floor mince you and rip your flesh. It is suicide to wait for another 180 degree turn, so you make the decision to jump off while the train is still in motion.

'The tight curve comes up in a flash of speed and the train slows momentarily through the goods yard points. You jump from the window (the painted door cannot open), aiming for the green baize verge. The surface bangs up at you suddenly and spear-sharp filaments pierce your skin. How soft the material seemed in its packet! The slope on the verge is practically 1 in 2 and you roll helplessly down to the rail surface, the roller-like wheels missing you by inches. The last swaying coach gallops past and disappears round the curve.

'At last there is a sort of silence, although under your soles the baseboard drums and thunders from the train's progress to the far end of the layout. Aching and limp, you stumble on to the track-bed. Here most pieces of ballast are the size of a rough-hewn football, but some are the size of suitcases. Walking over them is not easy. Eventually, you escape from the main line and stand in the maze of tracks that lead from the shunting-yard. You do not know from which direction to shade your eyes. The sky above seems hazy and full of motes like organic fragments of permanently floating paper. Six huge stars blaze upon you from high up in dull space. The shadows are confusing and make a dream-scape of the scene, an odd outer-planet panorama, totally flat up to the edge of your world, and above you are the silent, stationary suns. The light is very clear, but claustrophobic. Above each sun stretch three-feet thick hawsers up into that leaden sky. The effect is that of Milton's Hell in *Paradise Lost* – a confining dungeon somehow limitlessly vast.

'Gasping and dizzy, you stand balanced on a shiny, high rail and gaze up and around you. The drumming under your foot-soles tells you that the train is coming round again, bearing its grotesque sawn-off mutants upon another circle of their pointless journey. The noise hides a deep, rumbling whisper from much nearer at hand. Around your feet, the skin mites are being vibrated, and the motes are being moved heavily in the turbid air. Some instinct makes you turn, your six shadows turning with you, but you never see the driverless Hornby-Dublo 0-6-0 Class 08 diesel shunting engine that ploughs into your back, flattens you, and drags your legs up into its shark-teeth gears.'

Peter stopped, idly running his fingers in the

ballast of the nearest stretch of line. Now I looked at those pieces of ballast, they did seem a little over-scale.

'Well,' I said eventually, 'that is NOT how I see the railway. How these models are....' and I had swept my eye over all that beautifully preserved rolling stock from the '50s and early '60s, those clean stations with not a skin mite in sight, '....how the railway is, is, for me, how the world is.'

'Exactly. What I have been saying is how for *me* the world is,' replied Peter.

He always does things like this. All my life I have opened further doors into his personality. On that occasion I realised that I had not fully understood how fully he saw only the serpent beneath the flower. A most interesting guy.

Although bohemian and untidy, he was the son of a rather aristocratic landowner. His father's house, Startmont, was a short drive from Glenturret, and it had been one of Grandpa's wishes that Mike and I seek out and cultivate people who might be "Useful". He did not define, in my hearing, of what "Usefulness" consisted, but part of it had to do with what he called PLU. He had a deep horror of those who were not PLU – at least a horror of their establishing too great an influence on the family. This was, I now think, of a piece with his excessive courtesy towards servants; no one could have been more feudally *noblesse oblige* than Grandpa. It came from his consciousness of the huge perceived gulf which lay between them and himself – a sentiment already outdated in the age of *"Anatomy of Britain"* and *"That Was the Week that Was"*. Most of the human race was not 'People Like Us', of course, but Grandpa's low opinion of them was only expressed in private.

The Buchans, however, were very much 'People Like Us', if not a little more so by virtue of having titled persons in the close family, and Grandpa made every effort in the holidays to get us children acquainted. The initially enforced meetings with Peter, his membership of our gang and, finally, our mutual Sixth Form days, cemented a closeness which ended up with Peter spending most of the best years of his life up at Glenturret with me.

The great model railway we had was largely Peter's creation. An inveterate collector, more OCD even than I was, he had poured thousands of pounds into the museum layout, equipping it with every single item which, in the mid '60s, he and I had craved, but which sensible parents had denied. I too poured thousands into the railway, and into the narrow-gauge line which ran round the grounds, and the famous collection of toy cars and commercial vehicles, but it was the 00 gauge railway which had to take the brunt of two obsessives unable to see each other's point of view.

Naturally, we agreed that the period from 1914 to 1968 should be modelled, but we had never agreed on the precise years. I felt that the Great War should be left out, but WW2 be represented – Peter disagreed. I felt that early diesel haulage should feature: Trix Western "*Warships*", for example, and Hornby-Dublo's Metro-Vick Co-Bo, Rushton shunters, and certainly Deltics like "*Crepello*" – but Peter disagreed. He wanted steam only. I reckoned the emphasis should have been on mainline express passenger stock, but Peter preferred branch line and goods. I believed in toy buildings, especially the die-cast stations of the golden age of Trix and Hornby Dublo, but Peter thought the stations should have been scratch-built to proper scale, as at the famous Pendon Museum. I thought the trains should run through an industrial landscape, Peter wanted trees and fields. I liked night-time illuminations in structures and coaches, Peter preferred daytime. I loved old Dinky Toys and Matchbox vehicles on forecourts, but Peter liked scale kits. I wanted the bulk of the layout flat, Peter wanted it hilly. We did, in short, disagree about certain things.

The keenest area of disagreement was whether to have two-rail (as in real trains) or three-rail track (a centre rail being used to supply current to locomotives via shoes. The Trix system enabled two trains on one stretch to be independently controlled because one loco ran on left rail with centre return, and the other on right rail with centre return – hence their trade name "Trix Twin Railways". I collected their track until I had a vast mileage. Then came Peter Buchan onto the scene. With typical perversity, he failed to see any advantages in the third-rail system.

'It's too toy-like,' he would say.

'You can run two locos on it,' I would respond, quietly, but with an edge to my voice.

'It's not like the real thing. Only London Underground has a whacking great rail running down the centre of the track bed. Real railways don't.'

'Nothing about a model railway is like the real thing!' I would hoot, exasperated. 'Do models have an accurate representation of track length between stations, imbecile? Do we have real people getting on and off for real reasons, cretin? How else can we operate trains under different control, cuckoo? When shunting, for instance, dummy?'

'Okay, keep your wool on,' he would reply, and then, without a shred of understanding, would add, 'Two-rail is better. Three-rail is too toy-like.'

Peter, I'm afraid, disliked Trix products, but I thought they had character. And although my train mania had been kick-started by Grandpa's Hornby-

Dublo *"Crepello"* in its (wrongly-named) "Royal Scot" train-set, by 1965 I had become a Trix Twin collector through and through, largely because (though I didn't know it) the firm had slid into bankruptcy, and tons of its old models were going cheap through dealers and its own showroom in London.

Trix *"Scotsman"*, *"Coronation"* and *"Princess"* engines, even back in 1954, the year I was born, cost about eleven pounds. A plastic Triang *"Princess"* cost 17/6, (80p, or the equivalent today of forty quid or so: nine or ten times less than the Trix.). Going bust added to their allure, and even today I remain a member of the TTRCA (the Trix Twin Railway Collectors Association) even though I no longer search out and buy items from their range.

Whereas Mike was drawn to all things modern, Peter and I, in our different ways, liked all things old. In Peter's case this found expression in his wonderfully crafted dioramas of pre-1920 village scenes: the woods, the blacksmith, the horse-drawn wagons, the timbered cottages. His work for Glenturret's railway eventually became famous in the modelling press. Given my very different predilections you can see why we so often disagreed.

But I have grown sad writing about all of this. What we have lost has come flooding back. So – enough.

THE RAVIOLI RIOT

I'm going to pen the cataclysmic episode of The Ravioli Riot after I have asked myself some familiar questions. I went on, after Glenturret, to university, To King's College, London – and, as I gaze back from the 21st century, I wonder: Did I learn anything of lasting use? Why haven't I kept up with friends from that period in my life? I ask myself these questions periodically because, after all these years, I still don't know whether my time as a student was worthwhile. Mike never went to university, and built up a successful business in America. Peter Buchan did not go "up to the 'varsity" (as The Boiler used to put it), but he seems more acute and informed than most people I know – more so than I am, I think. Cardinal Newman's idea of a liberal education makes fine reading, but the model of a university depicted in his calm pages is unlike the reality I experienced. So too are all those books like *Zuleika Dobson* and *Sinister Street* and *Brideshead Revisited* – and the later *Lucky Jim* and *Changing Places*. In university-based novels spanning the best part of the last century, I have yet to read one that is not like someone else's dream-world: more vivid, more silly, more narrowing, more academic, more social, more degenerate and more adult than the gauche reality I recall in those years after I left Glenturret Academy.

From the cattle market of Freshers' Hop to graduation day, with Ma in her summer hat on a hot June afternoon – those undergrad years of life at King's – I received little that made a dent in my psyche. I grew knowledgeable about London: a different London from the misty-yellow, carefree city of our boyhood in Maida Vale, and my already over-developed historian's sense became fine-tuned to the point when it was sometimes an actual physical agony to gaze at, say, late 19th century photographs of Holborn or Clapham and be unable to get back to their time. My university days confirmed that I had contracted what I now know is a disease of so many British people of a certain outlook – a mental state of imprisonment in the present.

I guess my student days were tainted also by the sense of loss I felt by not being at Glenturret. I knew one other man at King's whose first year was rendered miserable by his leaving his boarding-school. I was, in an absurd, feverish way, homesick for my recent past. Absurd, because, apart from those vivid boyhood holidays in the '60s, Glenturret had not been my home for any time other than the six terms of my final school years. Absurd, because of the sense I had that without me there, it would change with the passing of the years, and dreadful things would happen to it, and I could not prevent this. Feverish, because of that thought that I could never return to it, ever, and that my life was to be passed in places uncongenial to my spirit. Feverish, because London, and its damp, exhausted air and miles of orange streetlamps made me yearn for the cold, bright intoxicant of the Scottish uplands.

From '76 to '77 I studied for my MA at Queen Mary College. I saw much, much more of Mike in that year. He was in the last year of the Sixth Form at his day school, and came racing across London by bike (when he eventually got a cheap replacement for the Ariel from Ma) to the East End to see me.

So, what of all those coffees and uncountable cigarettes and egg curries and four years of lectures on Pope, *The Dream of the Rood,* Laud, King John, Chaucer, Conrad, Shaftesbury and the Reform Bill, those all-night horror films at the Brixton Astoria, those thousands of hours in South Kensington and Bloomsbury? What of Soho and the high chrome stools in the salt-beef bars, the Hammersmith Odeon and Motown concerts, and all those words, frequent looks and very infrequent kisses, and the subfusc glow round Marshall guitar amps in the clubs, blurry in the endlessly rising smoke?

For some reason everything then made a smaller mark than perhaps it should have done, except to scribble a high carrier-tone on top of the calm, rolling wave of my eternal boyhood.

Meanwhile, as Doctor Costigan's regime at Glenturret moved on from 1970, the old building began to change. Naturally I was to make great changes myself, but my aim was to put things back, not to bring them forward. Some of Doctor C's peculiar ideas were ruthlessly annihilated. His 1972 rope-operated elevator, designed to raise trunks and boxes up to the top floor, went very soon after I took over – it ruined the main staircase; a clear example of the practical overcoming the aesthetic.

His auxiliary generating plant remained. I restored the Magirus-Deutz engine in 1982 and got a particular pleasure standing next to it in its sturdy brick outhouse as it roared away. Wisely Doctor C had ensured that it could produce 150 megawatts on a 120 amp supply, able to cope with heaters and stage lighting, should the need arise in troubled strike-bound times, or when winter storms blew down the power lines. I used it on a regular basis for powering part of the garden railway.

The oddest of the features of the Doctor's time, however, was destined to have a short life. I refer to his daft 1975 plan to put the school kitchen in the kitchen gardens. There was a sort of bizarre Costiganian logic in having the stoves and pans near to the veg which was to be cooked in them, but the practice of bringing all meals on trolleys from several hundred feet away through the back door was not conducive to *cordon-bleu* standards of cuisine.

In Grandpa's day, Glenturret had had a splendid Victorian kitchen and, annexed to it, a pantry, still room, server, and cook's and parlour-maids' sitting-rooms. This took up a lot of space on the ground floor, leaving only three other rooms suitable for classrooms. When I first arrived at Glenturret as a pupil there was no need for large numbers of teaching rooms; as I've already mentioned, there were barely seventy boys in the place. But for some unfathomable reason the school proved moderately popular, and Doctor Costigan attracted day-boys from the Dunblane and Stirling areas, so that in its fifth year of existence there was a desperate need for two further classrooms. The old kitchens must have seemed the obvious solution, and all those partition walls were pulled down, cook's room lengthened into a corridor, and abracadabra! – two more rooms on the ground floor, each capable of taking twenty-five tables. (Desks never did make an appearance at Glenturret Academy – I expect they were too expensive.)

Where now to bung the kitchen?

In the kitchen garden was that run of fine Edwardian greenhouses; museum visitors started their trip on the narrow-gauge railway from them. I recall many saying that the greenhouses reminded them of Kew. If they had been constructed entirely of glass, Dr C would probably have thought again, but they had brick sides and backs; in fact their backs formed part of the encircling wall. The greenhouse nearest to the main house had running water, and the new generator was alongside, so all the paraphernalia of Grandpa's kitchen had been loaded up and wheeled down to its new home: saucepans, cutlery, the huge Aga stoves, fridges, toasters, racks, knife-sharpener, dresser, deal tables, meat safe, marble blocks, meat hooks, game cupboard, bread bins, fridges and kitchen sinks all made the journey across the yard and round into the gardens, and all were connected up to produce a long, workmanlike kitchen under glass, like a ship's galley. The whole thing had been managed in the summer vac of '75 when I was recovering from bluffing my way through my degree and preparing to delay having to work for a living a little longer by starting to read for my Masters.

This grand but flawed kitchen scheme had, as I will explain, a short, sad life. By 1978 it was no more, and what brought about its demise was the saga of The Ravioli Riot.

You must have worked out what I had done; making the cardinal error, not just once, but twice, of forgetting the warnings about *never* jobbing backwards. But when the enormous uplands of the past lie on each side of the little valley of the present, stretching away into infinite distance on all sides, perhaps that little present is entombed, dimmed and diminished and the imprisoned soul cries out to climb out, up and away from it.

Yes, the moment my university days were over, I went back to Glenturret.

It was an act of unreasoning impulse, but I went back!

Dear Doctor Costigan, (I wrote),

As you may know, my university days have ended, and I have obtained an Upper Second degree (Hons) in History with English and an MA on 18th century literature, both from London University. I am at present seeking a teaching post, for I have felt for some time that the teaching profession is making overtures for my soul, and I have heard through my friend and former school-mate, Peter Buchan, that you are continuing to expand at Glenturret and are currently interviewing for the coming academic year.

I should be most grateful if you would consider my application for a general teaching post, for I believe that my future lies in school-mastering, and I can think of nowhere better to begin than at my old school, where I spent my happy Sixth Form days.

I enclose a resume of my education and

qualifications and I look forward very much to seeing you again, should you consider that my application for interview is worth pursuing.

Yours sincerely,

Anthony Crepwright

In the event I received a telegram from Doctor C which read: YES. WHY NOT? NO INTERVIEW NECESSARY. TERM STARTS SEPTEMBER FIFTEENTH.

Doctor Costigan was up a ladder whitewashing the hall ceiling when I blew in. His opening comments were not auspicious.

'Oh, it's you,' said he, gazing down from aloft, somewhere near the coving, after I had explained how grateful I was that he had offered me the job by telegram. 'Good God! I was thinking of someone else!'

Flattering, eh? I don't know that I was expecting the red carpet, the fatted cow, the "Well, well, my boy, I always knew that you would make a fine, perhaps a great, schoolmaster", but I hardly expected the convulsive leap of the whitewash brush and the squirming shudder of horror. Thinking of someone else, indeed!

'But it's too late now!' he cried, and poked his brush into the tin and continued his Michelangelo impersonation.

The very next person I saw was The Boiler. He clearly was not thinking of someone else. On learning that I was to join him in the groves of *academe*, a fellow employee, a valued colleague, he muttered something like, 'Merciful heavens!' and tottered into his classroom and slammed the door.

Of my personal experience in that first year of teaching, I will write little. Anyone who recalls their own time at school in classes taught by new, young teachers would be able to fill in the blanks. Put it this way: I realised all too soon what merciless little swine we had been to poor Pee-Wee Burgess. I discovered that it wasn't a question of strolling into a class of thirteen year-olds with one or two clever *morceaux* about Milton's cosmology which keeps the animals to the straight and narrow. I often tottered from a lesson soaked in a chilly liquor to find Doctor C staring frigidly down from a banister rail having been brought from his office by the blare of revolution from my classroom.

It was typical of my bad luck in those early days that, on the very evening of The Ravioli Riot, it was I who was on duty. There was practically no punishment on earth which would have stemmed the explosion which came about from exposing Glenturret's inmates to the sinister power of cold ravioli, and when I say that even the threat of "sitters" from the strictest prefects failed to subdue the ugly passions, old Glenturretians will know what I mean.

As a lot of this is unknown (and banned) in modern education, I'll briefly explain. Doc Costigan (by no means a bleeding-heart anti-corporal punishment liberal) had instituted the prefectorial system at the Academy as early as he could after its opening. The Head Boy and his deputy (as was not untypical in public schools, major and minor, in the '60s and '70s) were then invested with the power of caning juniors, if fellow prefects had ordered it. In the manner beloved of British schoolboys this was given an affectionate nickname: "sitters", because the chastisement was always given in the Prefects' sitting-room.

You could get "sitters" for breaking one of the vitally important rules of etiquette laid down by the prefects, such as not marching correctly down Library Gallery with your arms parallel to the ground, or having your left hand in your pocket if you were not a member of Burns Society, or wearing a red waistcoat or jumper when not a member of Games Study. A prefect's voice would suddenly cry, 'Chappie!' (You were always addressed as "chappie" by the prefects, even when they knew your name perfectly well.) 'Chappie, come here!' A languid finger would point to a spot some six inches in front of the prefectorial toes. 'You were not marching correctly down Library Gallery. You will have "sitters". Go!'

Hours of anticipation would then elapse, for "sitters" always took place after breakfast – not that you felt like having much breakfast. At 8.45 there would be a little queue on the landing leading to the prefects' sitting-room. By a fine irony, this landing boasted a large oil painting, given to the school by Doctor Costigan's mother, of Joseph and the infant Jesus entitled *The Love of the Child*. As the clock struck, you set off, marching, with arms parallel to the ground, down the prefects' passage. On one side were three of the senior boys' dormitory rooms – one of them my old haunt, Tennyson dorm – and some of the inmates were always lounging in the doorways. 'Hope the bugger bleeds,' one of them might say.

At the end of the passage was a small oak door. You gave it a single rap; just one – two was considered cheek.

'Come!' a voice would cry, never 'Come in' for some reason. In the sitting-room were all the prefects. They were supposed to witness "sitters" to ensure it was fair, but it was bad form for any to watch. To get over this difficulty, all but the Head Boy of Academy had a newspaper in front of their faces. Most punched little holes in their "Express" or "Telegraph" with a biro so that they could see, but not be seen to see. These papers began to flutter with excitement as your interview began. Behind your back, you were conscious of red, ferret-like eyeballs gleaming through their tiny apertures.

'Ah, chappie,' said the Head Boy of Academy, peering at you through his monocle (as affected, believe it or not, by one particular scion of the Anglo-Scottish upper-classes in my first year as a pupil), 'Not marchin' cowectly down Libwawy Gallewy. Vewy well, I shall give you six. Have you anythin' to say?'

You always replied 'No' to that question. A tirade about your pupil rights and the United Nations' negative attitude to child cruelty and abuse, would only have brought the response, 'Vewy well then – I shall give you twelve.' He would then stand and point with outstretched finger to a nearby chair. 'BEND!' he would cry.

And you bent down, down, over a battered Windsor chair, until your fingers came into contact with a thin wooden spar which ran just above floor level from one back leg to the other. This spar left just enough room between itself and the carpet for your fingers to curl round and grip it. In this position you were bent over so extremely that your trousers became like the skin of a snare drum; if tapped with a finger they would sound "bong"! The newspapers fluttered in a frenzy – you could see the pinpoint

240

eyes fixed on your bottom from between your legs. Behind you the Head Boy selected his cane. Would it be the thick one which bruised? The thin one which drew blood? The one with splinters? The papers rustled frantically. Head Boy took several paces back and then galloped towards your arse.

Whack!

After aeons passed, and the cane had lashed its allotted number, the Head Boy stepped back to his desk, breathing quickly. You remained bent over, gripping the bar with white knuckles.

'STAND!' he would cry. You faced him. His monocle flashed. Satiated, the papers would be still – a wall of white with crossed legs beneath. 'Let that be a lesson to you, chappie, to march cowectly down Libwawy Gallewy. GO!'

He would point to the door. You said, 'Thank you' – thanking him for taking the trouble to chastise you in time to prevent you becoming an even worse boy – and you left, going out of the little oaken door, down the thin passage, with arms exactly parallel to the ground – not 89 degrees, not 91, but 90.

'My God, the freak's blubbing,' would sneer the Sixth Formers as you walked past them on into the light of day, past Joseph and the infant Jesus, to your pals.

'What was it like?'

'Is it bleeding?'

'Let's have a look.'

These, and other expressions of fascinated sympathy, would greet you on your return to the world of mortals, but you didn't want to discuss things just then. What you really wanted was to be alone.

You may have noticed that I have slipped into the second-person narrative which implies that I too had been through this harrowing experience, and in case you're thinking that if I had it would have been as a Sixth Former myself, I must admit to the shame of being the only Sixth Former of my time to have received this essentially junior-boy punishment. But then I was the only Sixth Former of my time to arrange for an inky booby-trap to fall on the Head Boy of Academy (whom I detested) as the result of a bet. This was in my first term, in pre-*"Snow White"* days, however. After that show I found I had become a non-whackable "character".

Later I tasted the joy of "sitters" as whacker rather than whackee in my capacity as Vice Head Boy to Martin Landsgrove.

'Creppo,' he had said, 'I've got a dreadful hangover this morning. Would you mind doing "sitters"?'

I broke a nice whippy little cane on Lithgow's bottom, and how he cried when I was doing it! I remember the last whack coming down and Peter Buchan, Colston & Co trembling their newspapers like autumn leaves in the wind.

WHACK! went the cane.

'Ow-OOOOOGH!' roared Lithgow.

'Be silent!' I snapped.

'Yow, ow. Oooow!' cried the victim.

'Cease those absurd noises, Lithgow, or I shall chastise you again!' I had hooted. He did not cease the absurd noises, so I was compelled to administer further chastisement. I must have put extra beef into it, for there was a sudden splintering of bamboo, and the cane collapsed in my grip. I should have let Lithgow keep it really, for he whose arse breaks the cane becomes its owner, but I preserved it for myself (an early onset of museum fever), mended it with Sellotape, and had it hanging on my bedroom door for years.

This seems, by today's standpoint in schools, where "Every Child Matters" is the watchword, to smack a teeny bit of the abusive; but, as I've mentioned already, the attitude back then was more on the lines of NCM. Indeed, my later Glenturrent colleague Barry Larch's standard comment to whingeing pupils was: "Let's be clear. Me Teacher; you Nothing".

I've drifted a long way from The Ravioli Riot, but it is of importance to know that even the threat of "sitters" did not quench the fury of the rioters. Actually, I feel you can hardly be expected to remember why I'm even *telling* the story of the Riot. It was the kitchens – why they were moved back into the house from the greenhouses. Remember?

So: on with the events of that November evening during my early days as a master at Glenturret when the school was given a most unusual dish at suppertime.

The grub at the academy was never inspired, even when unaffected by being wheeled across the yard in freezing weather – as would be the case with a salad – so staff and pupils were always willing to vary the monotony of sosses and mash, egg and chips, mince and potatoes, shepherd's pie, fishcakes and small, fatty chops. Nowadays, of course, one can buy anything from anywhere, but in the late-'70s in Scotland you'd have been hard put to it to find an avocado anywhere between the border and John O'Groats, olive oil came from the chemists to treat earache and "foreign muck" was what people had on holiday in Spain.

Little bags of pasta filled with minced meat and swimming in tomato sauce had not graced the school's tables before. The boys liked this lukewarm tinned slime awfully, and were not perturbed when it cropped up again the following day at lunchtime, accompanied by mashed potato. There were a few sarcastic comments when back it came for supper the same day, sitting on top of soggy toast.

"Quiffy" Barnett, the bursar (a burly Scots ex-army staff sergeant with Brylcreemed hair, through the huge quiff of which he was constantly running a greasy metal comb) had clearly ordered several tons of canned ravioli, for we had it at lunch again the next day, for supper with chips, and again for lunch with Brussels sprouts.

Then an early cold snap set in, and the thermometer plunged.

The staff (who had their ravioli in common-room) one by one took to going to the Station Hotel in Dunblane for meals and, slowly, the murmurs of discontent among the boys grew.

Not only was the monotony causing unrest, but also the ravioli's temperature. Slopped into aluminium bowls, it made its torturous way from the kitchen-gardens on an open trolley, pushed by the cockney factotum, "Eddie" Edwards, and, stone-cold and squidgy beneath a layer of orange coloured oil, was chucked onto the refectory tables like slops. It wobbled under its oil up and down the sides of the bowls for several seconds after its arrival. Just seeing it made one feel queasy.

The refectory (Grandpa's old library, converted just before I came to teach at Glenturret) had several long tables in it, the ends pushed to the walls, on both sides of the room. Each table comfortably sat eight boys, although by the time of the Riot twelve were crammed on each one. The pupils chose which table they wanted to sit at and groups of friends would bag places at the aisle ends. The remaining seats at the walls were taken by smaller than average boys who had fewer, or no, friends. These tiny boys got very little to eat. Food always arrived off the trolley at the aisle end and the greasy trays of fried eggs or sponge pudding were grabbed by the big guys. One egg might find its way down to the dwarfs at the end and be fallen on, like a rabbit by starving wolf-hounds, and be torn to pieces. These tiny, ravenous creatures at the table ends were known as "the skeletons".

Meals were supposed to be eaten in silence and the prefects presiding at high table maintained this silence ruthlessly. Over the passage and down the hall was a smaller senior refectory (my grandmother's old morning-room) for those in the Fifth Form and the Sixth who were not prefects. I spent my first year as a pupil eating in this pretty yellow room, and very civilised it was, for talking was allowed and the only supervision was by a member of staff who sat where he liked. Food for the general mob, juniors, non-prefect Sixth and Fifth, was the same, and the serving was handled by Eddie Edwards' Italians – spiv-like young men from

Glasgow, known to us as "the dagoes". Eddie, who had come up to Scotland with Doctor C from the prep school, himself presided over Head of Academy's prefectorial table in the junior refectory. Here, the prefects had their special menu served with polish. While the peasants had cheese on toast, Eddie would wheel up a trolley to the Head Boy and prefects with a flourish.

''Ere you are, gents,' he would say, 'nice bit of chicken casserole and new pertaters. Very tasty.'

'Yaas, get on with it, Eddie,' would drawl the Head Boy, and Eddie would lay the thick white dinner plates out with a spade-like thumb pressed beyond the rim on to the centre of the plate.

''Ere you are,' he would wheeze, circumnavigating the table like a walrus. I remember, in my prefect days, getting a plate with a greasy dark splodge on it. 'Sorry about that,' grunted Eddie, grabbing it back, breathing on the mark to get condensation on the plate, and then wiping it clean between his jacketed arm and chest. 'Nice an' clean nah,' he gurgled. He kept a greyish serving-cloth under that armpit into which Peter swore he once saw Eddie blow his nose. He would bring in the prefects' custard "personal like" from the kitchen in a thick bowl. He carried it gingerly, tongue protruding, and his thumb was always an inch or two below the surface. '''Ere you are, young gents,' he would say, plonking down the bowl and pulling out his thumb with a "plop", disturbing the skin which had formed on the custard during its long journey, and wiping it under the arm-pit. You were much less likely to get food poisoning if served by the dagoes; being a prefect had its dangers as well as its privileges.

So there we were, much as usual, at suppertime: Prefects in control in the junior refectory, me the teacher on duty with the Fifth and Sixth in the senior refectory, and the ravioli wobbling in for the three thousand and fiftieth time that week. There was a universal sigh from all. The cold oily bowls were tilted towards plates, but at the sight of the sluggish puffy bags moving under the surface, a cry went up, 'Not bloody ravioli *again*!' Suddenly, a tall boy (called, I remember, Lewis) with soulful, bulging eyes, stood and screamed,

'I can't stand it anymore!'

He grabbed a brimming bowl, lifted it high above his head, and hurled it from him. About a quarter of a ton of ravioli sploshed over the tables and the floor. I laid down the fork with which I had been toying with a piece of pale, turgid pasta, and began to remonstrate.

'Er….,' I began.

But, as if at a great trumpet-call, the remaining bowls were seized and whoosh! Their contents rained down upon the just and unjust. I jumped to my feet in horror.

'Boys! Boys!' I hooted. No good, of course. A pound of mixed oil, tomato sauce and pasta bags got me between the eyes. Through the blur I was conscious of a scene like Dante's inferno: the figures of the damned scooping up handfuls of ravioli and ramming them down other peoples' shirt fronts and stuffing them down their trousers (Ho, Ho!), of tomato sauce pouring down the walls, of someone shoving a large number of bags down the back of my neck, of crazed faces coming and going in a blur of red.

Forgetful of my dignity as a schoolmaster, I sprinted for the door, and made my way in a daze of pasta to the junior refectory. I don't know why I did this; perhaps I had some atavistic belief that the magic power of the prefects and their threat of "sitters" might quell the riot.

The door of Grandpa's old library was a massy, oaken affair, neo-Gothic, of course, and brimming with carvings. I seized the door-handle. For a moment it wouldn't open, and my hand rotated, lubricated by oil and tomato sauce. I remember noticing that I had the equivalent of an economy-sized tin of squidge up my coat sleeve, and it slithered out as I grasped the knob. Eventually the door unlatched and I flung it open – awesome, I imagine, to those who first glimpsed me – and stood upon the threshold.

The noise of the revolution had clearly been heard from within the junior refectory, like Krakatoa from some neighbouring island, for there was a strained silence in the place and two of the prefects were on their feet, glaring about with flaming eyes. I noted that most of the bowls of ravioli were still half full, that the big boys at the aisle ends of tables had empty plates, but that the skeletons were busy with fork and spoon, tipping rucks of chilly ravioli onto their plates. Gobble, gobble went the skeletons, barely looking up from their first square meal for ages. Every other eye turned upon me wildly. I opened my mouth. Most of it was filled with ravioli. I gurgled, as far as I remember, 'There's – been – a – RIOT!' and flung my arm dramatically over my shoulder.

At the word "riot", and at the sight of a member of staff clothed in small pasta squares, with ravioli up the nose, sticking out of the ears, and decorating the gap between neck and shirt like an Elizabethan ruff, a spring seemed to snap.

Immediately, plates began to explode against the walls. There began a great baying shout and a clattering of aluminium bowls as these were dragged from the wall ends of the tables and hurled in the air. Above it all, like the squeal of chalk scribbled on a blackboard, came the keening cries of the skeletons, robbed of one of the few satisfying meals they had got that term, whose gobbling now ceased, to be replaced by lamentation, like that of Rachael of old, mourning for what was lost and unable to be comforted.

The prefects darted from their places, forgetful even of their tasty lamb stew. Eddie Edwards stood gaping. With burning eyes, the Head Boy of Academy and his myrmidons bore down upon the ravioli rioters.

"Sitters!" they roared, pointing at random.

"Two hundred lines, chappie!"

"Three hundred lines!"

One of them, a dark brooding fellow called Hudson, of whom I, a teacher, was a little afraid, ran from the room and, after less than a minute, re-appeared with a cane from the prefects' sitting-room. With this uplifted, he rushed into the fray.

"YOU, chappie! SITTERS! BEND *NOW*!" he bellowed. Hurtling forward, his right foot landed on an unseen mound of ravioli. Down he went, his cane thrashing the unfeeling air. Instantly a basin of ravioli was upended over his features. Judging by the way his bull-like roaring ceased, quite a lot got into his mouth. Ghastly guggles followed.

Up the windows went ravioli; the walls streamed. I sat on the floor near Hudson while my life flitted fitfully before my eyes. The heavy refectory benches were seized and out went the mob into the hall. There they met the rioters from the senior refectory. For an hour the uprising stormed through the building, crazed insurrectionists sliding and squirming on burst ravioli and ramming each other with benches. Only the skeletons were left stunned, unmoving, like Marius at Carthage, inconsolable among the ruins.

The lower part of Glenturret had to be closed for two days while industrial cleaners were brought in. During that time the boarders ate sandwiches in classrooms. Quiffy Barnett got the message, I think, for ravioli did not appear as the *plat du jour* again. Doc Costigan, going into the whole affair, felt that while the steady persistence of tinned ravioli on the menu had been a contributory cause of the rebellion, the fact that, day after day, it had been stone-cold on arrival had been the last straw. My own part in failing to restore order had not been unexamined, I'm afraid to say – although The Boiler stuck up staunchly for me, pointing out that at twenty-three I was not much older than the senior boys.

So the era of the kitchen in the gardens came to an end, and an extension was built on to the library to cook food on the spot. I pulled it down in 1992. It was a hideous eyesore.

Meanwhile as I taught away, steadily getting

better at it, and elucidating the mysteries of Shakespeare, Dickens, Keats & Co, the hand of Fate was clenching its fist above Glenturret. New kitchen, or no new kitchen, the winds of change were blowing from afar.

THE AVENGERS

So much for me in the academic year of '77-'78.

While I revelled in being back in Scotland, my brother resolutely embraced London life. For each particle of DNA I inherited from Grandpa, a cellular package which relished continuity, a liking for the old, a desire to stay in one place, a taste for the traditional, Mike had opposing particles from our dear father: a need for new experience, a restlessness of spirit, a dissatisfaction with the present and a yearning for a rosier future. I often thought that the only bit of Grandpa in Mike was his fascination with money.

Now that we share an apartment and he no longer lives in the USA, I wish I'd had a dollar for every time he has sighed when I've quoted Tennyson: "the saddest words of tongue and pen are these: it might have been". His last few years in L A, up to '99, had not been happy – problems with a mad female concept artist – and then he had his breakdown after her death and then his long recovery in England.

I am going to fill you in on his rather rackety existence from his eighteenth birthday. I've already sketched in Mike the intrepid motorcycle adventurer, so I'm now going to give you Mike the would-be rock-god, and Mike the terrible avenger.

'That cat!'

'Well, she is very annoying.'

'That bitch!'

'Careful. You're getting butter on the chair.'

'That cow!'

'I think you're being unfair to the dumb chums, comparing her with them.'

'That – that SLUT!' hooted Mike.

It was half-term at Glenturret, and Mike and I sat in my study having a meal which was halfway between tea and supper.

'Oh, my GOD! When I think of that *snake*!' Mike resumed his litany of least favoured quadrupeds and reptiles. The rain fell on Glenturret's lawns. I had bought a tub of hummus in Stirling and was dipping fingers of toast in it. One seldom saw the cuisine of the Eastern Med around Dunblane in the '70s, as I have explained, so it was rather a treat. 'Oh, yes! Yes! What I need is revenge!' shouted my brother. He stood up, hippily moustached and malevolent, his long hair swinging. He shook a fist at the ceiling. 'REVENGE!' he bellowed.

While I had been slaving away at university, re-sitting subsidiary subjects and then wandering like a lost soul in East London hounded by work for my MA, and then starting my labour on the chalk-face, spreading culture amongst the young gentlemen at Glenturret Academy, Mike had completed a couple of undistinguished senior years at his North London day school and had left – not bound for *academe*. By a part-coincidence and part re-introduction from me, he had met up again with Peter Buchan after a gap of several years, when just about to leave the Sixth form.

Peter had rather slid out of my life in the mid '70s. He had gone to Australia to work for a theatrical agency in Sydney. On his return to the UK he had toured with the Sabre Tooth Theatre Company, putting on fringe-like shows in unexpected countries such as Finland, Malta and Norway, and then landed a "proper" job in London about the time I was leaving it. For six months he had been a management assistant at EMI Records and then, briefly, had slipped into record production. Mike, during the months he spent after leaving school looking for jobs, was in-spanned by Peter to fill some sort of part-musician (he played electric guitar quite well) and part-dogsbody role at the studios. That's when he met Melanie.

'R-e-v-e-n-g-e!' he hissed once again, spitting out fragments of wet toast, dragging the word out to unnatural length and taking hold of my shoulders and glaring into my face with eyes like popping gooseberries.

'What has she done?' I asked at last.

Mike poured out the sad tale. Mr Chessman, Peter's boss at EMI, had been responsible for bringing them together during a refurbishment of one of the sound studios. Mike asked her to play tennis. Perhaps she liked young men whose idea of tennis was to thrash around near the net like a windmill about to lose its sails in a gale because she seemed happy to see him again. They had smoked pot together. And then Peter, although I gather he didn't really like Melanie much because she put on airs at EMI and sucked up to their boss, suggested she and Mike came with him to the Stonyhurst Ball at the Hurlingham Club. (Peter, you'll recall, was an old boy of the school). Peter paid for the tickets – he was going with his sister, Meriel – and Mike forked out for the hire of a dinner-jacket (or tuxedo as he called it). Mike was proud of being seen with a bird of Melanie's looks and, his long hair pinned back into a bun, felt he was cutting a figure with her. An hour before midnight, with the ball at its height, Melanie had turned to him and, with a smile on the lips he had learned to love, said,

'Do you mind if I spend the rest of the night with a man I know who is here? You are so boring to be with.'

She had then hooked on, Mike told me, clinging and clawing, to a bloke called Patrick, one of the ball's organisers, who was as clean-shaven, bronzed and mature as Mike was long-haired, thin and young-looking. He said he hardly knew what to do, short of throttling Melanie to death on the spot. One can hardly remain at a ball on a double ticket and dance with one's self, so Mike had gone home (a long, annoying trip on the last District Line train from Putney Bridge), frothing and snarling and ripping up his souvenir programme.

'Why don't you sort out this Patrick geezer?' I asked. 'After all, he's the one who led her astray.'

'He's a rugger-bugger,' replied Mike. 'He plays for London Irish.'

'I see.' And I did see. Mike isn't now, and wasn't then, the neck-twisting type – especially if the intended victim is a seven foot high gorilla. Clearly it had to be Melanie herself who was to be done over.

'But what can we do?' said I. 'You'll just have to accept that you're not every girl's choice.'

'Huh! I don't know what you know about girls, stuck up here with all your little boys.' He had struck a minor chord. Apart from one brief romance, I had not, by the age of twenty-four, secured a girl to call my own, as they say.

'Oh, fab! He wants his older brother's help, so he begins by smearing butter and hummus all over his armchair and then makes tactless comments about lonely, possibly deviant, schoolmasters. How persuasive!'

'Oh, per-lease!' wheedled Mike. 'You're not

doing anything this half-term. Come now, right to London and stay at Peter's; he's keen to catch up, and then we three can think of a plan to destroy Melanie. Please. Please. I couldn't manage it without you.'

'Ah, begging. Yes, that's more like it. I might come.'

So I travelled from Scotland to London and settled in for the rest of half-term at Balcombe (as in the famous hostages outrage) Street, in Peter's flat. There the three of us sat, racking our brains for some fate so terrible that Melanie would feel the divine smart of justice and penitence. The trouble was that Mike could think of nothing less than shooting her and I couldn't bring myself to believe that she had done anything so frightful as to warrant all this fuss. What *had* she done, after all? Refused to spend a whole evening with Mike – and for that many would have given her a medal for common sense.

'Oh, you're no help, are you? Here I am, sketching out scenario after scenario, and what do you do? Just sit whining and grizzling and saying this won't work and that's against the law. You haven't suggested anything. We might just as well ask the stupid bitch to dinner and give up trying to avenge my wrongs at all.'

I was just going to remind him sharply that *I* had no reason to avenge myself on the wretched trollop, when Peter (who had been silent for some time) leapt up, whooping.

'Something just went "Zing!" in my brain,' he cried. 'What was that you just said, Mike?'

'I said Anthony was just whining uselessly, and.....'

'No, no, after that. What you said after that.'

'What?'

'What you said about d-i-n-n-e-r. About asking her to *dinner*.'

'Well, what of it?'

'Don't you see? That's the thing to do. Ask her to dinner. Whatever you've got to do, Mike, you've got to do on home ground. You can't attack her in a public place, or assault her with a machete at her parents' house, can you?'

Melanie had a certain impregnability which derived from the fact that she lived with her parents in a road off Wimbledon Common. This was what had stymied several of Mike's plans – all elaborate and involving both of us in disguise – because he felt he should stop short of bringing her entire family to the edge of breakdown.

'Invite her *here*,' said Peter quietly.

'You'd invite that cow! Here! You don't like her any more than I do. And why here? After what she's done to me? You won't get me to join up! Never!'

'Hang on,' said Peter, getting in quickly before

Mike had some sort of conniption fit and started rolling on the carpet snapping at chair legs. 'Invite her here, and then you, and Anthony, can play a severe wheezelet on her, humiliate her, snub her, embarrass her – all in the comfort of home, as they say.'

A tremendous sneer appeared on Mike's face. 'Ah, I see. We are going to purchase a whoopee cushion, and........' he commenced. Then he stopped and I could see that something, at last, was also going "Zing!" in his brain. 'You are a genius,' he said quietly.

'You can use the flat, but leave me out of the torture session. I have to work with the girl, remember. And try not to do anything which will cause my fairly tame landlord to hoof me out.'

'"What cannot you and I perform upon th'unguarded Duncan?"' I whispered.

Peter riposted with, '"If we should fail?"'

'"We fail. But screw your courage to the sticking-place and we'll not fail".'

'Good old Shakesp. He's always got the words for it,' said Peter affectionately.

'Eh? Come again,' muttered my unread brother.

'Nothing,' smiled Peter. 'So, you invite her to *dinner*. Hm.' He rubbed his hands together in a Doctor Crippenish way that made my blood run cold. Slowly, our plan for Mike's Revenge took shape. If I'd had any idea that Melanie would be in hospital for two days, I would never have...... But it was too late; her doom was sealed.

There is something, even nowadays, about an invitation to din-nah that smacks of the fine, formal days of past times. Brunch, coffee, lunch, tea, drinks and supper are not the same. The very word "dinner" brings to mind candlelight, elegant frocks, four courses, sparkling silver, chocolate mints, witty talk. Melanie was invited To Dinner, the ostensible purpose being to introduce her to me – the clever, fascinating older brother – and another girl whom Melanie knew. Mike warned me not to make too much of this other bird, Annette Pearson. He told me that when first introduced to her at one of Melanie's parties, she had said, 'Quick! Talk to me! Please make it look as if I've got friends.' Less personality than a bunch of parsley was how Mike summed her up.

'Still,' he said, 'even if she makes a cheeseburger look like Barbra Streisand, she'll do. After all, no one's going to *enjoy* the evening, are they?'

Peter – ever the mischievous sport who couldn't resist something outlandish – and Mike and I set about getting the flat ready. Mike couldn't use his own digs over in Ealing: they weren't private enough – the motorbike chimpanzees never went out. Balcombe Street had a nice sitting-room with high ceilings and plaster covings round the walls. Peter rented it, of course. Back then, in the '70s, before the Labour Party's Rent Acts drove private landlords into oblivion for three or more decades, almost everyone we knew rented in London. This was an indispensable part of our growing up, and enabled us to have a more carefree outlook than was the case later in the century when young people were saddled with a sky-high mortgage from day one of living in an egg box. (Now, of course, property is so fantastically costly in London that renting has come roaring back.)

'Let's get these down,' said Peter, leaping towards his curtains and unhooking them. In a minute or two the long windows were denuded. 'Take those pictures off the walls, Anthony, while Mike and I do the carpet.' He wrenched one end of it away from the wainscot and they began to roll it into a sausage. 'Into the bedroom it goes!'

We paused and gazed around. Bare floor, bare walls, bare windows. Good. We gathered up the three side-lamps, the ceiling shade and all ornaments and shoved these too into the bedroom. Peter sprinted out to Baker Street and came back with an enormous 150 watt bulb which he put into the central socket. We switched it on. Blam! The blast of white light seemed almost to knock us off our feet. In that merciless glare, the big room seemed to shrink to a grimy, poky cell.

'Peter, can I?' asked Mike, gesturing to the sashes. Peter nodded so he hauled the panes right up and autumnal winds began to howl through. Peter darted to the gas fire and removed those white ceramic things which glow – the fire was now unworkable. We then dragged out every stick of furniture except two hard chairs and a box.

Peter whisked out to the bedroom and came back with an armful of reeking pants, socks and vests from his dirty-clothes basket. These he draped over one of the chairs, piled on the mantelpiece and shoved into corners. The most soiled items were given pride of place.

Mike and I raced down to the dustbins and returned with heaps of decayed food, old bottles and cans. These we sprinkled round the edges of the room. Peter stepped back and surveyed it all.

'Mmm. Not bad. Still a bit too cosy,' he muttered.

We went out again and returned with a few dozen empty beer bottles from behind the pub on the Marylebone Road. As we turned up Balcombe Street, Mike noticed a half-eaten packet of fish and chips in the gutter. He scooped it up and added it to his hoard. Back at the flat we arranged the bottles here and there and Peter had the brilliant idea of sprinkling talc on them to make it look as if they'd lain there a long time. Finally, he shot to the cupboard at the foot of the stairs where the cleaner's Hoover was kept and emptied its dust bag all over the floor. The acrid stench of dust blended with the fish, the chips, the vegetables, the sour milk in bottles, the beer, the socks, the pants and the sickly under-smell of talc.

'Needs something else, doesn't it?' murmured Peter. I nodded; it needed a hydrogen bomb on it. 'It'll come to me in a mo,' Peter went on. 'We had a set like this for Pinter's *The Caretaker* with the old Sabre Tooth; well, not as frightful as this actually. My God! Of *course*! Gimme a hand!' We followed him into the bedroom and manoeuvred his large brass bed across into the sitting-room. '*That's* what was missing! A bed.' On it was a lurid purple counterpane. Peter scooped up some pants and mouldy chips and arranged them artistically. Mike was despatched for the final time into the street and returned with a copy of *Playboy.* Opening it to its most revealing pictures, Peter placed it in the middle of the tarty bedspread.

The 150 watt bulb flared down its clear, penetrating light. It missed nothing. The squalor, filth and misery were lit as if on a stage. The room was now extremely cold and the wind went on eddying through the gaping windows.

'We need a final, organic touch,' cried Peter (by now completely carried away by these preparations and almost forgetful of why they were being carried out – a classic case of "the act worships itself", as the poet puts it) and he fished out a tin of Heinz Russian Salad from the kitchen cupboard. I know he always kept one handy because at twenty-firsts or stag nights he liked to empty some near the mouths of friends sleeping off their drink, to find upon awakening. When they saw the mound near their faces, their expressions were always indescribable. Peter sloshed some on the floor, leaving enough to put a realistically disgusting smear on the bed, near to some decayed fish.

One of the things I had heard Mike say about Melanie was that she didn't like the smell of cigarette smoke. In fact Mike (who puffed at least 30 a day back then) admitted that he had led her to think that he was a non-smoker, the great twit. He determined to smoke at least a packet that evening and had laid in a supply of Woodbines. Peter suggested setting light to a dozen or so of them on a plate. A miniature bonfire crackled and soon stale, sharp tobacco smoke filled the freezing room.

'Are you blokes ready?' asked Peter. 'They'll be here fairly soon, so I'd better skedaddle. I want to hear every detail about how it all goes later.'

'What are you giving them to eat?' I asked.

'Oh God! Thanks for reminding me,' gasped Mike, turning his attention to the culinary arrangements of the "dinner" for the first time. 'What've you got here, Peter?'

'Well, nothing. You know I usually go round to the Streamline Café or the pub.'

'Shiteroo. Can I just look?' Mike popped over into the kitchen and came back holding aloft a packet of Ritz crackers. 'Voila! Behold the grub!' he cried, slamming the packet down on the box in the middle of the floor.

'I'd forgotten about those,' said Peter. 'They've been there a long time. You're welcome to them.'

'It chokes me to even give the cow this much. Should I open the packet and pour them out, or wait until they're here? What do you think?'

'Oh, wait,' said I. 'Otherwise they won't know that it isn't just another pile of crap from the dustbin.'

'Right. I'm off. Good luck, kiddoes,' said Peter. 'I'll be back at eleven, and I'll want my bed, so make sure you've finished the torturing by then.'

Left alone, we gazed for the last time around us, making sure that everything was just so – drinking in the glaring bulb, walls, floorboards, salad, dust, pants, gaping window panes, bottles, chips, cabbage, socks, gas-fire, purple bed, *Playboy* centrefolds and fish. Then we had hysterics for about quarter of an hour, lying on the talc-covered floor and drumming our heels on the boards.

'You're MAD, you are!'

'You're mad, you mean!'

'Peter's more bonkers than both of us, isn't he?'

At length we picked ourselves up. Melanie and Annette were due in quarter of an hour.

'What are you wearing?' I asked. It had already been decided that I should wear black leathers (which I already possessed), tiny jet-black dark glasses and a swastika made of horseshoe nails, a trinket which I'd picked up in the Portobello Road. I had this gear ready in a hold-all. Mike had opted for a string vest, a huge pair of tartan knickerbockers (borrowed from an Ealing motorcycling gorilla) and Doc Marten boots. He explained that he deliberately hadn't washed since we had mooted this scheme – several days before – and his moustache and hair were more unruly than ever. Robinson Crusoe wasn't in it. We changed quickly.

He burnt a few more Woodbines in a saucer and fished out our choice of music for the evening, an LP of the sound track of what had been Dad's favourite film: *The Ten Commandments*. We then sat on the two hard chairs and waited. By now it was eight o'clock.

Trrrring! The doorbell downstairs! At last!

'I'll go,' I said.

'Right, right,' muttered Mike, lighting a fag and sticking it in his mouth.

I think, now the time had come for committing outrageous acts against all the codes of polite behaviour on which we had been brought up, we were rather nervous. Still, too late to have doubts.

Down I went to the street door. I could see the silhouettes of female forms through the opaque upper panes. I swung the door open.

'Hello. Come in,' I grunted. 'It's upstairs.' I didn't bother to introduce myself. Mike and I had decided not to speak at all unless spoken to, and then only to reply in the briefest way possible. We thought that long, long periods of silence would be marvellously embarrassing. The girls trooped ahead of me, while I grinned derisively in the darkness. Melanie had brought a bottle. I took it from her without a word. Mike, Peter and I drank it the next day.

'This flat belongs to my colleague from work, Peter Buchan,' explained Melanie to the other girl, Annette Pearson. 'Mike really has digs out at Ealing.'

'Oh,' said the other girl, trying not to tread on her dress as she ascended.

At the flat door I stepped aside.

'In,' I said, turning the handle.

Mike sat on the floor between some pants and a fish skeleton with a Woody hanging between his lips. The bulb blazed down on his soiled string vest, tartan shorts and huge boots. He dragged himself to his feet, advanced towards the girls, stumbled and caught hold of Melanie's long frock, nearly pulling it off. There was a rending sound.

'Strike me pink!' he cried. He then had a most realistic attack of coughing. Masterly. With the fag dancing between his lips, he retched and spluttered. 'Christ!' said he, 'I've gobbed on your dress,' and he reached out a grubby hand towards Annette's frock. She gave a little scream and darted closer to Melanie.

'I don't think we've met,' twittered Melanie in an attempt to rescue the situation, and holding out her hand for me to shake. I stared at her and ignored it.

'Gimme a fag,' I said to Mike. I lit up and we blew smoke in the direction of our guests.

'Hrrugurr, uurgh!' coughed Melanie, 'What's *happened* to you, Mike?' She gazed wildly round the room.

'I've become a hippie,' he replied, and spat copiously on the floor. Then he had another coughing fit – probably real. Phlegm spattered on the bedspread, as he bent double over it. I caught the girls' horrified glances as they noticed the *Playboy* centrefolds for the first time.

When I say that the evening tumbled downhill from this point, you will get an idea of what we went through.

Mike put on *The Ten Commandments*.

Peter had good quality hi-fi, as befitted someone who worked at Abbey Road: a Rogers amp, Transcriptors hydraulic record player, Stentorian studio drive units in Lockwood enclosures, a Brenell stereo tape deck and Leak tuner – all British, which he was proud of, and, I gathered, still to be fully paid for. A sheet had been chucked over this set-up for the night. He also possessed a cheap Woolworth's special which he'd had in the Sixth Form at Glenturret. It consisted of a small blue plastic case with a shrill, tinny speaker under the record platter. This platter was of the sort that leaves half the record dangling off the edge. The needle-arm was so heavy that it probably tracked in pounds rather than grams – the sort of arm you only play an L P on a few times because the needle practically goes through to the other side. It was astonishingly shrill. This machine was on duty for the dinner party.

'Weeeeeeeee!' went *The Ten Commandments* in a silence unbroken except for Mike's retching cough. I'll tell you how heavy the needle was. Mike was making his way across the room to get another fag and he kicked the record player heavily with his Doc Martens. It went sailing through the air, still playing.

'Weeeeurrrgh!' screeched *The Ten Commandments*.

When the side ended, Mike simply put the needle

back to the beginning.

Once Melanie tried to say something in between these endless playings of side one, but we never found out what it was because Mike had another of his retching fits and knelt on the floor spewing out bits of wet Woodbine. It's the sort of thing that inhabits a girl's merry chatter.

Mike and I lounged, legs apart, in the only two chairs, so the girls had to perch on the edge of Peter's bed, and they shifted their positions uneasily Between the bulging protuberances of *Playboy* and the decaying food and pants further along.

And so the evening wore away.

'Eeeeeeeeeooooooooooooo!' shrilled *The Ten Commandments.*

Annette began to cry.

At length I could feel hysteria welling up inside me so powerfully that I knew I'd have to get out of the room. I caught Mike's eye and realised he too was on the verge of an explosion.

'I'll get a drink,' he gurgled, and he and I left the sitting-room and went across the passage into Peter's kitchen. There we collapsed helplessly behind the closed door.

'Oh *GOD*!' we shrieked, as we rolled round on the lino between the oven and the fridge. 'Oh God! It's wonderful! What a revenge!'

'Why don't they just walk out?' I gasped. 'I can't

believe they're just sitting there.'

'We must get something to drink and get back in, I suppose,' said Mike.

We tried to pull ourselves together. But when we thought of those girls in there, in that awful room, perched on the purple bedspread; and when we heard, muffled by two intervening doors, but still piercingly shrill, that "Weeee!" from the record player, we had paroxysms again and thrashed on the kitchen floor in hysteria.

'I must have a coffee!' gasped Mike. 'My throat's killing me after all that smoke.'

We dragged ourselves to our feet.

'Are we giving those two a drink?' I asked. It was at that instant the cosmos stood still, for our eyes fell at the same second on a smallish tapered bottle.

We looked at each other with horrified brotherly understanding.

'Surely not?' I whispered.

'What d'you think?' he mouthed.

We reached up with trembling hands. There, on a shelf above the fridge, at the very top, was a dusty bottle of *Vitalis* hair lotion, left by some previous tenant, we supposed. Mike lifted it down gingerly. 'She won't actually drink it, after all,' he said. And so we made coffee – one lot for Mike, Annette and me, and a "special" for Melanie. We thought she would be further discomforted by getting a cup of coffee which was undrinkable, while the rest of us sipped away. We arranged, as the kettle boiled, that I should say something like: "Hm. A most unusual blend of coffee" and he would respond with: "Yes, I got it from Harrods", or something similar, while Melanie sat with the undrinkable in her hands.

And I can tell you that coffee made with *Vitalis* hair lotion is undrinkable all right. We boiled all of it in a saucepan. The stink was unbelievable. We then added Nescafe and milk. The milk instantly curdled into greyish clots, and the Nescafe coated itself in oil and remained undissolved in clammy lumps. The oil and alcohol separated so that eventually in Melanie's cup there was a layer of alcohol, a layer of curdled milk droppings and a layer of heavy oil full of coffee powder. Mike held the cup at arm's length as we left the kitchen.

We re-entered the living-room. The squeal of the L P hit us again like a blow. I thought something was wrong with the record – I mean more than usually wrong – and I couldn't for a second work out what it was. Of course! The side should have come to an end long ago while we were in the kitchen. It hadn't because the needle had got stuck, presumably having gouged into the vinyl. The sound was sharp and repetitive, like piglets having their throats cut, one by one, in an abattoir.

'Weeeeskrt! Weeeeskrt! Weeeeskrt!' went the

record, but Melanie and Annette seemed too miserable to do anything about it; or they just noticed no difference. They sat in dumb suffering on the bed, hunched and shapeless as two wet sacks.

'Here's your drink,' said Mike ungraciously. I, as arranged, said my bit about unusual blends. We sipped. Mike and I watched Melanie, fascinated, knowing that she could hardly bring the cup near her face, let alone drink from it.

Then the extraordinary happened. Whether the unnerving screech of the music had disorientated her, or whether the stench of fags, socks and rotting food was so strong that she couldn't smell the *Vitalis* mixture, or whether she wanted to commit suicide as the only way out of this hell, we didn't know, but, in front of our horrified gaze, she downed half a cupful of the vile concoction. I could almost see the curdled lumps of milk going down her delicate throat. After this one great gulp, she put her cup down gently, got up from the bed, rushed over to the packet of Ritz crackers, tore it open and crunched ravenously. I supposed she was trying to take away the taste. We sat stunned – at least, I was stunned, but Mike's eyes glistened like those of Genghis Khan after a successful mass-murdering expedition.

Within ten minutes the party broke up. The wonder was that it had lasted so long. With a few muttered words the girls left, Annette tear-stained,

Melanie completely white and tense-looking. On our own once more, Mike and I had further hysterics, and then started the awful job of clearing up before Peter's return.

As we finished cramming everything into black sacks and had moved the bed back over the passage, the phone rang.

'You monsters! You mental patients! You should be locked up!' came Annette's scream as we pressed our ears to the same receiver. Apparently, seized by violent pangs on the way home, Melanie had been taken to hospital for a blast with a stomach-pump. She was later detained there for two days. It was interesting to learn that hair oil can make you so sick, though Mike was inclined to blame the elderly Ritz crackers.

Just when I thought I'd heard the last of avengement, I had a phone call in the New Year at Glenturret, a few months after Melanie's doom.

'Hello?' came the shouting voice, on Jan 2nd, three days before term began. 'Can you hear me?'

'I can hear you, Peter,' I assured Buchan; he was, after all, only ringing from London, not Vladivostok, 'Happy New Year!'

'Sod that. What I want is revenge!'

'What! Not you! Revenge on whom? And why?'

'That bitch!'

'Which bitch? You haven't got a girlfriend.'

'My bloody sister.'

'Meriel!' I cried.

'The same.'

'But "she is oftener upon her knees than on her feet", surely?'

'What the hell are you talking about?'

'Sorry. Quoting from *Macbeth*. I mean Meriel's a saint, isn't she?'

'No, she bloody isn't.'

'This is ridiculous. You've caught this from Mike, haven't you?'

'I do realise that when a woman treats you badly you need to fight back – yes. Yes, I suppose I have learnt from that Melanie biz that they can't always have their own way and expect nothing but chivalry in return.'

'But what's she done?'

'That's what I'm going to tell you – if I can get a word in sodding sideways.'

I propped the receiver to my ear, and Peter unfolded his sorry tale. The Buchans had had a New Year's party at Startmont, a party to which I had been invited, but which I had not been able to grace because of being with Ma and Mike. At this do, Meriel (a stunner with all the looks which she and Peter should have shared) had found fault with Peter's demeanour after he had quaffed about four

litres of Guinness and champagne, and had pushed
him out of the house, and kept him out by locking all
the doors. He had spent that chilly night of
Hogmanay nestling in a dustbin by an outbuilding.
This had annoyed him. His first thought had been to
drive round to Glenturret and beg a night's kip. Then
he remembered that his car was in London and then
that I would not be there, and then that even the old
Boiler and Doc Costigan went off somewhere for the
holidays and the place would be shut up. By the time
morning had come his blood pressure was over a
million and he had caught a cold. Even the gallons
of Guinness had not staved off frostbite. His need of
my moral support was imperative.

'I'm coming to see you,' he shouted down the line.
'I can't work with this cold anyway. We'll think up
a scheme. What do you think?'

'Well, I don't want your cold.'

'Self first, as per bloody usual. You can't stop me.
See you tomorrow.'

His first words on arrival were: 'I've got a plan.
But it means going down to Manchester.'

'Oh God! When? I mean, why?'

'I'm at Startmont, but Meriel has gone back to
Manchester to do some studying.' (She was in her
penultimate year of a medical course at Manchester
University and lived, I gathered from Peter, in a flat
off Palatine Road.) 'You've still got a few days

before the brats return, haven't you? Well, I've invited us to spend two nights with her at her flat. It's there we do the deed.'

'The deed of dreadful revenge?'

'Yup. Got it in one. And do you know what that deed is going to be?'

'It's not something too beastly, is it?' I asked. 'Don't forget that, well, Meriel and I – you know.....'

'Oh, that! That's been over and buried three years or more, hasn't it? You and Meriel! She wouldn't touch you with a bargepole now. Now that she's engaged to The Lapdog, I mean,' added Peter hastily, realising he was putting his foot in it. 'Look, I've thought of something so outrageous, so complete a revenge, that I can safely say that she may never recover from it.'

'Peter, really..... I don't honestly think that I *can*.....'

But, in the end, I did, of course.

MERIEL AND CHRISTINE

I was tepid about being involved in an act of violence towards Meriel because, a few years earlier, she and I had been intimate – when I was twenty and she eighteen. Friends of the family or not, the Buchans would not have approved of the extent to which Meriel and I got to know each other in that summer holiday at the end of my second year at university.

In our Glenturret Gang period, Meriel had seemed too kiddish for me to bother much about her. She had just been Peter's younger sister.

The day that changed all that was a sultry, rainy one in August 1974. I had had a late summer invitation to Startmont before university term started and Peter, Meriel and I had been for a ramble across the tough, wiry heather of Sheriffmuir, when Peter had said,

'I'm so starving. I wish we'd brought a picnic. Let's go back.'

He had parked the car – his newly-acquired, but elderly Mini – down by the Memorial stones at the edge of the moor.

'Oh, let's walk a bit further,' I had said (this was at a time when I had actually *liked* walking), and he, with an under-meaning in his voice, replied,

'No. I'll go. You and Meriel tramp round to the

sheep walls if you like. I'll meet you there in, say, forty-five mins, and I'll bring sandwiches.'

With a nod to me, he had gone striding off towards the car. I could see its blue roof in the distance. We hadn't come far from the road.

'Oh good,' had said Meriel. 'I didn't want to go back yet. We've been stuck in the house all week.'

That was the first time, in eight or nine years of mutual acquaintance, that Meriel and I had been alone in each other's company. The sensation was curiously disturbing. I was struck by the reflection that Meriel was very attractive. This had not occurred to me until that moment – although she was just the same that day as she had been the day before. She had lovely eyes, smoky and finely lashed. She had pretty teeth and a fascinating mouth. It dawned on me that I had found her mouth delightful for some time – but had not been fully conscious of it until then. Her hair was tawny and the light made it shine. I realised, taking covert glances in her direction, that, as is true of many girls of eighteen, she could have been older.

'Well, come on,' she laughed, and she walked on uphill. I followed, and found myself noticing how the damp atmosphere caused her shirt to cling to her, and my heart pulsed. The swiftness of this had taken me completely unawares.

We walked on over the crest of the moor and down towards the other road, where Peter had agreed to meet us in the car. We reached the sheep wall, and Meriel jumped up and sat on the boulders. We had spoken not a word since breasting the hill. I could hardly understand my new-found shyness. I wished Peter would return, and at the same time dreaded his doing so.

'Meriel....,' I said, and, just as I opened my mouth, the summer rain started to fall again, drenchingly. We backed up against the sheep-wall's gate-post. There was a thorn bush by it, but it was poor shelter. I scanned the road; there was no sign of the Mini, and only twenty minutes had gone by. I took off my jacket – I had been too hot in it – and draped it over Meriel. My fingers lingered on her shoulders and droplets dewed her lashes and hair.

'Let's shelter in there!' she cried. She pointed across the road to the field beyond the wall. A low granite shed was an easy distance away. We could see that its door was open. I took her hand and we splashed across the ditches. I let go her hand and ran over to the shed. Inside it was dark, but not so dark that we could not see square bales of straw lining the walls. We jumped onto the nearest bales. Across the doorway, like a curtain, the warm rain scudded over the empty moor. Meriel laughed.

'This is great! Look at that rain!' She pulled my

jacket from her shoulders and laid it down on the bale. 'Isn't it humid? You shouldn't have lent me your coat. You're soaking.'

I looked down at my shirt. The fabric was transparent and clinging to my chest.

'Oh, it's okay,' I muttered.

'Take it off,' said Meriel, 'and I'll squeeze it dry.'

She began to unbutton the shirt. Her tanned fingers burnt as they touched my skin. The shirt fell away. Meriel began squeezing and wringing it.

'You've got nice arms,' she said. My face flamed in the dim shed.

'Where on earth is Peter?' I muttered.

'Oh, we'll spot him. You can see the stone gatepost from here, but he won't be able to see us. It's nice here with the rain falling on the roof, don't you think?'

I nodded dumbly. That afternoon my ability to put words in front of each other had vanished. I was intensely conscious of my bare torso. Meriel looked me up and down.

'Peter's told me about you – all you boys – when you were at school at Glenturret. He tells amazing stories.'

'Peter's good at telling stories,' I replied. 'And some amazing things did happen.'

'Oh, I know they did,' she grinned.

Hardly able to believe how daring I was being, I

then said,

'You're wet too. Shall I wring out some of your things for you?'

There was a pause.

'Yes, it would be sensible to hang our things on those nails to dry in the air for a bit,' said Meriel. 'My skirt is soaked through.'

She pulled the pin from the tartan she was wearing and unwound it from her hips. She stood on a bale to hang it on the wall. Her legs were strong and elegant. In the dim light, her flesh seemed glistening and brown and her eyes sparkled.

'Your shirt is wet too,' I croaked. I hated that unsteady croak.

'So it is,' she replied, and unbuttoned it, shook it out and hung it up. She then sat cross-legged in the skimpy underwear that remained on her, facing me.

I felt that I should be in at least as incomplete a state of undress as she was, but I had no idea how to remove my trousers. It seemed such a silly thing to do – like something from a *Carry On* film. Besides I was tremendously self-conscious about what would be revealed when – if – those trousers were slipped off. No girl had seen me unclothed before. How had I got myself into a barn in the rain on the point of having to remove my trousers? Less than two hours ago I had been sitting in the front of the Mini, with Meriel the kid sister on the back seat. Four hours ago

I had been trying to decide between Mrs Buchan's home-made marmalade and honey at breakfast – and now this! I felt the steady pressure of Meriel's eyes on me, and I knew I was being challenged. I could not have been more aware of the difference between boys and girls than if I had been Adam and she Eve, in the immediate post-apple stage.

'Stand up. They're soaked through. I'll undo the buckle.' Her deep, clear voice came to the rescue. With feminine insight, she had known that I would have hesitated for hours before autonomously divesting myself of my defences. She yanked them to ankle-level, so that all I had to do was step gracefully out of them.

'Peter's quite a prude, but he has told me about things you did at school.'

I could of nothing to say to that.

She remained on her knees in front of me. I placed my hand on her hair. She slipped off her bra.

'What *is* that?' she suddenly asked. My eyes flew to my last garment – my underpants. My hands whizzed after them defensively. I stood, like Venus surprised while bathing.

'Oh, er, you mean….? It's not surprising, Meriel. It's what happens when…..that is…..you with nothing on…..'

'No. I mean what do you keep staring at in the roof?'

Of course I wasn't staring at anything, but her words brought to me the fact that all during the trouser-removing stage I had been gazing soulfully upwards like Archbishop Cranmer burning at his stake.

So I too knelt down and we faced each other, knee to knee. Now that I could see her face, I spotted the flicker of helplessness in her eyes for the first time, and she saw that I saw it.

'Meriel,' I murmured, 'don't you think that.….?'

'Look, Tony, I haven't done anything like this before. But I want to know what it's like; what men are like – and who else do I know as well as I know you? We are friends, aren't we?'

At the word "friends" I knew that this odd day was going to turn out all right. Up to now I had been aware of the muggy air around us, of the harsh prickly straw digging into my bare legs, of the wide gap of the door and its curtain of rain. These vanished behind the ramparts of a different, exciting awareness.

'I want, first of all, just to look at you', said Meriel. 'Oh, please.'

As I knelt I pulled my last garment down, drew it over my knees and ankles, and sat back on my heels in front of her. 'You are the same as other boys, aren't you?' she added, as if having taken a look at my nakedness raised doubts about this. I assured her that we were all much the same – though some were circumcised – at least I knew that for a fact.

I recall that we kissed and that her mouth was slightly sweet, like the surface of a currant bun. We began to explore each's other's contours. She was at ease; I was at ease. The fact that she accepted me made my limbs feel straighter, my skin more light-bearing, my muscles and hairs more springy. It was a stupendous feeling. I have *never* recaptured that sense of certainty and pride in the physical. I suppose Olympic swimmers or marathon runners feel it all the time.

I know I lost my head too. I had no idea of being cautious; Meriel, with that greater regard for consequences which distinguishes the female mind, and having told me to gasp through exactly what was happening to me, twisted strongly away just in time. She said she experienced her first completely satisfying feelings, which pleased me. With a shock I realised that well over an hour had slipped past, and that Peter had only gone a few miles up the road.

'Where *is* Peter?' I asked, lying back on the straw with Meriel's head on my stomach.

'Well, you didn't want him to walk in on us, did you?' There was such an undertone in her voice that I looked down and searched her eyes.

'What do you mean?' I asked.

'I *had* to know about things,' she said. 'Mummy was driving me mad with hints and warnings. She wanted Father to "have a little talk" with me, but he thought I should speak to one of the nuns at the convent. Last time anyone did that, they were told to put a newspaper, folded double, on the boy's lap before sitting on it. That was Sister Philomena, and she was seventy-four then. I can't talk to Peter; there's something inhibiting about speaking to your brother, and, as I say, he's rather a prude, I think. It's Stonyhurst and the Jesuits in him still. Anyway, that's what made me determined to find out about things with *you*. I knew it would be nice and fun – like one of our old kiddie games.'

From the road came a shrill Mini-esque peep.

'There he is. Get dressed,' said Meriel. Then she grasped my arm. 'There are more things I want to know about. The lessons aren't over yet, are they?'

'Sorry I was so long,' said Peter. 'But I've got the nosh. Good job you had each other's company.'

I thought Meriel looked quickly at him as he said this, and I knew for certain that she had arranged for him to leave us together. But his look was opaque and unconcerned, which I felt it wouldn't have been if he knew I had been making love to his sister – and yet…..

'Your sister is, naturally, wonderful company,' said I.

I don't know why I wanted to explain this. I think I sensed I might come over in these writings as, and be pigeon-holed as, a sort of closet-gay, priestly bachelor. I have never lost my love and liking for Meriel Buchan and that holiday with her is among the multi-coloured moments of my existence; I have never lost my desire to be with her and to hold her – even though she married, has children and, in 2004, moved to New Zealand. She was, perhaps, after all, the greatest loss of my life.

'So this revenge is not going to be too horrible, is it?' I asked. 'I can't be involved in putting her in hospital like Mike's Melanie, can I?'

Peter looked slyly around, as if imagining that Meriel's spies lurked under the furniture. He put his mouth to my ear and hissed,

'Pin this to your underpants, lover-boy. We are going to go and talk to her.'

'Talk to her?'

'Sorry. Talk *at* her.'

'Talk at her, eh? Hm, I see. Why does that constitute a revenge?'

'Talk AT her non-stop, for forty-eight hours, is what I mean,' explained the banana-case.

'How do you mean: non-stop?'

'Well, obviously we've got to go to the bog, eat, cough, and all that, but – and this why I need you –

when I'm not talking you take over the jabbering, and vice-versa.'

'Oh honestly, Peter. It can't be done.'

'Of course it can. Surely you remember Park?'

I did, of course, remember Park. Andy Park had been a fantastically fake, cool, Timothy Leary figure who had taken us for A Level English in our last year in the Sixth. He had sat, legs apart, far back on a tilted chair, with fingertips pressed to his temples, while we read our essays to him. We suspected him of never reading the few essays he infrequently collected. Wild bohemian ticks had zig-zagged down the pages. He never gave marks; it was probably too much of a fag to think them up. (I know myself how difficult it is for a teacher to decide on any mark between 10 and 90; I always seemed to give 56.) Sometimes Park tore off a straggling comment – short, out-of-date hippy – such as "Wowie Zowie!" or "This is my bag". He would nag at us to read "the rare sources". Where he thought schoolboys at Glenturret could get hold of *The Cambridge Review* Vol XXIV, May 1951, pp 118-121, or *The Critical Quarterly:* Romborg on Metempsychosis and Morphism in *The Prelude,* I can't imagine.

The A Level class decided to try out a few "rare sources" on him. Gingerly at first, I had introduced Y. M. Teprac, critic, on an inspiration while gazing at the prefects' study carpet the night before. It got a wild, approving tick. Peter quoted the African novelist (from Bulawayo Community University) Kefu Asper (anagram of Park's nick-name: Super Fake). A tick and "Fab! Always research!" was scrawled near it. Our best efforts came when Park requested bibliographies at the end of each essay: "A gentleman always acknowledges his sources". Pussy Lindsay and I got by well enough with our Bulgarian commentator Gianu Madick Spufe (author of *D H Lawrence and The Screaming Id*). It had taken Peter several minutes to work it out, until I told him that four of the words were: "I am a pseud" and all he had to do was sort out the missing adjective. The only time we saw Park annoyed was when he got Peter's booklist consisting of one lonely work: *The Ladybird Book of Great English Writers*.

Anyway, Peter and I had once talked without pause through one of his periods, getting on towards an hour, on dreams in *Othello*. The fact that there are no dreams in the play did not hamper us. Park's idea of pupils' talks had been to let a few stumbling comments slip by and then to chip in and collar the rest of the lesson himself. What Peter intended me to recall now was how exasperated Park had been. If the eclectic and easy-going Park had been maddened by an hour, what effect would forty-eight of them have on Meriel?

Armed with throat tablets, we set off for

Manchester. Our excuse for staying with Meriel was that there was a Hollies concert in the city and Peter, as an employee of EMI, the group's record label, felt it would be disloyal not to see them. She had seemingly forgotten the New Year quarrel and was, Peter said, quite the cloying lil' sis' on the phone. The tickets for the band were for the Friday, so that gave a full Saturday for the torture process.

We burst in at teatime, reeking of *Fishermen's Friend* lozenges, and shrieking at the tops of our voices. We talked solidly until the three of us had to set off for the show. After it, we resumed in the bus back to the flat. We jabbered on until one in the morning. We told her every plot in the canon of Shakespeare, related tales of dear old Boiler and Costigan at Glenturret, lamented the demise of Bronco lavatory paper in favour of Andrex, touched upon the economy, sang several Hollies' songs, especially *He ain't heavy, he's my brother* and speculated about the recent space missions. Peter gave a prolonged impression of a Saturn rocket taking off.

We seemed to be getting away with it. Our hostess gazed at us, every now and again opening her mouth to try to interpose a word or two. She had less chance than a curate on a bicycle in the fast lane of the M1. Then, all of a sudden, without warning, she reached out and grabbed my ear in a pincer-like grip. She then marched to the door with it, and I – having little choice – decided to go with it. In the passage she pushed me against the wall, and banged the door of the room we had just left. I heard a yelp. I know Peter, at first stunned, had leapt up and rushed after us. I expect the door got him on the tip of his nose.

'Right, joker,' said Meriel, letting go my ear and seizing my collar, more in the manner of a Chicago moll than of a medical student. 'What's all this about?'

She reached behind me and there was a click.

'What are you doing?' I gasped.

She slipped something into the pocket of her slacks.

'Get into the bedroom, you!' she hissed and whirled me through into the next room. 'Right. What the hell are you two up to?'

'Oh, er, nothing, Meriel. What do you mean?' I blustered.

'You think you can play one of your idiotic tricks on me, do you? I suppose this is one of Peter's infantile schemes of revenge.'

'You'll have to ask Peter,' I said, with as much dignity as I could muster. 'I have no notion of what you are getting at.'

'Peter isn't in a position to be asked anything,' she said sweetly, 'because dear Peter is locked in the sitting-room and I'm not letting him out until you come clean.'

'Meriel!' I twittered. 'Is this sisterly? First you lock him out and now you lock him in.'

'Ah, I see. *That's* what this is all about, is it? Revenge for New Years's Eve. Well, let me tell you, Peter behaved like the drunken, insane pig he always has been on New Year's Eve and upset a friend of mine. He deserved everything he got, and more. But, my old childhood chum, I want to know what precisely you two mental cases thought you were going to do this weekend, before I even *think* of releasing him.' Even as she spoke, there was a sound of muffled calls from over the passage. I made a convulsive movement. 'Let him stew,' said Meriel. 'Now I want the facts, Mister Avenging Angel.'

So I told her. Not just because Peter was in durance vile, but because her manner was so imperious in a Queen Victoria-ish sort of way. I could not help remembering how close this girl and I had once been. She put me, English teacher as I was, in mind of Keats' "When your mistress some rich anger shows, let her rave, and feed deep, deep upon her peerless eyes". In fact I was about to inform her that I thought she still had peerless eyes, very poor moment though it was, when there was a bellow from next door, followed by banging from the flat below. It was about two in the morning and I suppose the neighbours were tiring of Peter's frantic yowls.

'I see,' she said, in a steely voice, when I had told her of our great forty-eight hour plan. Then, surprisingly, she added, 'Well, you may be able to do it yet. Stay here.'

She took the key from her slacks and stepped across the passage. She unlocked the sitting-room and Peter came shooting out like a greyhound from its cage.

'I know all, creep,' said Meriel, before he could open his mouth. She pulled him into the bedroom with me.

'Look here....' began Peter.

'Sit down,' snapped Meriel, pushing her brother roughly. He overbalanced and plumped down on her bed. 'You can sit down too,' she added, shoving me down next to him. 'I've heard about the Grand Plan, Peter, and it's no good looking reproachful – I knew something silly was going on. Well, you can forget about practising your ga-ga schemes on me, but since you're here, you can bloody well apply them to someone else. Your visit will not be a total waste.'

We gazed at her with rolling eyeballs.

'Yes,' she hissed. 'I'm the one who wants revenge, and I want it bad.' Her eyes took on a faraway, slitty gleam. I turned to Peter. He shrugged his shoulders in a bemused way. But I thought I saw what she was getting at.

'You don't mean The La.......?' I began. She interrupted with a snort.

'Yes. The Lapdog,' she said, her voice suddenly shooting up the scale, 'and I *wish* you wouldn't use that *ridiculous* name for him! I've told you before.'

'We didn't use it,' said Peter. 'You did.'

'You started it.'

'Well, maybe….. Anyway, he *is* a lapdog,'

'OK, he is,' conceded Meriel.

'So,' resumed Peter, getting up and crossing to the mantelpiece, which he began to straddle "like a Colossus", 'you need our help in bringing this Lapdog to his knees. Very well, I speak for both of us when I say that we will do the deed. But there *is* one condition.'

Meriel stamped her foot, like actresses playing exasperated little women in '50s movies, but before she could speak, Peter hurried on, in measured Bertie Wooster style,

'The condition, Meriel, is that you apologise fully and without reservation for causing me to spend one of the coldest nights of the year: to wit, the night of the thirty-first of December, *inst,* in a garbage collection receptacle.'

For a second I could see that Meriel was thinking of telling him where to stuff himself. But common-sense prevailed, and with a gulp she muttered,

'All right. I'm sorry.'

'Very sorry,' said Peter, pushing his luck, I thought.

'*Very* bloody sorry,' cried Meriel, her voice rising again.

'Right,' said her devoted brother. 'Rely on us.'

Thus came about the abandonment of the plan for The Breaking of Meriel and the hatching of the plan for The Breaking of The Lapdog.

Harmony between the three of us restored, we sat on Meriel's bed in a row and plotted the morrow's campaign. Meriel made tea and I, starving, joined her in the kitchen and cooked sausages for a midnight feast. Meriel grew cooing as our machinations took shape and wasn't even cross when Peter dropped a sausage on her dressing-gown and left a zeppelin-shaped mark.

At eleven the next morning, the doorbell rang. It was The Lapdog – a young police inspector seconded to study social trends at the university. Meriel had met him at a lecture on "Modern architecture as a cure for city crime". He was good-looking, in a rozzerish, stolid sort of way, but I couldn't see what Meriel saw in him. I believe that I had not quite lost the old belief that she and I might become a couple, permanently, so I automatically disliked other men whom she liked. I was elated by the scrapping of The Revenge on her; my heart had not been fully in it.

The Lapdog had arrived to take her to lunch, on her own. His Vauxhall Viva waited outside. Peter and I piled into the back before he could stop us. Jabbering fitfully, we were borne into the centre of Manchester. Meriel said she wanted to do a little shopping at Kendal's (Manchester's equivalent of Harrods, or so they used to claim) and The Lapdog was to carry the booty. Peter and I trailed behind them trying out underarm deodorants and bras, and squealing to each other in high, camp voices. The Lapdog shoved over to us and growled, in his most threatening police manner,

'Will you *stop* this! There are people I know here. People are looking at us!'

I caught Meriel's eye. She winked devastatingly, and I minced off to shriek over an angora jumper. Peter bought a lipstick, and began to apply it, uttering little squeaks of ecstasy. All around people were indeed goggling. The Lapdog grew very red.

At lunch Peter and I shared their table, bickering shrilly over the first course. Peter took The Lapdog's arm in a meaning manner and began asking him all about his job, feeling his arm muscles, eyelashes fluttering like a couple of Japanese fans. The Lapdog, in a constrained voice, started to explain his police work.

Suddenly Peter cried, fixing his eyes on a man less than ten feet away in the restaurant, 'Oooh, sweetie! No, no, dear! Not a T-shirt with those arms! Look at her pectorals! She thinks she's Mr Atlas! No, sweetie-pie, get *real*!' and after a pause he returned his gaze to The Lapdog's and, with parted lips, breathed, 'I'm sorry, dear – you were telling me about being a big, butch bobby.' It was a fine performance. Peter told me that he simply copied the outrageously camp mannerisms of a fellow EMI employee, the producer Jools Farthingale. At the time I had no idea that this Farthingale and I were going to be involved in a further vengeful project a year down the line, about which more in a page or two.

We left Meriel and The Lapdog alone for only a few minutes to go the gents – when the bill came. It avoided a politely wolfish debate about how to split the cost because, upon our return, skilfully timed, The Lapdog had paid up. It must have been expensive, because Peter and I had eaten a great deal and ordered the most expensive things. We noticed The Lapdog was perspiring freely.

On the way back to Meriel's flat, Peter and Meriel got into the back of the Viva, and I, to The Lapdog's distaste, sat in the front next to him. Catching Meriel's eye in the mirror, I put my hand on his knee and squealed,

'Oooh! You're such a *marvellous* driver! I feel so *safe* with you, duckie!'

He tried to squirm his knee away, but couldn't do so without taking his feet from the pedals. He probably didn't want to make a scene with Meriel either, so he had to put up with my hand travelling further and further up his thigh. In the back, Peter kept up an endless monologue about the state of his complexion and what he was buying for it. 'I want *radiance*!' he pouted. Seeing Meriel's eye again, gleaming wickedly, I mused as to why she wanted us to do this to the poor, harmless copper; she had not really explained to us.

All afternoon Peter and I jabbered. That evening, Meriel and The Lapdog had invited some chums round, ostensibly to meet her charming brother, and her brother's friend. We sucked blackcurrant lozenges to gird our larynxes for the supreme effort.

At eight o'clock the first of the guests arrived; by eight forty-five all were assembled. They didn't stand a chance. Stunned and horrified, they sat in a paralysed circle as Peter and I talked and talked in increasingly shrill and camp voices. When not actually chattering, we sang every Beatles' song we could remember – me on drums (a tin waste-paper basket), Peter on Meriel's guitar. A pretty, fair girl, who had spent most of the evening sitting close to The Lapdog, asked me why we were doing this.

'Doing what?' I cried. 'Don't tell me Miss Brain-Dead hasn't any party conversation. Intelligent discussion is the breath of life, sweetie.'

'My sentiments too, duckie,' said Peter, leaping up and standing menacingly over the poor girl. 'You'll be telling us next you consider Dostoevsky a finer novelist than Conrad! Oooh, and *don't* you dare deny it. We've heard all about you and your opinions on Impressionism, haven't we, love?' A merciless review of Conrad then followed. You couldn't have cut the atmosphere with a chainsaw. The Lapdog put his arm round the girl and helped her to her feet. 'What about *The Nigger of the Narcissus* then?' screamed Peter. 'Ooooh! Aren't we the helpless little *cow*? We can't think of a *thing* to say, even about one of the short stories, so we have to be rescued by our brave bobby.'

Without a further word, The Lapdog led the girl from the flat. A few minutes later, unable to bear any more screeching contemptuous invective, the remaining guests also departed. Peter and I were left in possession of the field.

'So, *that's* why you wanted revenge,' I croaked, my voice huskily going back to its normal range.

'Peter knows,' muttered Meriel. 'Her name is Primrose. He calls her *Primmie,* for God's sake. He's been all over her for weeks. I can't believe he had the arrogance to think he could keep stringing us both along. But what a sap! Today was the test – and, boy, didn't he fail it!'

Meriel kissed each of us.

'What about those friends?' asked Peter.

'Oh, most of that lot are pals of his. You don't think I'd have asked proper friends of *mine* to meet you two, do you?'

We did not croak a reply. I realised that we couldn't have kept up her persecution, as originally intended, for forty-eight hours. Being Queens of Camp for twelve had nearly done us in.

My final reflection on these matters is this: Is it not amazing that The Lapdog did not hit us? Why did those guests just sit in silence, paralysed? I think if you are prepared to go so far beyond the boundaries of manners and social expectations of others, you are accorded an impregnability.

Jools Farthingale. Peter's colleague at EMI, about whom there is a quite a bit to relate, with his platinum hair and fur handbag, was one of these disturbing extremists. He featured in the final adventure of The Avengers – the Harrowing of Christine.

It was in the spring of '78, as I sat in Masters' Study, my feet on the fire-grate, Tchaikovsky's *Pathetique* on the record deck and exercise books at my elbow, that there was a clawing at the door and

Peter drifted in.

'Good lord! What are you doing up here?' I cried.

'Oh, I just came on up. No one's about except brats; I didn't run into Costigan,' replied Peter.

'No. I meant what are you doing in *Scotland*? I didn't know you were here.'

'Well, it was mother's birthday on Tuesday, so I took some time off. I thought I'd nip over here to see you. In fact,' added Peter, coming to sit on the arm of my chair, and lifting the needle off the record, 'I need your help.'

He patted my shoulder, then got up and draped himself in front of me by a corner of the mantelpiece. Since I had last seen him he had grown his hair and looked like a witch from *Macbeth*.

'How –erm – how do you feel about another spot of revenge?' he asked.

The room spun round me. I seemed to hear a mournful sighing like the endless breakers on some lonely shore, but it was only the needle running on the label; Peter had not lifted it off properly. A year or more on from The Lapdog – and nothing, it seemed, had changed.

'Oh surely not! What's Meriel done now?'

'Pah! It's not Meriel!' snorted Peter.

'Who then?'

'You know her,' said Peter.

'"Be not a niggard of your speech",' I murmured.

'What?'

'Sorry. Just quoting from "Maccers".'

'What? From *"Macbeth"?* You're getting worse than The Boiler, Tony.'

'I was merely, nim, nim, nim, trying to intimate that I was desirous of learning the name of the lady to whom you refer in your, nim, nim, nim, nim, nim, postulation of avengement,' I twittered in Boiler-speak.

'Yup. Right. Well, I'll tell you. It's Christine.'

'Not *the* Christine?'

'The very one.'

'You took Christine out and she dropped you....?' I gasped. I was amazed. No one would have taken Christine out.

'No. No. No. Of course I didn't take her out. Would *you* take her out?'

'Of course not. I've met her a dozen times, and I can safely say that if Christine and I were trapped on a desert island for the whole of our lives, and the rest of the world dead, I'd be a Trappist monk and dedicate myself to celibacy.'

'Not very original,' said Peter, 'but you put it well.'

'Can we start again? You said you wanted revenge on Christine. Why?'

Peter slunk to a nearby chair. He began in a dull, toneless voice, his eyes bulging, his hands clenching and unclenching.

'Day after day there is a tap at my door in the evening. I come back from EMI, often late, always tired, and whatever time my footsteps are heard, Christine wakes, like the monstrous beast in that poem…'

'….by Tennyson: *The Kraken Wakes'*, I put in.

'Yes, yes. Just listen, will you? She comes in and she homes in on her prey. Sometimes it's after midnight,' said Peter pathetically, 'and you know how I need my sleep. Tap, tap at the door. I've tried not answering, but she goes on tapping more loudly until I *have* to answer it. I open the door a crack, and, BAM! – she's in. She's taken up knitting. She says, "Don't mind me, Peter dear. I'll just keep you company", and she sits, gazing at me, meditatively, you know, like a shark selecting its victim. I've tried everything. I've told her I have a migraine; she massages my temples. I've had diarrhoea; she dashes out to the all-night chemist. I've lost my rag and screamed at her; she simpers and says "I know. You've had a hard day". Every evening this last bloody month,' snarled Peter, seeming to bite off the words rather than uttering them, 'she has come barging in and *knitted*. I wouldn't mind as much if she talked, if she sang, if she engaged me in discussion about Goethe or the Labour Party, but she does and says nothing! Nothing! She just squats on her huge buttocks, her shirt sagging open under the weight of those giant knockers, and looks at me in silence. I can't *stand* it anymore! And then,' cried Peter hysterically, 'on Saturday she brought her mother in to see me!'

'Her mother?'

'Yes! And you can see what *that* means, can't you?'

'Can I?'

'Of course you can. It means she is sizing me up with the old folks for approval as the son-in-law! She's after me, Tony, like – like a radar-controlled torpedo!'

'But if you don't like her, surely you....?' I began.

'I know what you're going to say. Be cruel; speak the truth; surgeon's knife. But the awful thing is that there are times when I feel myself weakening. I mean, she does obviously like me, and I can't say that about everyone I know. One day I'm sure I shall break down and kiss her. It's like making confessions to the KGB. You do it in spite of yourself. Ha, ha, ha!' laughed Peter, like a maniac. 'Caught! *Me!* Trapped! And by Christine! You MUST help me! You must! I want to get rid of her, but I also want some sort of revenge for all those ruined evenings. Revenge for...... Urrgh! Guuurgh!'

Here Peter got a frog in his throat and underwent a prolonged coughing fit, while I dutifully slapped him on the back. Gasping, but no longer actually choking, he slumped back in his chair, limp as a leaf, and gazing at me with mournful eyes. He whispered, 'Help me!' once more, and then was silent.

'Hm,' said I.

As I've mentioned, I knew this Christine. I had kipped on several occasions at Balcombe Street and each time had glimpsed the mountainous female. It may have been an overheated regard for the irresistible nature of my own charms, but there had been times when I had fancied Christine's glances simpering in my direction. Like Peter, I too found my inner being withering away at the thought of such a thing – like a slug under an inch or two of salt. Plumpness can be attractive, but it should not step over the dividing line between the cuddly and the morbidly obese. Christine had long ago so stepped. Her choice in clothes was unfortunate: why is it that really big girls are devotees of mini-skirts and tight jeans? And she had a mop of frizzy ginger hair; and often one or two inflamed spots on forehead or chin. But infinitely more terrible than mere personal drawbacks of appearance – and, after all, if a person's plain they're plain, and it shouldn't matter – was that quality which Peter feared more than all the others: a quiet, intent persistence. Having moved, some nine months ago, into her eyrie above Peter's virginal flat, she had entertained lascivious thoughts of him and so had started the long business of making herself indispensable.

'Hm,' I mused once more.

'Come and stay with me!' begged Peter. 'Please. We might be able to think of something. I don't feel safe alone.'

'Why don't you move?' I asked.

'Why should I?' he riposted. And he had a point.

Off then on Friday night (The Boiler taking my weekend prep duties) to Balcombe Street. On Saturday morning, soon after our tousled late awakening, came the lumbering which told either of an escaped rhino on the staircase or the arrival of Christine. Peter's eyes met mine in silent horror.

'Just a minute!' he called, as the first tap-tapping began. We dressed rapidly and then crept to the kitchen window. The sash was heaved up, we trod carefully into the sink and then out and round to the alley at the end of the terrace. Five minutes later we were on the tube heading south to Waterloo.

'This can't go on, you know,' sighed Peter. We had gobbled breakfast at the Festival Hall café, and were now leaning on the balustrades of Westminster Bridge, perhaps subconsciously seeking comfort from contemplation of the Mother of Parliaments, perhaps, in Peter's case, drawn to the dark peace of the sluggish waters below. Wordsworth had been on this spot in the throes of creative fervour, and I quoted him reverently,

'"Dear God! The very houses seem asleep/ And all that mighty heart is lying still".' It wasn't all that apt as it was mid-morning and buses and cars were roaring past, but something of the great poet's fire must have been rushing in our veins, for Peter began to intone:

'When Christine comes around, I'd love to smash her face in.'

Softly I began to hum, tapping on the parapet:

'When *CHRIS*tine comes a*ROUND*, I'm *GON*na smash her *FACE* in!' And Peter chanted above the traffic:

'When *CHRIS*tine comes a*ROUND*, I'm *GON*na hang her *HIGH* up from the *CEIL*ing!'

'So *NO*body can *HEAR* her urgent *SCREAM*ing!' I sang.

'When *CHRIS*tine comes a*ROUND*, I'm *GON*na make her *SORR*y she's bin *LIV*in' - A-ha, ha!'

Peter than punched me on the chest. 'Listen! Listen!' he howled in a different key above the traffic's roar:

'Her *EYE*ball's *SIT*ting *NEAT*ly in its *SOCK*et:

I *THINK* I'll rip it *OUT* and *PUT* it in my *POCK*et!'

'When *CHRIS*tine comes a*ROUND*, I'm *GON*na kick her *SHINS* in….' I chanted.

Like loonies we sang and tapped on Westminster Bridge, just as I'm sure Wordsworth did when he realised he'd got his sonnet just right. Within ten minutes we had the lyrics, the tune and a revenge of sorts.

'I'm going to get this made into a single, or die in the attempt,' said Peter later that day after we had refined the song and committed it to paper. He went through everyone he knew at EMI who might be able to help, muttering and shaking his head, until his face lit up. 'Of *course*!' he cried. 'The *very* man.' Jools Farthingale was going, eventually and annoyingly, to enter my life.

When Christine Comes Around was recorded a few months later at studios in Denmark Street, was banned by the BBC and became a cult song. Tap the title into *YouTube* today and it'll immediately pop up. It is performed by punkish groups all over the USA, and I can tell you the royalties are hard to chase.

But overarching all other preoccupations, as the turbulent, strike-bound '70s began to fizzle out, came three enormous bombshells, with as great an impact on our lives as new Prime Minister Maggie Thatcher would have on the UK.

1. Glenturret Academy was forced by the scandal of a demon-worshipper into closure.

2. Grandpa died.

3. Mike and I came into huge piles of money.

Of these the first was the most disturbing to my peace of mind for a long time; a strange, sinister link was to weave its way from The Cold Spot of our youth to the insanity of my actions on the edge of old age. The second was not unexpected – though I mourned the passing of the dear old tyrant. The third was the stuff of ridiculous novels, having no real connection with life as I lived it, and I never got used to being rich.

Just as well!

CYRIL'S DEMON

Glenturret's curved corridor, the haunted passage of my youth, had, in 1979, living accommodation beyond it. In the nearest room, built where the Cold Spot had perplexed Grandpa, lived one of Doc Costigan's senior masters, Cyril Ritter. They said that in this bedroom he gave birth to a demon. I was not actually in the building when the events which follow took place – so everything I know about them is hearsay; and I can't say I really believe they happened as reported, even all these years later. But I came to realise one thing: as a result of the catastrophe Glenturret was finished as a school.

Cyril I knew as a colleague, of course. He was regarded as an enigma. For a start, although always referred to as "Old Cyril", he was not all that old; a little over sixty, I'd have said, though he could have passed for seventy-five. He always wore a ghastly olive mackintosh with its collar up and great rents round the hem. He perched NHS tortoiseshell glasses at an odd angle on his beaky nose. One of his grey trouser legs had a long tear up the inside of the calf – the right one, I think it was – and as he never seemed to change these trousers, the rip grew longer as the years went on. He chain-smoked Senior Service cigarettes all day long, even when teaching. His hands, freckled and with long nails, were orange with nicotine, and a streak of orange ran from the corner of his slit of a mouth up through his eye socket and into his peaked hairline. He never spoke in the Common Room unless spoken to. His voice was clipped and educated. The Boiler told me that he had been in training to be a vicar thirty years before, but had not made it to ordination. He was a fine golfer and was rumoured to have been a cricketer of genius; indeed, it was said he had coached teams at major public schools in the past. He taught Latin. I was terrified of him.

Where Dr C had obtained him, no one knew – although it was agreed that he must have had some sort of reference. Why he was prepared to teach at Glenturret after a career in major schools, no one could guess. Glenturret Academy, like many small, rickety, financially insecure independent schools, was a haven for two types of staff member: the young hopeful in his first job who doesn't stay too long if he knows what's good for him, and the battered cynic at, or near, retirement age, who wants a last, cushy billet with small class sizes and low academic expectations. That there is a third category was evinced by the existence of Cyril: that of the man with a "secret" and "a past".

The boys were as frightened of him as of cholera. He joined the staff when I was myself in the Upper Sixth. I was never taught by him, as I didn't do

Latin, and thanked heaven for it. He could be extraordinarily violent. Once, not long after his arrival, a pupil got in his way in a doorway. Cyril picked the boy up and began systematically to clout his head. Clump, clump went Cyril's hard hand until the youth was losing consciousness and had dropped to the floor. Cyril stepped over his body and said very slowly,

'Next – time – me – first – chum.'

The incident was around the school within an afternoon and it made Cyril's fame (which may have been his intention.)

When teaching in the late '70s, I saw, from the old library windows, Cyril's methods with his Latin class. Outside one of Doctor C's hideous classroom huts (erected hastily during the expansion of 1972-73) a line of boys stood shivering in the drizzle. They were in a soldierly file along the wall of the hut with books under their arms, waiting. After some minutes, Cyril came in sight, fag in his slit-like mouth, smoke running up through his glasses into his hairline, mackintosh pulled around him. He stopped at the head of the line of boys and, raising his hand, snapped his fingers and pointed to the hut door with an orange fingernail. In silence the class filed in and stood to attention at their desks. Cyril followed them in, faced them, snapped his fingers again, and the boys sat down. He scrawled "Page

22" on the board, snapped his fingers once, and pointed downward. Immediately all began to write. Cyril stood in front of them, trembling slightly, eyes bulging, while he lit another Senior Service. At intervals I looked out and across to the hut. For the duration of the forty minute lesson no word was uttered, no question from the class, no head lifted from paper. When the bell went, Cyril ground out his cigarette, snapped his fingers and the boys closed their exercise books and stood up. With a final snap he pointed to the door. They filed out. Five snaps was all it took to overmaster a class of fourteen-year-olds who did exactly what they wanted in my English lessons.

Towards the end, when Cyril was going ga-ga, he spent a whole series of days in bed and no knock or entreaty would bring him from his room. In a free period on one of those occasions I had to take one of his junior Latin classes. In the hut I asked the boys what work they were doing and they told me they were on page eleven of their Latin primer. I suggested they moved on to the exercises on page twelve, but they looked very worried.

'Well, get on with it, you twits,' I snapped. 'What's the problem?'

'Oh, we always only do page eleven, Sir,' one of them said. 'We can't go on to twelve.'

They then told me that Cyril had come in,

scrawled "Page 11" on the board, and snapped his fingers for them to begin – every lesson that term. It was true. I looked at one pupil's exercise book and page after page was headed "Page 11" and the exercises, absolutely identical, marched after each through the book. None had been corrected. The small class of thirteen year-olds had been far too frightened to say anything to Cyril personally, or to anyone else, for that matter.

The Boiler had been most puzzled one day to find Cyril standing right up against a wall, his face to the stone, near the squash courts. He had been making walking movements, but had only pressed his features further into the wall; his cigarette had snapped into an L-shape. The Boiler had led him back to his room. Not a word had been spoken.

Cyril often took violently against certain pupils and made them stand throughout his lesson. He would send them out to make tea or coffee for him during the cold winter lessons. That they might miss valuable instruction did not worry him.

A story about Cyril and his least-favoured pupils circulated in the mid-'70s. How true it was I couldn't say, but apparently one youth had had the temerity to place a drawing-pin on Cyril's chair. Cyril had spotted it the moment he entered the classroom, but I shouldn't have thought the prank would have worked anyway, for Cyril generally stood the whole lesson through, chain-smoking and scattering ash down his mackintosh.

Contrary to what the boys had expected, however, Cyril did not blow a gasket.

'Which – of – you – has – done – this?' he articulated quietly, picking up the pin with finger and thumb. No one owned up. With a grim smile, he went on, 'If anyone here is bright enough to get ME to sit on a drawing-pin, you know what I shall do?' (He had said "me" extra loudly and now leaned forward over the front row of desks, so the story went) 'I shall give that lad five pounds. But…..you'll NEVER do it!'

No one else in that particular group ever did dare to slip a pin onto his chair, but in a more senior class an African boy named Senanu Ulanu was said to have managed that difficult feat. Sent to make Cyril a cup of tea (with the usual grim warnings in his ears: Too hot – detention, too cold – detention, too sweet – detention, not sweet enough – detention), Ulanu had mixed laxative with it. Cyril always had twelve teaspoons of sugar (for Our Lord and each of the disciples, minus Judas, so it was believed) and could be relied on not to notice the change in taste. The boys, who knew about this plan, watched fascinated as Cyril sipped. After half an hour, Cyril gave a grimace and clutched at his middle. Aware that the class was staring at him, he rapped,

'Get on with your work. And take a hundred lines each.' Then he gave a horrible gurgle and left the hut, presumably to go to the lavatory. In his absence, Ulanu had put on Cyril's chair not a mere drawing-pin, but a whacking great upholstery tack about two inches long, securing it firmly with BluTac. Cyril, pale and perspiring, had re-entered the hut and thrown himself into his chair. The tack had driven into his bottom and he had leapt up again like a Polaris missile, ascending ceiling-wards and shrieking like a banshee. Upon removing the tack from his arse, he had held it up, trembling, and had hissed,

'*Who* has done this?'

Ulanu (who probably went on to become a military dictator in one of those hot countries where reckless bravery is prized above common-sense) stood out and faced Cyril.

'It was I,' he said clearly. 'Because you are an unfair teacher and you treat us badly.'

The horrified class stared at Cyril, expecting him to begin disembowelling Ulanu with his bare hands, but Cyril withdrew a battered wallet from his pocket and took a £5 note from it.

'My – debt – as – promised,' he had articulated, shaking Ulanu by the hand and presenting the note. It was said that the whole class clapped and cheered and that a wintery grin, like the glint of moonlight upon a sarcophagus, had come briefly to Cyril's slit of a mouth.

That, if true, was the only time Cyril was known to have acted with magnanimity, and with a smile. I feel the story might have had some elements of truth in it (notwithstanding the rather hackneyed presence of laxative, which often features in hilarious schoolboy tales) because I was personally the recipient of the only joke Cyril was heard to make; a joke which proved that he did have a hidden but magnificent sense of humour.

We were driving back to Glenturret in the school minibus with two other colleagues from Stirling after a regional exam board meeting, and had been passed by a lady driver in an old Morris Minor. She had, dangerously, a little poodle sitting up on her lap between her and the steering-wheel. Cyril, leaning over towards my ear, had said,

'I am surprised that dog can drive *at all*, sitting on top of that woman.'

We had hysterics the rest of the way back – I and the other two, that is. The quip was all the more amusing because it had come from that surprising man.

Such, then, was the enigmatic schoolmaster whose private world was to spill over into normality and destroy Doctor Costigan's academy. I thought, at the time, that it was horrific that something in

Grandpa's house might have been responsible.

Cyril lived in the "haunted" area beyond the old curved passage. But the police investigation made us realise that he had some very peculiar tastes. His books were gathered up by them after everything had gone wrong. He had the life of Alisdeir Crowley, the self-styled Wickedest Man in the World, a treatise on the practices of the Grimoires, that fascinating material about the link between the crusading knights and alchemy, some writings about the Faustean legend, and a little book about Moloch – the demon God of biblical days to whom children were sacrificed. This slim volume alone did a lot of harm when Cyril's tragedy became public.

As I have explained, I neither witnessed nor was present at what others were involved in, and I'm sure, looking back, that much of what I heard had its embellishments. My colleagues said that Cyril was one of the few to have been an unlucky possessor of a runic paper. According to legend, a piece of parchment is in permanent circulation. Upon it, in runic script, is rumoured to read: "My name is Choronzon. You know me as The Beast." When, after someone barges against you in the street, and you find this paper in your pocket, you must get rid of it at once by "casting" it, that is to say, by passing it on. You must not destroy the paper; your visitor then stays with you forever.

This was the demon of the runic paper thought to have possessed the soul and mind of my colleague, Cyril Ritter. Why else, said everyone after the tragedy, should Cyril have written: "I see him. I see Choronzon!" in boot polish on the mirror of the bathroom which all who lived off the curved passage shared? And why else the extraordinary and ghastly events of that night in the summer of 1979?

This is what I was told had happened:

Cyril had gone to his room early after prep. At his desk he had taken a great swig of whisky from the bottle, lit a Senior Service, and begun a study of drawings. Some of these were very odd indeed, the pictured consumption of parts of the anatomy, living and dead. The fact that he possessed these at all in a school added to Costigan's later problems. (The police were later critical of us, his colleagues, for not seeming to have noticed, in our small community, how disturbed he had been, and for how long. Yet that is one of the problems in schools – every member of staff is more or less partially round the bend, and you go on making allowances.)

After perusing his drawings, Cyril had taken a further deep swig of whisky and lain down on his bed. He had begun to undress for the night. Cradling the bottle in one hand, he had opened his shirt front with the other, and had fallen back in a stupor while some of the contents of the bottle had splashed out near his pillow. The room reeked of whisky when the police arrived.

At about this time, Alan Ferrier, the Maths master, who occupied the room next to Cyril, had heard, over the sound of a programme on his radio, sharp banging. He thought this might have been Cyril falling over – everyone knew he was often intoxicated by nightfall. Alan was the only one to whom Cyril had spoken briefly. A week earlier, Cyril had told him that he had noticed a large piece of fluff in the corner opposite his bed. He had been strangely reluctant to go near it, but could not tear his eyes from it when in the room. Four days after its first appearance the ball of fluff burst and Cyril's room had been filled with transparent seeds. All had wings. Cyril had watched, fascinated, for they seemed beautiful in the room's peachy light. Most fell to the floor and, after whirring for a short time, shrivelled. Others whizzed as far as his bed and landed there. These too soon stopped and shrivelled, but a few hit Cyril's face, and he could feel the fast beating of their tiny, pointed wings. He told Alan that he had inhaled some of them which had found their way, buzzing, into his mouth. He had felt the sherbert-like tingle of their wings on his tongue.

Alan hardly knew what to make of these confidences. He asked several of us if we thought Cyril should see a doctor, but, in spite of everything,

Cyril had told him that he had never been happier. For the first time since early adulthood, he had felt complete physical well-being: no hunger, no thirst, no aches – just a glorious cosy repletion and ease. It did not seem necessary for Cyril to receive medical attention.

So to Cyril's last night, half undressed on his bed, his whisky scenting the room. And then the banging heard by Alan, who, alarmed, went next door to see if Cyril was all right. He had pushed the door open and his eyes had gone straight to Cyril's mouth. Cyril was sitting up, with hands supporting him on the mattress, his hair on end and his mouth wide open, so that the lips were cracking at the edges and the teeth sticking forward like a dog's snarl. From that mouth, it seemed to Alan that there was emanating a long, transparent worm, glassy as ectoplasm, but solid enough to push Cyril's jaws apart, and nearly two feet in length. When it had nearly emerged from Cyril, Alan saw that it had dark, pin-like eyes and, half-way down its length, a black, angular shape was moving. The worm had slid down Cyril's chest and had lain, like a rolling-pin, on his sheet.

Alan had been so stupefied with disbelief that he had remained with hand frozen to the doorknob. Nothing would have brought him nearer to the bed, he said afterwards. The black shape within the worm stood up and tore at the transparent film from the inside. The worm wriggled off the sheet and flopped over the side of the bed and, for a second, disappeared from Alan's sight.

Alan remembered that he had given a long cry from his position at the door.

The worm had then reappeared, moving its way along the floor to the wainscot. There it curled up. The thing inside it resumed tearing until it was out and crouching. It grew slowly – intensely black and humanoid in shape. The worm's pin-like eyes, Alan said, had seemed to have transferred to its offspring. A second later, it seemed to have entered the wall itself.

As this was going on, two more of our colleagues, Chris Cave and The Boiler, had been drawn to Cyril's room by Alan's cry. The Boiler hung back, but Chris came right into the room beyond Alan. Cyril banged his bottle again and it broke, leaving him clutching the neck and a circle of jagged glass. Alan's statements were never wholly clear about what happened next. Suddenly Chris Cave's face was bleeding and a gash had appeared across his left eye, tearing the eyeball and the cheek below it. Unreasonably, Alan swore that the black demon had seemed to dart out of the wall and jump up onto Chris' face, biting and ripping like a cat. But then again The Boiler saw Cyril jump out of bed waving the jagged bottle at Chris.

Alan had bowed his head briefly to vomit on the floor near the lintel. When he raised his head again, the dark demon had vanished, and Cyril, the bottle no longer in his hand, was hunched on the bed. Alan had come up to his side and straightened him. The Boiler had helped Chris away to ring for an ambulance and to awaken Doc Costigan. In the five minutes or so which elapsed before Doctor C hurried to the room, Cyril had died. An hour later the police had arrived.

By the afternoon of the following day, it was known that Chris had lost his eye. He was not to return to the school, and I never saw him again. Alan Ferrier's story was told and re-told. He admitted that he might have been deceived by a trick of the light, but was fairly certain that Chris had not been blinded by Cyril, and that a second entity had manifested itself in the bedroom from out of the wall. For three days the Stirling police were in the house and the boarding pupils were sent home, the day boys given a week's leave, and the school closed. The story spread everywhere, growing ever wilder in the re-telling and reviving old local memories of Glenturret's haunted room and the famous Cold Spot.

As the more peculiar elements of Cyril's disaster were revealed at his inquest, parents began to withdraw their sons from the school. Alan Ferrier resigned. The Boiler was next, taking the opportunity to go into genuine retirement at last. By the end of the new Christmas term, it was clear that Glenturret Academy could survive no longer – proof of the axiom that it only takes one scandal to bring a school into difficulties for terms to come. The trouble was that Costigan hadn't the capital to ride out a period of disaster.

The other day, before typing up this admittedly unbelievable episode, I looked through the press cuttings I had kept about the events surrounding Cyril's demise and Cave's terrible blinding. Here are samples:

Drunken homosexual teacher's 'pact with Satan' blinds colleague.

Satanism causes death and injury in a boys' school.

Staff complacent about demonic practices in boarding school: one dead, one blinded.

Mass resignations at Glenturret Academy after night of drunken perversions leads to death.

Alcoholism, death and the occult at minor crammer cause rapid drop in enrolment.

From *The Daily Mail* to *The Times Educational Supplement,* from *The Scotsman* to *The Mirror* they came – none positive, few restrained. This was an item of news after every reporter's heart, and the public lapped it up. What could you expect at one of those places? Everyone knows what goes on at boys' boarding schools.

Where had I been during that fateful summer weekend? In London with Peter, recording, at last, our song of revenge against the persistent Christine. And no sooner had the twin shocks of becoming a collaborating songwriter with a 45rpm disc to my name, and realising that one of my professional colleagues had expired giving birth to a demon begun to subside, than the sad news came from Prince's Gate that Grandpa's latest apoplectic fit had been his last.

RICHES TAKE WINGS

Grandpa's eminent doctor, Sir Walter Blunt, had (as I have related) the brilliant idea of keeping Grandpa alive by dint of a weekly dose of *Top of the Pops*. In 1979, this BBC show had never been more popular, scooping up 19 million viewers in the UK, although if 18,999,999 liked it, one certainly didn't.

'Ah!' my grandmother would cry. 'Pops again! Right, Guy, in you go!' And the old boy would be shuffled, and later wheeled, into the large airy sitting-room at Prince's Gate and the TV switched on.

'Bah! Tchah!' he would cry. I know he had a particular dislike of Suzi Quattro, and although antique chivalry towards what he thought of as the frail sex prevented him from barking his thoughts at the screen, his upward-leaping moustaches and purple forehead told their own tale. David Bowie was another matter and usually brought forth commentary: 'Queer! Queer! National Service would have cured him! The nasty little tyke!'

Sir Walter's advice had worked wonders for the frequently dropping pressure from which Grandpa had suffered for so long and by Christmas '79, in spite of appalling weather and endless bad news about the economy, he had one of the most stable blood pressures in Knightsbridge. Of course, it was important that he did not become too purple and agonised, so my grandmother alternated *Top of the Pops* with *One Man and his Dog,* (a sheep-dog programme filmed on the hills up and down the UK, which he loved), so that shepherds and collies chivvying bemused herds could act as a pressure balancer.

Opinions are divided about which group of artistes brought about his demise – the result of a seizure in mid-programme – but I believe it to have been the January 1980 *Top of the Pops* performance of *My Girl* by Madness. No doubt the mixture of cockney accents and white tuxedos had been too much.

Sometime in the mid-'seventies, my grandmother had engaged a plump Estonian woman, Lily Samsa, to act as a live-in carer for Grandpa, and it was she who rang me up to break the news of his death, my grandmother being, I imagined, too distraught to cope.

'You, mister. The sad has happed, isn't it?'

'What? Is that you, Lily?'

'The so sorrow has happed, mister. At last happed.'

'What has happened, Lily?'

'A real English gentlemen, isn't he? But not any more.'

'Who is a real English gentleman, Lily?'

'You come.'

'Come? Come to what?'

'She is in pieces. Psah! Hasn't that so typical when arrows and slings are not yet fortunate. I have been persecuted, so I haven't broken into many pieces when outrageous is Fortune.'

'Come to what? You said: Come. But come to what, Lily?'

'Now.'

'Now?'

'Now. That Madness he do them, isn't it?'

'Madness? Whose madness?'

'He.'

'Oh, you mean Grandpa. What, mad as in cross, or mad as in ga-ga?'

'Madness he not make him on into February – or March.'

'Quite, Lily. Well, goodbye. Nice to talk to you, as always.'

Of course I had absolutely no idea from this conversation what had occurred, so I didn't do anything. I thought that if the message Lily was trying to get over from Prince's Gate were serious, someone would ring back. Consequently more than a week passed, and it was sheer luck that I had this other phone call from Mike.........

'Hi, Bruv. Awful, isn't it?'

'That you, Mike?'

'Of course it is. Where are you staying?'

'How do you mean – staying?'

'Staying for it.'

'Oh, *staying*! Oh, right. Well, we're all clinging on here. A lot of the boys have gone, but Costigan wants us to remain to the end of March to wind things up. He's quite generously paying us all until the end of the Easter term, so we feel a bit *noblesse oblige*. Quite a few boarders have parents overseas and they won't be doing anything for a bit – even if they've heard. In fact, Costigan's hoping they haven't heard. After all, they may not have seen it all in the papers.'

'STOP! Stop! What on *earth* are you talking about?'

'I thought you asked me what I was doing – going or staying – now the crap's hit the fan at Glenturret.'

'NO! I'm not asking about that old "Randy Wizard Rapes Four Boys" business, or whatever it was. I don't mean where are you staying *now* – I mean where are you staying for *it*?'

'What "where" are you talking about, Mike?'

'Oh God. What are you wearing, then?'

'Ah, *that* "wear". Sorry, I thought you meant "where". You mean "wearing", as in clothes?'

'Yes, you twit. What? Suit and black tie?'

'Eh? No. I've got on a tweed jacket, that teacher-y one with leather patches, some cords, my yellow jumper, if you must know. It's pretty cold up here, of course.'

'What! No, at the *funeral*!'

'What do you mean: funeral?'

'What – are – you – wearing – at – the – funeral? You burk.'

'Whose funeral?'

'WHAT!'

'I said: whose funeral?'

'Whose funeral, he asks!'

'Yes, yes, yes, yes, yes, yes! What blasted, goddam funeral are you talking about?'

'Are you nuts?'

'Eh?'

'Have you been drinking?'

'Come again?'

'You've been boozing, haven't you?'

'Listen carefully, Mike, because I'm going to ask you this just once more before I put the phone down. WHAT FUNERAL?'

'Grandpa's, of course. Who else's?'

'Grandpa's!'

'Yes, Grandpa's.'

'You don't mean to tell me he's *dead*?'

'Of course he's dead. Why else would he be having a funeral? What's wrong with you today?'

'But do you mean to say that Grandpa – our grandfather – is dead?'

There was silence at the other end; then I heard Mike's voice mutter softly,

'Christos termurgatroyd! He's flipped, I suppose.'

'IS GRANDPA DEAD?'

'Well, he hasn't been resurrected.'

'Look, you cretinous moron, I didn't *know* he was dead!'

'Didn't *know*?'

'No! I didn't know! When? How?'

'But didn't Lily tell you?'

……..or I'd have missed the funeral.

Grandpa's funeral was a grand and impressive affair. What stands out at this distance in time was the walnut coachwork of the Rolls-Royces which swept us up to Golder's Green crematorium, and the taste of the egg-and-cress sandwiches and tiny game pies back at Prince's Gate afterwards. I also recall Geoff Bradley, Grandpa's old stock exchange crony, sidling up to me, as Lily, dressed in swathes of black, handed round glasses of champagne.

'The reading of the will is going to be interesting, my boy,' he said. 'Your dear grandfather left a very great deal of money. The firm – his old firm – would naturally give you any advice you and your brother need.'

The old chap's watery-eyed solicitousness was the first indication I had that Grandpa's death might make a difference to mine and Mike's lives. I had no idea how much of a difference and returned to the slowly emptying Glenturret to await events. The reading of the will came quickly, and, in due course, the clan assembled in a high room overlooking Lloyd's at the head office of the merchant bank which had handled Grandpa's affairs. I smelt in the air a strange, polite, anticipatory rapaciousness. Darting glances flitted across the room. People I hadn't seen for years had turned up, dressed formally and awkwardly. There was Hector McAird, representing his dead father, with shiny, slicked down hair, and a tiny moustache, like that odd singer in Sparks (a group hated by Grandpa in 1980), with the vaunting expression he wore in the days when he had taunted Mike and me with being "custards". There were past gardeners and farm workers from the old Glenturret estate. There was Barable the gardener, very old and wizened, with fly-buttons done up. There was my mad aunt, her wig at a jaunty angle. There was Ma, over from Italy and looking faintly embarrassed by the glances of cousins, colleagues and dependants. There was my grandmother, dignified and silver-haired in a boardroom chair, gazing across London. Expectancy enlivened every face but hers.

The door opened. Several people rose to their feet. Mike nudged me in the ribs.

'Here it comes,' he whispered.

"Young" Mr Jaffrey, representative of the famous firm of Jaffrey and Bothwell, Grandpa's solicitors since the 1920s, came forward with a sheaf of paper in his hands.

'Do sit, ladies and gentlemen,' he drawled. The original Jaffrey had been poor and ambitious with Grandpa in London just after The Great War. His son had the suave deportment of a senior diplomat. He waved a plump hand. We were silent. The reading of the will began.

Contrary to what I had been led to expect of such a function from films, the smaller beneficiaries were dealt with first. Old Barable brought a handkerchief to his eyes when he heard the size of his generous bequest. The reading went on in silence until all Grandpa's erstwhile staff and colleagues had been covered. How many tens of thousands of pounds had totted up, I could not have calculated. Hot at English, History, Geography and Religious Studies though I might have been, my maths had never been equal to a task like this.

'Now I come to the members of the family,' intoned young Mr Jaffrey. Aunts and cousins round the room stiffened sharply. More bequests were read out.

Suddenly I was aware of my own name being articulated. Detached all through this ceremony, although aware that Geoff Bradley's comment was worth pondering later, I had felt like an observer at an interesting event – at it, but not of it. I pulled myself together, but it was too late; I had missed hearing what Grandpa had left me. I had been conscious of a gasp which came as an echo after my name. Then, busy trying to recall whatever figure had passed me by, I missed what Mike had been left. By that time Jaffrey was on to Ma, and I took in that her days of living comfortably in Italy were assured. She had known her father's intentions, so it hadn't been a surprise, but a confirmation.

The reading came to an end. Champagne was brought in and I was aware of old Geoff Bradley pumping my hand and exclaiming, 'My dear boy! My dear boy!' Mike was punching me on the arm and intoning, 'Good old Grandpa! Good old Grandpa!' I left that room still not knowing what sums I had been bequeathed. I had spent the last minutes of the gathering talking politely to Hector McAird. I remember asking him what he was doing these days, and dimly I heard his reply,

'Aye, ah'm in local politics in Stirling, y'know.'

I'd like you to take with me a fractional pause at this point. Stirling is the large historic town west of Glenturret and affairs in the region are run from its city hall. Note that reply of Hector's, for it bears pertinently on the ultimate fate of Glenturret: 'Ah'm in local politics y'know'…..

That evening, I learnt, in the bosom of the family, that, coming up to the age of twenty-six, I need not have to work for my living again. Dear Grandpa – it was all of a piece: the model railway in childhood, the long, happy holidays at Glenturret, the payment of school fees, and now this. A stream of munificence had come my way since 1963. And it was for a purpose, I felt. Why else should I have been singled out, to the astonishment of aunts and cousins, to receive twice the sum of anyone else in the family? I believe that Grandpa knew I had always been at home at Glenturret; Dad had hated it, Ma liked Italy, Mike was London-based. I had elected to finish my schooldays at the house, and then to teach there. Grandpa's wishes, though not expressed in so many words in his will, were clear enough. I was the only member of the family likely to reverse that step which Grandpa had never wanted to take: the treacherous selling of his house.

I saw my next step with twinkling clarity. To Doctor Costigan's aid I would come, scattering riches like manna. When the period of waiting was at an end, and all trace of the Academy gone, Glenturret would be wholly mine!

My brother, freed from an obsession such as this,

had other plans. Grandpa had been very generous to him too, but I could see that Mike was going to make the fur fly with his new riches. From October 1979, after leaving EMI as Peter's temporary stooge, Mike had been quite successful, in a slimy, Chelsea-ish way, pushing property with Dorrell and Stringer as an assistant to an unpleasant creep called Clive Atwood. When Atwood moved on and up to Porter's Properties on Sloane Street, he took Mike with him. By 1980 Mike was everyone's idea of a young, thrusting, money-mad, early Thatcherite go-getter. I felt, with reason, that he was amused by his bookish, schoolmaster older brother, recently embowered in his old boarding school pushing Shakespeare on Costigan's modest salary.

To celebrate his new wealth, Mike insisted on taking me, Peter Buchan, Lucille (his latest bird: a model) and two pals in real estate (likely to be partners with Mike in a new firm, I gathered) to the Savoy Grill.

Mike had always drooled over The King's Road and Glebe Place, where he had dossed in the late '70s, after leaving the bike nuts in Ealing. He had managed to re-create himself as an essentially Sloane-y, Chelsea and Kensington sort of person. The epicentre of his world lay somewhere between Peter Jones and Parson's Green, and his eateries were the bistros, crepe restaurants and Italian trats of that zone. The Savoy was out of his territory in those days, and I remember the vaunting but defensive manner he assumed as we roared under that famous hotel sign in his newly-purchased Rover 3500.

'Can you park here?' I said from the back.

'Of course, old bruv. We're dining here, aren't we?'

He stopped the car with a flourish and nipped round to open the door for Lucille. A doorman appeared from inside the foyer. Lucille put out a shapely leg and wiggled from the car. There was a rending sound.

'Oh bollocks!' she cried, as the stately doorman came into earshot. 'Me skirt's caught!'

It had got snagged on the seat adjuster. Her pants were all too much in view. Mike reddened with vexation.

'Hang on,' said he, and dived over her lap to effect the necessary rescue. From the back of the car I caught the doorman's superior smirk.

'Sod it, Mike! Get yer 'ands off me bum!' squealed Lucille. The doorman tapped Mike on the shoulder.

'You can't park here, Sir,' he intoned. Mike straightened up and heaved Lucille to her feet. One of her shoes slipped off and dropped under the sill of the car. 'You can't park here,' repeated the doorman.

'Look,' said Mike, fumbling for a pound note,

'we're dining here.' Lucille hopped on one foot, clinging on to Mike's arm as he clutched at his wallet.

'Shit, Mike. I've put me bleedin' foot in a puddle. Can't you get me shoe?'

'What room number, Sir?' asked the doorman with a fine touch of irony.

'I've just said we're dining here,' boomed Mike. 'We're not staying, just eating. Park the car, will you?'

'You'll 'ave to find a meter, Sir,' said the doorman. 'Only hotel guests can leave their cars here.'

Mike gave up the struggle. He asked me to take Lucille into the foyer, after grovelling beneath the Rover for her shoe under the sarcastic grin of the doorman, who had pocketed the pound, but did not seem much disposed to do anything else. With a red face, Mike got back into the car and, by mistake, put it into reverse. There was a shrill cry from Lucille, as she and I jumped for our lives. With a swirl of exhaust, Mike disappeared back into The Strand. In the foyer, Peter, and Mike's two smooth-looking, top-of-the-market real-estate bosses, were waiting.

'Jolly good of your brother to stand us a feed,' said Peter to me. Then he noticed Lucille. 'Why, *hello*,' he chirruped. 'Haven't we met before?'

'No, we ain't,' snapped Lucille. 'I got to find a

safety-pin or me skirt'll fall down.' She disappeared to ask for the Ladies. The smoothies exchanged glances.

'Er, well, what about drinks?' I said. 'Or shall we wait for Mike?'

'Wait for Mike,' said one of the slimies, no doubt fearing that he might have to pay.

Just then, the revolving doors whirred and Mike marched in. He had recovered his composure.

'Did you find a meter?' I asked.

'No, but I'm right down behind the theatre. Near the river. It's a double yellow, but it should be OK at this time.'

Lucille returned. She too had had time to adjust herself to her surroundings. She looked very pretty. Like the stars of the early talkies, she was fine until she opened her mouth.

'Sorry I was a bit snappy,' she said to Peter, oscillating her hefty black lashes.

'Oh, not at all,' smiled Peter gallantly, reluctantly lifting his eyes from her hem-line – not that his eyes had far to go, for Lucille was 99% leg.

'So, look,' said Mike, 'Let's go straight to the table. It's past eight. We'll have drinks while we're choosing.'

He headed towards the back of the hotel to where the fine dining-room overlooks the river. I was sure he had said that we were noshing in the Grill Room, and that was round to the left of the foyer at the front. These days it's all been re-modelled, so I've read – and I haven't been back in over ten years, so I don't know how much has changed.

'Are we going the right way?' I ventured to remark.

'Who's giving this dinner?' asked Mike. He swaggered up to the little desk at the entrance to the dining-room. He gave the name. The *maitre d'* justraised his eyebrows.

' 'Ave you booked, Sair?'

'Of course I've booked,' replied Mike hotly. 'Just look, will you?' The *maitre* looked.

'Your name ees not 'ere, and we air full,' he said. The smoothies nudged each other.

'What!' cried Mike, grabbing the book from the stand. 'I rang yesterday to book a table for six in the Grill Room.'

'Zees is not ze Greel Room, Sair.'

'Oh.'

We traipsed back to the foyer. Just above the spot where we had been waiting for Mike was the sign I had noticed: GRILL ROOM.

'Bah!' snorted Mike. 'Come on.'

Lucille swept into the Grill Room.

'*Bonsoir, Mam'selle,*' said the head waiter. Peter and the smoothies followed her.

'*Bonsoir, M'sieu,*' said the head waiter to me. I

went in, anxious to sit next to Peter during the meal. I somehow felt that the smoothies and I would have little conversation in common.

'You cannot go in,' said the head waiter to Mike. He put up an arm and Mike ran into it.

'What do you mean?' gasped Mike, quite red with annoyance.

'*M'sieu* is not correctly dressed,' said the head waiter. I had turned back to see what was happening. Mike drew himself up.

'I was told on the phone that there was no need to dress formally for the Grill Room.'

'Certainly *M'sieu* does not need black tie, but *M'sieu* does not have on a jacket.'

He looked down at Mike's attire, and I noticed for the first time that my brother was dressed differently from the rest of us. We four men had suits on. I wore one because it was the only thing in my wardrobe that wasn't a tweed jacket; remember I'd been teaching for five years. Peter's suit had seen better days, but it was quite formal looking; I suppose some instinct that it might be appropriate had urged him to don it. Mike was paying the price of being a trendy. He had on a sort of bomber-top in gingery leather and an open shirt with medallion round his neck – a bit pimp, now I came to examine it closely. The other denizens of the Grill Room all resembled Harold Macmillan (or today's Jacob Rees-Mogg) with old Etonian ties. Some of them were gazing at the doorway with raised eyebrows.

'*M'sieu*'s jacket is not really a jacket,' the head waiter explained. '*M'sieu* will have to go to the Hall Porter to borrow one, and, of course, a tie.'

Speechless, Mike turned back into the foyer. I accompanied him for moral support. His old enemy, the doorman, pounced on him.

'I have been sent to borrow a jacket,' mumbled Mike through gritted teeth.

'Certainly, Sir,' cried the ironist of the Savoy. 'I'll take your jumper, Sir.' The bomber-top changed hands. A dark-grey jacket, slightly sweaty-smelling, was handed to Mike. He donned it. The sleeves were at least three inches too long. 'A perfect fit!' cried the ironist, holding out his hand. Another of Mike's pound notes slipped into new ownership. The Hall Porter meanwhile had been riffling through a box from his office and now produced a tie with the air of a conjuror. It was one of those outdated Carnaby Street psychedelic kippers like a large slice of surrealist pizza. Mike fumbled a knot into it. 'You look a treat, Sir,' said the doorman.

Resembling a patient on an outing from a mental referral unit, Mike and his long sleeves re-entered the Grill Room. The old Etonians returned their eyebrows to normal level as he dropped into his place at table.

'Bit pongy, that coat!' squealed Lucille, giggling shrilly, her fingers to her nose.

The menu came. Mike ordered lavishly, even exuberantly, insisting we all had the most expensive of everything.

'My treat, you blokes!' he kept crying. There was a slight tussle when I insisted on trying Eggs Arnold Bennett in honour of the great novelist; Mike took exception to the fact that they were half the price of all the other starters except soup.

'What will *M'sieu* drink?' asked the wine waiter.

'Er, what shall we have?' said Mike, looking round.

'Anything,' said Peter.

'As long as it's wet!' twittered Lucille, with the air of one making up a startlingly original witticism.

'Up to you, Mike' said one of the smoothies.

'Right! Right then,' boomed Mike. 'Bring us two bottles of *Beaujolais Nouveau*!'

The wine waiter gazed at him. He then went over to the head waiter. They both returned to the table.

'Does *M'sieu* ask for *Beaujolais Nouveau*?' asked the head waiter.

'Certainly, if you have it,' replied Mike.

'But, *M'sieu*, we certainly have the *Beaujolais* when it is *nouveau*, but now it would be rather *vieux, n'est ce pas*?' He and the wine waiter exchanged smiles of great superciliousness, amused by the joke.

Mike went pink, then white, then pink again.

'We'll have two bottles of the *Cheval Blanc* '47, please,' said the smoother of the smoothies.

'Certainly, *M'sieu*. I commend your choice,' said the wine waiter – slightly stressing the "your".

He went to fetch them.

'It's all the same to me, whether it's Lucozade or *Mateus Rose*,' giggled Lucille in an effort to retrieve the situation. Good-hearted as she was, she could see that my not quite twenty-two year old little brother was out of his depth, and strove to minimise his embarrassment. The faintly malicious slimies seemed frankly to enjoy his discomfiture.

You may have got the impression that this was not one of those successful evenings, and I hardly like to relate that there was more disaster to come. Over coffee, Mike produced a terrifically swish cigarette case and proffered it to each of us.

'Turkish or Virginia?' he asked, like a villain in a '30s film. In the case were ten beautiful oval fags and ten fat round ones. Each had Mike's initials on them.

'Good God!' I gasped. 'Where did you get those?'

'Oh, I'm having them made up by Sullivan and Powell's in the Burlington Arcade.'

Further quizzing elicited the fact that each gasper cost as much as a cinema ticket. Mike was definitely making the fur fly with Grandpa's money. We each took a cigarette. The gold initials twinkled.

I had noticed that since the arrival of two further bottles of wine beyond the Cheval Blanc (red this time, but I hadn't taken in what sort), Lucille had been giggling more often and more explosively than earlier. I only twigged that she was three-quarters pissed when I saw her stubby fingers fish out an ice-cube from the water jug and drop it down the back of Mike's shirt collar. There are certain things which aren't done in the Savoy Grill; this was one of them. Mike gave vent to a sound like a tube door closing as he inadvertently sucked in breath, and the cigarette (Turkish oval) that he was smoking vanished into his mouth. Taken externally, that expensive cigarette was delightful; taken internally it was not. Mike leapt from the table, screeching like a tormented soul in hell, and spat out gobbets of tobacco while attempting to retrieve the ice-cube from his neck. He caught the table-cloth, it dragged after him, and two cups and saucers and a heavy coffee pot crashed to the floor. Unfortunately, the pot was nearly full.

'Laugh! I'm nearly crucified!' hooted Lucille, slapping her shapely thighs with mirth.

The head waiter was at our table in a trice.

'Perhaps *M'sieu* would like the bill?' said he to me. I suppose he couldn't believe that Mike was the founder of the feast. 'There will be an extra charge for……,' he murmured, gazing at the smashed crockery, the pool of coffee and the overturned chair. The Old Etonians concentrated elaborately on their bread-and-butter puddings.

''Ad a good evening, Sir?' asked the master of irony at the desk as Mike's bomber-top was brought forth.

The real-estate slimies left us at that point to go back to Chelsea. Lucille, pouting because Mike had been such a bad sport, and clinging on to Peter's arm to show Mike that he wasn't the only pebble in the Savoy, and Mike, horribly silent, like Attila brooding in his tent before a campaign, and I, sorry that Mike's celebration had not turned out as he'd hoped, went down the steep little road behind the theatre. The Rover was gone. While Mike stood, rooted to the spot, I found a policeman who informed us that it was at the Elephant and Castle car pound over the river. Lucille cried,

'Sod that! I might as well get a cab. Ta, Mike, it was quite fun. I'll ring tomorrow if I can.' She thrust her heavily lip-sticked mouth forward for a kiss. Mike pecked her cheek unenthusiastically.

'Er, I'll help you find that taxi,' muttered Peter, unsubtly announcing his lack of enthusiasm for the tube ride to the Elephant. 'Thanks, Mike. It was – er – great.'

My brother and I were left on the pavement. I

toyed with going after Peter, but loyalty and blood won the day. We went together to pick up the car. The fine was steep. Mike said, as he dropped me off at Prince's Gate where I was staying with our grandmother, 'I think I'm going to see about working somewhere else – maybe America.' The Rover disappeared down Exhibition Road in the direction of Chelsea and civilisation.

Mike was as good as his word, and, with an introduction procured from Geoff Bradley to a New York real-estate tycoon, left the UK about 18 months later. In New York he had his big idea about bringing re-locators and vacant property together, changed his name to Greville and named his consultancy Royal Greville (cheeky, but effective) and set out for the West Coast, where his share of the sum left over from the will began to multiply with startling speed.

I now come closer to one of the most serious of my errors of judgement. I know that I should not have pleaded to do my Sixth form years at Glenturret. These compounded the strange fetishism I was developing for the old house. I have already lamented my letting go of Meriel; of not taking seriously the feelings I had for her. I had been unwise, I see now, to have taught at Glenturret and then bought the house from Doctor C. It turned out to be a further boxing-in. But going ahead with the lunatic idea that materialised next was down there with the worst of my whims.

'I'd like to have a meeting with you and Jools Farthingale,' said Peter some weeks later, as we sat in Balcombe Street. I don't suppose I looked very enthusiastic; I'd had more than enough of producer Jools during the making of *When Christine Comes Around*.

Peter seemed at a loose end. He was involved in the production of a terrible LP of orchestral classics accompanied by a rock combo, but the sessions at EMI in Studio 2 had not been going well and priority was now being given to the recording of a new Cliff Richard album. Peter blamed the delays on everything but the real cause: the unending vapours of Jools and his rows with musicians and arrangers. I thought that the eventual non-appearance of *"The never-before attempted synthesis of the Golden Favourites of Yesteryear with Today's driving disco beat"*, as the record sleeve blurb was later to put it, would be no loss. I disliked the concept behind this ridiculous LP and had heard enough of what had been laid down already to know that "yesteryear" and "driving disco" did not make easy bedfellows. Peter had brought home the stereo master tape of what was to become Side 1 and had subjected me to an hour of torture on his faithful Brenell reel-to-reel tape recorder. The *Farandol* from *L'Arlesienne*, the waltz in C sharp minor of Chopin, the Chinese dance from *The Nutcracker* and Dvorak's fourth symphony were by no means enhanced by a thunderous accompaniment of bass, rhythm, lead guitar, synthesiser and drum-kit. Particularly bizarre was *Jesu, Joy of Man's Desiring,* in which Bach's sweetness of tempo was jammed with a hefty disco beat and lead guitar through fuzz-box and wah-wah pedal. It was a crass marketing ploy – but not untypical of the time: those dying years of LPs.

When listening to these tracks I had the same sensation of disconnectedness and nightmare that I'd experienced as a student when trapped into seeing a surrealist play in which an elephant and a midget sit on pink triangles of rock in the Sahara desert and discuss the existential qualities of *The Song of Solomon*. I've now forgotten who wrote that play, but it didn't work. Neither did I think that Jools Farthingale's project was working, but it was no use telling Peter that the LP was an abortion.

'He's a *genius*!' cried Peter, besotted. 'I know he's temperamental – all geniuses are – and sometimes we spend all day on eight bars of music. But, you see, he gives it *soul*!' Peter snapped his fingers soulfully – probably to make the point. 'Look! Why don't you come to a session? We could go out for a meal afterwards and then I could put my plan before you both. How about a posh curry?'

'Plan? What do you mean? And I can't hang about in London for too long. Now we've signed the contracts, Costigan is only sticking on at Glenturret until he hears about his new term dates in Athens. I promised him that – but I must get back. There's a lot to sort out.'

'Ah, yes. But that's all connected to my really *stupendous* idea, old recent millionaire pal of mine.'

He and I were having spaghetti Bolognese for supper that night. I prefer it *al dente*, as the natives say, not too squidgy. Peter errs on the squidgy side, and I had a large ball of glutinous knitting-wool on my fork with the adhesive properties of gaffer tape. Just as well, for when Peter explained what his stupendous idea was, my fork jerked so spasmodically that, had the spag not been so gluey, it would have splattered the ceiling.

I had not thought further quite *what* I was going to do with Glenturret now that I had bought it from Doctor C. I simply wanted to be in it, minus 100+ schoolboys. I had not imagined that I was going to recreate the days of my childhood hols: tea under the library windows, croquet near the Gothic folly, dinner at 7.30, shooting on Sherrifmuir; the times had changed too much for that. Grandpa's way of life had been getting anachronistic in the '60s;

besides, you have to be elderly to live like an Edwardian squire, and you have to be married.

When asked exactly *why* I had repurchased Glenturret, just when everyone else in the UK was moving into little neo-Georgians, I could only answer that I had not wanted to lose it again. I expect that Mike's decision to emigrate to America had disturbed me; I think I had hoped that he and I might cooperate in a brotherly plan to run the old place as a business. Indeed, we had once discussed its viability as a hotel, but had not got further than speculation. Mike, of course, had shorter and less rosy memories of the house – he had been only eleven when Grandpa sold it. I had seventeen years of association as against his meagre five years as B.O.P.

Peter's plan (once I had absorbed the startling zaniness of it) gave me the answer: Glenturret was going to be a recording studio. As I say, my acceptance of the proposal gave little evidence of my sanity; only a banana-case, would set up a sound studio for serious professional purposes nearly five hundred miles from Leicester Square.

Jools Farthingale, however, was all over the idea when, at last, Peter brought us together during a break in the recording of The Abortion. I had slipped into the control room of Studio 2 at Abbey Road in the late afternoon. Peter and Jools were crouched over the mixing desk and from the 18" Tannoy dual-concentric drive units in their huge Lockwood cabinets came a squealing of violins under a battering of drums. I had dropped into a chair by Peter's side. The famous Jools, whom I had met only once, just before the recording of *When Christine Comes Around*, was screaming into a microphone.

'Can you hear me on cans? I want SOUL, sweeties, SOUL!'

What I thought might have been *L'apres-midi d'un faune* was squeaking despairingly in the far background. The bass and drum track shook the big cabinets. The air was full of smoke and the surfaces were littered with dirty coffee cups. 'Hello? Violins? Violins, duckies!' cried Jools. 'You're drowning the drums! Keep it limpid, sweethearts, limpid!' *L'apres-midi* disappeared. The roar increased in tempo and volume. After a few more bars it ceased. Peter leant back, and in the corner a dark-eyed youth with an air of suffering snapped off the Ampex recorder. With the tapes still, and the mikes from the studio floor muted, there was a delightful peace.

'Jools,' said Peter. 'You remember Anthony? He is now the Man with the Cash.'

Jools proffered two limp fingers for me to shake.

'I'm not likely to forget,' he smiled. 'I loved them rotten, right down to the camisole, you might say.'

'He means the lyrics of *Christine*,' interpreted

Peter.

'Of course I do, silly! What else would I love after such a short acquaintance? Honestly! Making everybody think I'm Dolly Drop-drawers!'

His fingers grew sticky in my hand, so I was glad when he disengaged them in order to insert a cigarette between his yellow teeth and full lips.

'Bruce! Light my fire!' he called, and the dark-eyed youth in the corner slouched forward with a lighter. 'Oooh!' cried Jools, as the flame leapt up. 'Go easy! I can't afford to get a burn on the tip of me thing, you silly queen, you! I meant nose, sweetie, actually,' he hissed at me, puffing smoke in my face. 'Who's got a mind like a docker?' He hoisted himself archly onto his stool at the control desk, and flipped his hand at the youth, Bruce. 'A good sound engineer's a useful tool,' he grinned. 'You're useful, hey, Brucie, aren't you?'

Peter smiled indulgently, like an uncle tickled by the precocity of a favourite niece.

'Tell Anthony what you think of the Grand Plan,' said he.

'I love it! Peter has absolutely *sold* me the idea. I adore being in the countryside. I'm never happier than among flowers. More like a little monk than a bold, bad record producer, really. And I mean, dear, you don't have to grovel – not to your Jools. I *said* I'd come in as a partner, and I will. There!'

Back in Balcombe Street, I said to Peter,

'Are you *sure* you know what you're doing? Why did your Jools use the word "partner"? That was never explained. There's no question of some sort of split ownership of the studio, you know.'

'Oh, I realise that. He means partner in the creative sense. Leave it to your Uncle Peter. I know Jools. He's a brilliant producer. Mad, of course, but he'll be ideal. You'll see.'

I was doubtful, but then we had just been out for a curry at Veeraswamy's with Jools after EMI, and I was still perspiring from the embarrassment of being seen in public with so outrageous a queen, whose high, querulous voice had filled every corner of the restaurant, and who had made such a pet of our Indian waiter that I expected to hit the pavement in Swallow Street long before the end of the meal. But Jools had revealed a sharp financial mind and had costed the fitting of a 24-track studio into a Victorian baronial manor-house down to the last hundred pounds. He was optimistic about the studio's appeal. 'Look, they'll come tearing up there with tongues hanging out. Studio time is London is a tenner a chord. But you'll have to offer 32-track before long. Anything less will be last night's dirty sheets by 1984.'

He painted a picture of creative, bonhomous weekends with musicians strolling downstairs refreshed by a quiet night's sleep and a lie-in, and then straight into a capacious, attractive studio where they would be safe from stray background noise like tube trains and aircraft, with no worries about parking, and with a set recording fee based on number of tracks cut rather than on hours spent in studio time.

'Dead right,' Peter had interposed. 'Half the problem with London places, like Air, de Lane Lea or TPA, is the pressure of racing against the clock, and then having to break off and start cold the next day. At Glenturret, they could play half the night and sleep it off, and no fuss about hours clocking up.'

'You'll recoup twice the cost of outlay in a year!' cried Jools. 'And you could tender for classical music sessions and have John Williams and Pavarotti flocking up to use the place, and screaming queens in chamber sextets!'

'And jazz!' Peter had shouted.

'And choir boys!' screamed Jools.

'And Anthony Hopkins and Shakespeare!' howled Peter.

'Right. Right. I see what you mean,' I had replied.

Later, as euphoria was succeeded by detailed planning, I asked Peter what Jools' proper name was.

'Oh, it really *is* Jools – that is, it's short for Julius. His middle name is Vespasian, believe it or not. His parents were classical scholars and mad on Roman history. They now live on a kibbutz – but his father doesn't speak to him anymore.'

This info joined the other many misgivings I was beginning to have about the Grand Plan and Farthingale's involvement in it. But it all seemed too late to back out. Upon return to Glenturret, the contracts signed and representatives from Leevers-Rich, Neve, Bowers & Wilkins and Revox due to arrive with equipment and advice, I stood alone in Grandpa's old library. I had planned to make this the performance studio, but as I looked out through the triple-arched windows towards the blue Ochils, I could almost hear the slow tick-tock of the grandfather clock, and I saw that I was on the threshold of committing blasphemy against the dead. Suppose Madness or David Bowie ended up singing in this very room?

I turned on my heel and went into the stone-flagged hall. There, on the left, was the old disused ball-room of my childhood in which, years before that, a sarcophagus-like radiogram had dispensed Glen Miller and Al Bowley, and in which, more recently, *Snow White* and the Ravioli Riot had woken the echoes. Next door was what had been my grandmother's morning-room, and lately Quiffy Barnett's office – ideal for the control desks and tape machines. A double-glazed window could be let into the wall near where the escritoire had stood.

So be it.

The deep bell tolled in the hall. Stifling any last shreds of doubt, I went towards the main door to greet the first of those helpful and professional men who were to ensure that I spent the next six weeks in a haze of signing cheques.

363

FLYING SAUCERS HAVE LANDED

The disaster which, in 1985, befell the studio was so staggeringly ridiculous and unnecessary that it makes me hot under the collar to type it up – even though so many summers have passed.

I'll start by explaining that, for about three years, Peter, Jools and I made money and a bit of a reputation. The market for singles had vanished and the extended rock work had replaced it. By the early '80s things were changing again – swiftly – as vinyl LPs were succeeded by tape cassettes and, from '83, the CD. At Glenturret we offered increasingly sophisticated mediums for recording and, as Peter had prophesied, attracted clients from a wide musical base. I might have been happier if we had concentrated on classical music, for I had long grown away from rock; indeed I still thought of Pink Floyd's *Dark Side of the Moon* as a newish disc in '83, although it was over ten years old. But Jools and Peter never wanted to stray far from what they thought of as chart bestsellers, and they encouraged a fair number of well-known bands to come and make records.

Although I grew tired of an endless troupe of strangers in the house – often drunk, sometimes stoned, always noisy, egotistical and demanding – I appreciated the profits that came in and spent them on additions to my collection. Slowly, all that bit of Glenturret which was not part of the studio filled up, with shelves, cabinets and drawers bearing witness to my increasing collector's obsessiveness. Peter and I began to vie in mania over the model railway at this time. Actually, I've found that, in common with schoolmasters and clergymen, electronics men are often hot on trains. Jools was an exception, and I should have known from this fact alone that he was a wrong 'un all along.

'Oooh, choo-choos!' he had squealed once, when I was trying to explain my interest, 'all those long, shiny things plunging into tunnels! It makes me tingle from the dentures downwards!'

I realise that by today's viewpoint, I seem to be painting Jools in a very non-PC, LGBT-annoying sort of way. But he really was as outlandish as described; not, perhaps the best advert for gay guys. What was wrong about Jools was not that he was almost ridiculously camp, deliberately putting on a show, but that he was arrogant and nothing like as competent as he (and Peter) thought he was.

Everything began to go wrong on the October day when Jools rushed up to Peter and me waving the just-delivered day's newspaper.

'Look!' he cried, shoving one of the pages under our noses. There, near the bottom, was a small article entitled: *Flying Saucer Hunt.* It announced that, following a large number of sightings of UFOs in and around Warminster, there was going to be an organised vigil on the Great Ridge on Salisbury Plain from eight o'clock at night to eight the next morning. After twelve hours of scanning the skies with infra-red cameras, it was hoped that a sighting would be confirmed. Although the public were not permitted to take part, people from the RAF were going to bring special equipment, and the press, TV and recognised experts would be joining them. This proposed jamboree was due to take place in a fortnight.

'Gee-hosa-phat!' cried Peter, grabbing the paper. 'We're in on this!'

'Flying saucers! Isn't it astonishing luck!' gabbled Jools. 'Honestly, everyone is bonkers about space at the mo. *Star Wars, Star Trek,* Spock and all that. I couldn't believe my peepers when I saw this....'

It did seem an interesting coincidence. Jools, Peter and I had finished the recording of a cosmic, outer-space LP which we had decided also to release as a CD simultaneously, ready for the Christmas market. The studios had been quiet for over a month, and Jools had convinced us that it was a God-sent opportunity to produce something for ourselves. Peter had been itching to engineer a sort of heavy-metal/glam-rock production using all the new facilities I had paid for. 'Sort of *Queen* mates uneasily with *Led Zep,*' as I had put it to frowns from the other two. I privately thought their idea sounded unoriginal; *Queen* had already made their *Hot Space Tour* in the US and *Star Fleet Project* LP. Our fictional band (a group of session musicians whom Jools had arranged to front this work) was to be called *Aliens*.

Most of the music was instrumental, featuring synthesisers, but several numbers had lyrics. Jools came up with pretentious bollocks, sounding deep but meaning sod-all, and Peter and I seemed to have exhausted our creative depths with *When Christine Comes Around*. Here's a sample of something I wrote for the album which proves the point:

> *When, yeah, when I'm far from Earth*
> *Then you'll know just what I'm worth*
> *When my ship has hit the stars*
> *Beyond the Moon and far from Mars*
> *Then you'll lie in bed and cry*
> *Oh, baby, Cry-y-y-y-y-y-y*
> *I came, yeah, from outer space*
> *In my craft to your sweet place*
> *I needed love I couldn't find*
> *On the world I'd left behind*
> *But you just made me cry*
> *Oh, momma, cry-y-y-y-y-y-y*

Here's some Jools-crap for contrast:

Break, lonely chancellors of strife
As the womb trip, seed ship, cries dartingly along
Planes of pendulum forever parallel
And every birth struggle's imminence fleshes
Future forgetfulness, forgiveness featured in
Prophecy, bewilderment and Merlin's ken –
Archetype of both philosophy and Men

The recording sessions always began in the same way during this Flying Saucer period. Peter and I would be downstairs and in the control room first. Half an hour later, Jools would appear, tetchy, garish and tousled. It was always an effort for him to rise before eleven. The three of us would then potter about switching on equipment. I would go into the studio and point microphones at snare, tenor tom-tom, bass drum hi-hat and cymbals, Peter would fiddle with the singers' mikes in their cubicle, and with the Marshall floor amps (we didn't always feed electric guitar direct to mixer). Jools would sort out synthesisers and the elderly but tried and tested Binson *Echorec* reverberator bought from Pendulum Studios when they closed. We then emptied ashtrays, chucked yesterday's beer tins, moved stools, put on lights, turned others off, and wandered from room to room. At this stage, Peter would shout,

'Where *are* those idle bastards?' And Jools would sniff,

'Don't come the fishwife with me, sweetie. I need to be calm, calm, calm before a session if I'm not to be Mister Mediocre.'

'Oh, I'll make some more coffee, damn it,' I would say, and the three of us would sit amidst humming equipment with the red lights winking in an empty room until it pleased the band to waken from their drugged slumbers and join us for a spot of creative art.

By lunchtime we would be ready to do some balancing and to test vocal levels. The VU meters wavered as singer Rory coughed tobacco-coloured phlegm onto the mike heads. Jools' voice squealed down the cans to our drummer in the booth,

'Kevin! Kevin, dear, we know what to ask Father Christmas for, don't we? A bloody hearing-aid! Kev-in, your fairy godmother's calling! Come in, come in, the one with the Y-fronts.'

Eventually Kevin would look up with a dazed face and eyes like old, putrefying oysters.

'Yeh?'

'Kevin, ducky, would you give us some level on the drums?'

Kevin would toss back his thinning yard-long hair and throw his head behind him, so that from the control room window only a white Adam's apple and unshaven chin could be seen, and bring down his sticks. Like falling rocks, the roar came bursting out of the B & W cabinets. 'Stop!' Jools would hoot. 'Fine. Thank you, dear.' Then he would snap the cans mike off and turn to us. 'Oh, what a caveman! I know him from punk sessions in the 'seventies. Lucky he's got round to using sticks; it used to be meat-axes for the loud bits and lead piping for ballads. What a hunk!'

And Kevin, noticing Jools' mouth moving in silence behind the thick glass, would growl,

'Warrer you three cows whisperin' about?'

Balancing of lead guitar, rhythm and bass guitars, organ, piano and backing vocals mikes would come next. Peter sometimes joined in and Jools seemed able to make his out-of-key yowl seem quite funky by judicious use of echo and infinitely variable speed mixing. I helped on additional percussion, like maracas, gong, bells and wood-blocks and was sometimes given the job of playing piano or organ. I mustn't give the impression of being Daniel Barenboim – in fact, I couldn't read music – but I would be placed in front of keyboards and Jools would tippex 1, 2, 3, 4 on various keys. At a signal I would press the keys in sequence to an agreed tempo – this being kept in my headphones by Kevin tapping a stick on the edge of the sound-desk. When six or seven minutes of this 3 or 4 key riff had been recorded, it would be played back to me while I pressed new tippex-ed keys. By this means a pro sounding keyboard track was built up and laid down on the master tape. All the recording of *Flying Saucers Have Landed* was done through multi-tracking and superimposition, there being only one other musician apart from Rory and Kevin – the bassist, Ian. This took a long time.

Jools was not always a demanding perfectionist. He could be pragmatic, as when he took the 10-inch 4-track master stereo mix of the first four items of *Flying Saucers Have Landed* to EMI to play to a couple of engineers there who had had experience of sending source material out to Japan for CD manufacture. He went from Euston to Swiss Cottage by tube and nearly wiped the lot. In spite of working with electronic equipment for years, the great twit had not remembered that the magnetic field of an electric train motor is enough to erase recording tape, and he had sat over a motor-bogie in the lead carriage with the tape in a briefcase at his feet. When it was popped onto the big Studer at EMI, he found that the first track had had its sound warped and twisted into bizarre, swooping fades and spiky, jagged peaks. Track two had all but vanished, and three and four were distant and muted – as though the highest frequencies had been wiped.

None of this would have mattered had this stereo

master merely been a copy. But it was the final product of hours of editing of the 32 track superimpositions. None of the originals had been kept, because the tape had been re-used over the weeks. There was no hope of repeating the sessions to re-record either. Kevin, Rory and Ian had gone their ways, one to join a band to tour Holland, the others starting on incidental music for a TV series. I had, to be honest, grown tired of the UFO CD/LP project and was spending more and more time planning how to exhibit my expanding collection of ephemera. Paragon scissors, Pedigree can-openers, Ewbank sweepers, Kilner jars, Ever Ready torches, Swan and Esterbrook pens, Bush Radios and Tilley lamps were more to the front of my mind than every flying saucer spotted between Vladivostok and Inverness.

The news that Jools had wrecked the work of weeks went down badly.

'Cretin!' cried Peter.

'Cuckoo!' said I.

'You should be locked up!'

Jools waved his hands wildly at us.

'Sweeties! Sweeties! Leave it to me! It'll be all right! Leave it to me!'

Peter and I did leave it to him. We had little idea what to do with the wretched remnants on the master tape. Back at Glenturret, we listened to the first track closely. The fades and peaks came regularly through until the end when they speeded up. The vocal line faded and peaked with the rest.

'Don't you think it's actually *better* than the original?' asked Jools, making the best of a bad job. 'It's more space-ship and weird, like – like the pulsing of an object in the sky. Well, dears, I'm going to record my own sweet voice over the top, with tons of echo, singing the vocal line all over again. Then I'm going to pulse the vol up on every fade and add a single piano note recorded backwards each time I pulse – the whole lot through the graphic equaliser, of course. I'll do it on a 4-track, so it's separate from the master, and if you two don't like it, we can change it.'

So, that's what we did; and I added the sound of a bottle being blown every third pulse in time with the reversed piano; not with every fourth – that third percussive note created a new, at odds tempo, annoying on one level, but arresting too. We played the whole thing back, and Jools basked in the knowledge that he had been right. The first track was much, much better than the first recording.

'It makes *Good Vibrations* sound like Benny Hill!' cried Jools, tickled pink by his own cleverness (and showing his age by those comparisons). I could just hear him in the future, impressing some new recruit at Abbey Road: 'Oh, yes, ducky. I could see it was useless – I mean useless, dear! So I took it for a ride on the tube to doctor it. What, sweetheart! You don't *know* about tube trains and recording tape? Well, let me tell you, it was lucky I knew all about it! Blah, blah, blah, sweetie…..'

Peter poked a finger into Jools' ribs.

'OK, Mr Genius. What about the other three tracks? One's just a hiss. Try blowing a bottle over that.'

'I said, leave it to me!' shrilled the master.

So came two of Jools' most pragmatic of expedients, and Peter and I had to admit to a tiny flicker of admiration. To sort the problem of tracks 2 and 3, he took a number from further on in the CD – one that had not been mastered for a trip to EMI, and was still in 32-track mode, unedited. Then he phased it slightly and lowered the tape take-up speed onto the 4 track machine. Over this he and I put some bongos and a tambourine – very far forward and very bright. A reggae-ish flavour emerged. Something had to be done about the vocal line. There was stray backing vocal on the master (a girl group had come from Manchester to do this on several numbers), but it was now too slow and sounded like Lee Marvin affected by mongolism.

'But the dominant chords are all there, surely?' said Jools, picking them out on a keyboard. 'So why not add an instrumental line, down an octave, superimposed on the girls. Ping! A new track. No one will notice it's another one slowed down, and even if they do, so what? Variations on a theme, sweeties.' And, as if to prove his point, he took the very same track *again* and reversed some of the mix on the 32-track master and added a strange, wailing electronic line of vowel sounds. ('Like a whale calling, duckies. Very ecological.') Amusingly, a year later, one of his beloved *Star Trek* movies, *The Voyage Home,* about an entity in space calling to lost earth whales, featured just such sounds. Too late for us to capitalise on it, though.

So we now had three tracks recovered. The fourth had more or less gone. Peter suggested leaving it out, but Jools objected that the CD would then be too short. We had no more new material. Peter had been musing broodingly during our discussion of what to do with the gap and then grinned.

'Do either of you remember The West Coast Pop Art Experimental Band?' he asked. Jools had heard of them; I hadn't. 'Well, on one of their LPs in the late 'sixties they had a track called *Anniversary of World War Three*, and you know what? It was absolutely silent.'

'So?'

'Brilliant idea – but so?'

'So, we fill up the space on our CD with silence. Absolute. Where track four would have been. All we need is a title.'

In the end after about twenty-five attempts, we settled on *Beyond the Asteroid Strike.*

We then edited the whole of the melange – the recovered stuff and what we had already – onto a final 4 track master-tape and boxed it ready for manufacture into CD and vinyl. *Flying Saucers Have Landed* by Aliens was complete.

This was why flying saucers were on our minds when Jools waved the newspaper under our noses.

'See what it says here,' he gibbered, poking at the article with his pointed nail. 'Over four hundred sightings have been reported in the Warminster area since 1970. We must go! We're bound to see at least one.'

Jools, I must tell you, professed to believe in the existence of UFOs from other worlds and had swallowed every word of Erich Von Daniken's *Chariots of the Gods,* which had made a great impact in the UK in the 'seventies.

'We could go for a giggle,' said I, 'but it's a long way from here. Can anyone just turn up?'

'No,' said Peter, who had been peering at the article, 'it's not open to the public. But are *we* the public? We will go as members of the press, of course. I'll get us credentials.'

'Oh, yeah? Where from? *The Guardian*? *The*

Times?'

'*Flying Saucer Review.*'

'What!'

'I'm sure I've heard of them. I'll see what I come up with.'

A few days later, Peter slit open a brown envelope and three round little badges dropped out. They read: "PRESS. *Flying Saucer Review.* ADMIT TO PASS." He had done some homework and found out that this venerable rag was delighted that he had volunteered to cover the event. He had to agree to give the editor a 1000 word summary of what had happened on return. Payment for this was to be six free copies of *Flying Saucer Review.*

On a damp, foggy evening in November the three of us sat in the bar of The Old Bell Hotel in Warminster, tanking ourselves up before the long night began. Jools, who had had jaundice a couple of years back and should have gone easy on alcohol, was pushing back lager and lime and had gone a peculiar yellow. Peter drank Scotch and gurgled to himself on a greasy sofa. I decided to go to the reception desk and ask the girl the best way to the Great Ridge. As I caught her eye and was about to speak, I was shouldered out of the way and a clear, hard voice said,

'Is the table ready for my crew and me?'

I looked at the speaker. Tough, glossy, early '80s

executive-woman with a firm jaw. *Crew*, she'd said. Crew? Not a boat's crew, surely? Film, perhaps? Television? TV! I clutched at the desk.

'Er, excuse me,' I began, forcing my voice to a deep, impressive bass, 'did I happen to hear you mention the word "crew" a moment ago?'

She turned and looked at me, as if from a great height.

'Yaas,' she drawled distantly, and then turned back, instantly dismissing me from mind, as I could see.

'You mean TV crew, of course?' I asked.

'Yaas. BBC Roving Eye team, actually.'

Roving Eye! I was impressed, and could barely keep a quiver out of my voice as I asked,

'Are you......er......you're not by any chance covering the – the flying saucer hunt on the Great Ridge, are you?'

'Actually, we are. Yaas.' Her drawl had become more distant, and I could sense that she was about to make an escape from me, so I hurried on,

'Well, I'm reporting the event for an international publication…..' (And here I had the sudden inspiration to add academic respectability to my name)….. 'I am Professor Anthony Crepwright.'

She gazed at me. I think I hoped in a wild moment of madness that she might say, 'Not *the* Professor Crepwright…..' but she didn't.

'You may have read my book,' I continued. 'It's a study of extra-terrestrial intervention in pre-history.' I was pleased with that sudden inspiration – it seemed so right, so believable.

'Oh. Oh, no, I'm afraid not,' she said, turning to face me for the first time, now that she understood I wasn't just any old Joe off the street. Her voice had a completely different note in it. It had gone from icy drawl to cooing turtledove in six words.

'I am with my colleagues,' I continued, 'Doctor Buchan and Doctor Farthingale.' (I couldn't bring myself to raise Peter or Jools to my status of professor). 'We are researching these recent sightings.'

'Oh, how *rude* of me,' she simpered. 'I'm Cheryl Haynes, BBC. How nice to meet you.' She paused fractionally. 'Would you and your colleagues like to give us an interview?'

I could hardly believe it. I know Warhol pointed out that everybody on the planet would eventually have their few minutes on TV, but I hadn't expected mine to come about as easily or as soon as this. I almost burst into a laugh as she stared reverently at me. I tried to look like a busy international expert on extra-terrestrial intervention in pre-history.

'Interview, hm? Well, I do not normally give interviews to the populist media, and we shall be busy with the specialist press, of course, but, yes,

yes, I think we can fit you in.'

'Oh, thank you! Thank you!' she gabbled. 'We are bringing a mobile studio up on to the Ridge at ten o'clock. Come to the producer's van whenever you like.'

I rushed like a *scirocco* back to the bar. There, in a corner, were the other two "experts", both gurgling, one very yellow. I grabbed at them.

'Wake up, you drunken pigs!' I hooted, shaking Jools until the lager and lime frothed in the glass. 'We're on TV!'

They goggled at me. I explained. They cried,

'You're insane!'

'What do we know about UFOs?'

'What does *anyone* know about UFOs?' I retorted.

And so the long night began. Every weirdo in the UK had been drawn to The Great Ridge by the modest publicity attending this event, and there were cameras and sound recorders; there was ITN News, filming something for their light spot at the end, and, astonishingly, CBS and Fox from America. Peter and Jools and I flew from one to the other, posing, with outstretched hands pointing at the skies for the cameras. Jools' camp squeals rang out over the rounded hills.

At ten o'clock, as the fog grew very dense, a roaring of diesel engines was heard and the BBC studio and support vehicles came ponderously up the muddy track which had once been the Roman road from Old Sarum to Monkton Deverill. Before long a generator was throbbing, and arc lights were set up. I introduced Peter and Jools to Miss Haynes. She blinked rapidly as Jools slapped her roguishly on the arm and hissed,

'What I could tell *you* about spacemen!

We were ushered into the studio van and were prepared for our interviews. Our inquisitor was a long drink of water called Jeremy Ridpath, whose face I recognised, having seen him on current affairs programmes. He spoke to us separately on camera. We were given plenty of time to speak. I thought initially that they wanted a lot of material, and had the night before them, but soon realised that Ridpath had little talent for shutting people up. The fear I had had about not being able to utter more than a sentence or two evaporated under the lights. I talked until my video tape ran out. My subject was "Propulsion of extra-terrestrial craft by the generative forces inherent in colour". Having explained that at current rocket speeds a NASA ship bound for the nearest star in our galaxy, Proxima Centauri, four light years away, would have had to have left earth at the time of Henry VIII, (and I've since discovered that it would be a lot further back than that), I moved on to the point that until we grow out of the "burning dead trees" era of fossil fuel dependency, we would never get beyond the solar system. UFOs from other worlds, however, had explored "colour propulsion". They make no noise because this power harnesses the energy that is present as one colour of the spectrum merges into another. This piffle flowed so copiously that I almost came to believe what I was saying, and grew combative when Jeremy Ridpath sought to contradict me over some little point about gamma rays.

Peter adopted a broad (and to my ears unconvincing) Welsh accent and spoke of his childhood experiences in the hills above Portmadoc when he had "been entranced, look you, by the blue pyramids which rode like spirits in the heavens above my rude cot." Why he couldn't have adopted a *Scots* accent and set his tale in the Ochils at Startmont where he was brought up, and thus have sounded more believable, I don't know; nor did he. 'I was rat-arsed, I suppose,' he said later.

Jools drooled about archaeological digs he had been on in Mexico and Algiers, at which indubitable proof of visitations from other galaxies had been found. The slur induced by many lagers-and-lime and his yellow, jaundiced tinge, seemed to give his words a Buddha-like and ascetic power.

Jeremy Ridpath interviewed about thirty people

that night, some for a short time, some (probably because he couldn't stop them) for twenty minutes. His interviewees included a vicar from Buxton who had had visitations to his rectory of tiny, disc-like craft, and a twitchy man with a strong West Country accent and huge sideburns, who claimed that he'd been taken in a saucer to a planet in the galaxy of Andromeda, had married an Andromedan princess, had learnt their language, and had been returned to Earth (near Honiton) as ambassador to all Earth's peoples. Much of his interview consisted of phrases like: "Sgraptic glopplblilp nardh" and "Jer nardin prongzopflub."

In all the excitement we had rather forgotten the flying saucers we were supposed to be watching for; but – to condense the night's events – the fog had closed down solidly by one in the morning, and we couldn't have seen a UFO if it had landed on the BBC van's roof. At five o'clock, frozen and starving, we three set off to drive back up the A303 to London. Over brekker in a Little Chef, we agreed that we would hear no more about the Roving Eye report and its UFOs. Peter and I went back to Glenturret, and Jools dropped out of sight for three weeks. He was going to make the contacts necessary for pushing our CD/LP, he told us.

During this time a letter arrived from the BBC. It was addressed to me.

Dear Professor Crepwright, (it read),

I write to inform you that the programme for which you gave an interview during its OB recording is due to be screened in the spring. Prior to this, I invite you and Doctor Buchan to the above address on Monday, 11th February 1985 at 5pm to take part in the recording of a studio discussion which will supplement the existing material. I extend an invitation to Dr Farthingale to join the studio audience. Please let me know if you are able to take part by returning the slip sent with this letter. When you arrive, kindly present the enclosed cards to the staff at reception at or around 3pm in order that there is time for make-up and refreshments before recording begins.

It was signed by Cheryl Haynes, siren of the hotel foyer at Warminster. I shoved it over to Peter.

'Bloody Nora!' he gasped. 'This is insane! Someone's bound to find us out.'

'They haven't yet,' I replied.

'But they might if we really do appear on telly.'

'How?'

How indeed? Considering the number of politicians and CEOs who aren't found out year after year, I thought we'd have a good chance of coming over as experts in the field. It was extraordinary that no one had asked us for proof, but I reasoned that if we hadn't been asked on the first occasion, we were unlikely to be called to account on subsequent occasions. It was an interesting reminder – particularly to one who had been teaching for some years – of the uselessness of qualifications once you've got them. Once you're in the system, you are in. Most people are honest, unsuspecting and, more important, fundamentally incurious (because more interested in themselves), and take people as they find them. I knew this from what Mike had done in his rise and rise in real estate in the US. While Jools, Peter and I were mucking about with our flying saucer recording, Mike was using the Jesuit church in New York as his business address, satisfying the American authorities that he had the status of an employer, rather than a seeker of work, and was scooping in cash as quickly as I was losing it.

Jools, incidentally, was as mad as a weasel that he hadn't been asked to contribute to the programme but had been relegated to the audience. I couldn't help being pleased. Peter boomed in Welsh, I baffled with bull about gamma rays, and the knowledge that that dummy Jools, that maniac Jools, that incompetent, dishonest, greedy, vain, reckless queen was left out spurred me to even greater levels of verbose obscurantism.

You may have noticed a teeny bit of anti-Jools sentiment creeping into that last paragraph. If so, you have noticed correctly. By the time of that BBC final recording at the television centre, Jools and I were barely on speaking terms.

Three weeks after Cheryl Haynes's letter came another – much more peculiar and disturbing. It was from Sugden's in London. This outfit, whose huge warehouse can be glimpsed behind the chimney pots off Seven Dials and whose entrance is so modest and so contradictory to the great spaces which lie behind it, was our distributor to the record shops of the country. Sugden's, since 1947, have distributed countless millions of discs as far asunder as Smetana's *"Ma Vlast"* with The Bournemouth Symphony Orchestra and *"Aston Villa Heroes Sing Songs From The Terraces"*.

Their surprising letter congratulated us on our forthcoming TV appearance, confirmed that Mr Julius Farthingale's requirements had been undertaken as per instructions, informed us that Denon in Japan had pressed the CDs and that the cost of each, trade, was to be £4.91 including jewel-case and full colour front and back covers and interior details (to be confirmed), that 150,000 pressings had arrived from Japan following the sell-out of the original 20,000 LPs, and reminded us that settlement of the enclosed account for manufacture, storage and distribution would oblige. It was signed by Benjamin Moshe himself – that well-connected entrepreneur who had made so many millions since the craze for the pop 78 had begun back in Bill Haley's day.

'What d'you make of this then?' I said, chucking it over to Peter. He peered through it with bulging eyes.

'Is it some sort of joke? I don't suppose Sugden's have sent this at all. It's one of Jools' silly japes.'

'But what's all this about the TV appearance? Roving Eye hasn't screened us yet, if it ever will, and what's that got to do with the record anyway?'

Even as I spoke, fiddling with the letter, I glanced at the "settlement of account" invoice clipped on to it. The invoice for Denon's production (outsourced by Sugden's on behalf of our independent record label Ozymandias because, as yet, no British company was producing CDs) of 150,000 discs was huge.

'You don't mean – assuming the letter isn't a joke – that we owe Sugden's *money*?' gasped Peter. He really could be extraordinarily dense at times. 'A hundred and fifty thousand CDs at five quid each? But that's over half a million pounds!'

No amount of looking would make clearer what this cryptic communication meant. Obviously, since it seemed that Jools was in the know, the next thing to do would be to wait for him to return and throw light on it all. Peter, slow to grasp the point at first, but quick to reach hysteria once he had grasped it, was all for ringing Sugden's straight away, until I pointed out that it was Saturday and they would be closed, and that Jools was supposed to be back on Sunday night.

Sunday night. Peter in ferment, me strangely calm, Jools a curious mixture of defiance and sheepishness, and a shadow hanging over Glenturret.

You hardly need to have it explained that that imbecile, that fumbling, dishonest con-artist Jools had RUINED us. On the strength of our possible forthcoming appearance on a TV documentary about UFO freaks, Jools had had requested Sugden to release the whole of the original 20,000 LPs (manufactured in the UK) to him, purchasing them himself with our money, and had arranged with them the swift manufacture of CDs on the premise that, with 20,000 notionally sold, we would be somewhere in the top 50 LP chart.

We were stunned into silence as he explained that *Flying Saucers Have Landed* was a sure-fire hit and needed coaxing up the LP/CD charts by what he called "primary source investment" – that is, buying up your own stock and causing an artificial rush of demand, and securing (on that basis of 20,000 sales) automatic air-play of the title track on Radio 1, and possible exposure on The Old Grey Whistle Test on BBC2 TV. All this before the public had bought a single copy. He had prepared press-releases to DJs in which Aliens' TV appearance was specifically mentioned (and inducements to play were suggested). A sorry tale of chicanery and payola.

You might think – so what? This had happened all the time in the '60s and '70s. What was new about the pop music industry fixing sales and buying success? Fine, if you have the money, and if you are not dealing with Sugden's. Peter and I turned, like wolves, on Jools.

'How could you do it without even *asking* us?' shouted Peter.

'Oh, you two! You're a couple of Aunt Hildas! You're so wet, you could sail a regatta on you!' squealed Jools, going on the offensive at our combined attack.

'It wasn't *your* money!' I cried, thinking of Grandpa's legacy.

'Look, sweetie, I *know* this business. Just leave it all to me.'

That phrase again: Leave it all to me!

The crash wasn't long in coming. We could not immediately pay Sugden's for the Denon CDs, so there was a nasty legal wrangle which took more than two years to sort out, though the debts were finally cleared. The CD did not stampede to the top of the album charts because, of course, there was no TV promotion for it. We were left, eventually, with over 70,000 CDs and 17,600 LPs of *Flying Saucers have Landed* in boxes in the garages at Glenturret, where they remained to the end. Well over a quarter of a million of Grandpa's money was lost, and most of what we had made as a studio. Jools' absurd gamble having failed, we parted ways. My interest in the Ozymandias label, never more than tepid, evaporated completely. Jools returned to London, and later emigrated to the USA. The last I heard of the stupid git was that he had opened a dog-manicuring parlour in Miami.

As 1985 trickled towards 1986, the studio was dismantled, the equipment sold off, and Glenturret underwent the last of its metamorphoses. I thought that all disasters were now behind us and calm, bright days in my ever-growing museum, with its torrent of summer visitors, lay ahead – my brain painting it as a carpet of bright colours stretching into infinity.

The Roving Eye report? It did come off after all. Peter and I, and Mike, back to see us before moving out to California from New York, and two other pals, sat round my old Bush black and white TV at Glenturret and watched the "in-depth" investigation. First man on was Peter, screeching in his corny Welsh accent about "purple pyramids over the mountains behind Capel Curig, look you", then the loony clergyman, who got a good few minutes, then the husband of the Andromedan princess. I had the longest exposure of all, and am now convinced that UFOs *do* propel themselves by the inherent power available at the boundaries of the spectral colours. And joy of joys – Jools was cut completely. The programme ended with Jeremy Ridpath gazing at the camera like a fish in a bowl and intoning solemnly: "You can be sure that, although you might never have seen one, flying saucers *have* landed." All rather ironic.

THE LOSS OF GLENTURRET

When I began to jot down what Peter calls "Crepwright's Codswallop" I didn't think anyone else would be reading it any time soon. I had children or grand-children in mind – not mine, of course, but Mike's perhaps. And I had wanted to end this portrait of the high points in Glenturret's later existence as I always thought I would end my own time – at peace, serene, and with a life's work all around me. I imagined that, on what Grandpa's old solicitor used to call "The Sad Day of Final Reckoning" I should be leaning nonchalantly against some pinky-gold buttress of cloud having a surprisingly informal conversation with God.

Mind you, I've always thought God would be rather a snubber. I recall meeting an old Stonyhurst man at a dinner to which Peter had invited me. It was the week after the famous gales in 1987. "Dweadful business, the gales," said this man. "Oh, quite," I replied, "and worst of all in the South-East. My aunt in Putney lost a lovely cherry tree and an apple in her garden. Did they affect you at all?" The Stonyhurst man gazed at me. "No, no," he drawled. "But ma cousin, the duke, lorst five hundwed orf his estate in Sussex." That is what I think God would be like; all too ready to put one down. All that terrific omniscience and omnipotence, and knowing Adam

and Eve and the angel Gabriel would make a snub or
two almost inevitable.

GOD: So what were you doing at the turn of the
last century, my son?

ME: Well, God, I was preserving the past in a
house I more or less inherited. I held back the
obliterating molars of time for quite a while,
M'Lord, keeping and treasuring ordinary domestic
things. Not great works of art, because, as you know,
after the studios crashed I didn't have that sort of
money, but everyday things like radios, biscuit tins,
toasters, toys – the things by which people really
measure the passing of the years.

GOD: You'll never believe what I saw outside
The Athenaeum Club! The Duchess of Argyll eating
ice-cream from a cone!

ME: *I* eat ice-cream in the street.

GOD: Well, that's *hardly* a comparison, it it?

ME: Why didn't you give me a chance to
complete my work, God?

GOD: No, I didn't give you much of a chance,
did I, my poor boy?

ME: Was it because, as Hamlet says, "there's a
Divinity that shapes our ends, rough-hew them how
we will"?

GOD: Precisely. You must see it as a lesson not
to go around doing so much *planning*. Not to put too

much reliance on material things. I had to do exactly the same to your brother, you know.

Up to just before the bitter end, my outlook on life had been sunny. Optimism, fun, japes, *joie de vivre:* these had characterised my existence. I have never been seriously ill, have enjoyed almost all meals, have not sampled an hallucinogenic drug – even in the '70s – and have escaped addiction, have not come out at the short end of a messy divorce, have inherited a lot of money, done one noble and useful job (teaching) and one glam and creative one (music production). My great love of the immediate past has been consummated by my crusade of the collection of minutiae, by my museum at Glenturret. I have done what I wanted to do, have lived in a time of peace in one of the most well-ordered and well-intentioned of democracies; have travelled freely in the free world and, upon return, wallowed in the delights of a place in which I had always wanted to live. Not a cloud in the sky.

Well, I should have heeded those nameless shadows which had already crept over the surface of my life: demons, death, scandal, greed, vanity, folly, loss and blindness to consequence. Nothing is causeless, or fails to have its seed-time in your own actions, I have discovered.

Remember the name Hector McAird? I had seen him only once since our childhood – at the reading of our grandfather's will. In our boyhood days, as the chauffeur's son, he was constantly being reminded by us of his status as servant, as you may recall – and that was because he asked for all he got, the little creep.

I vividly recall the morning he re-appeared. I was cleaning out clinker from the locomotive *Topsy*. Peter stood on one of the irregular tracks behind the engine; the sun was warm and sent up odours of tar and resin; behind us, uncoupled, were six tiny carriages, two of them bought from The Ravenglass and Eskdale railway in Cumbria and restored – their bright malachite green and coachwork varnish twinkling back beams which filtered through the pines. An equally painstakingly restored Morris Minor pick-up was backed into position near the loco's cab. In it a sack of coal waited transhipment into *Topsy's* bunker.

While Peter waited to load up, I pulled the stoking-iron through the fire-grate to dislodge remaining slag. I was dusty and oily, yet utterly absorbed, filled with that contentment which used to come over me when, as a boy in the mid '60s, I sat in the Odeon cinema, Edgware Road, watching a Western in technicolour and thought of the train set in my bedroom, and the warmth of bed and the happiness of that glow under the door, and breakfast, crisp-skinned sausages, perhaps, to come in the sunshiny morning of autumn.

Oh, and Mike was back from America, investing in a Brit TV project, and I was seeing him again after our many years apart. So all was bliss.

Hector arrived in a small brown Nissan, his head shiny with unfashionable Brylcreem, his eyes pebbly behind steel-rimmed specs.

'Hector! Well, well! You haven't changed a bit.' I said. 'How *are* you? It's been quite a few years, hasn't it? Come in. Come in.'

I found myself twittering a little, as I do in the presence of silent, pebbly-eyed people.

'Aye, well, I think I must have changed a certain amount,' said Hector. 'Can we talk aboot a wee matter of business?' he added, coming immediately to brass tacks, and ignoring Peter, who was stacking the engine's tools and empty sacking in the pick-up.

'Oh, er, yes. Yes. Come up to the house and have some coffee. I – I'll just get out of these clothes.'

Hector looked fastidiously at the oily rags in which I had been tending to *Topsy* and moved back a foot, obviously fearful of smuts. He was dressed in a light grey suit and sported a blue tie with a rather civic looking coat of arms on it. He carried a thin briefcase. For someone who had been brought up in the countryside, he had a very provincial townee look about him.

'I thought I'd call on you ma'sel, rather than let you get a wee letter,' said he mysteriously as we went in.

'Make yourself at home,' I said, ushering him through the baize door into the private part of the building. 'I'm just going upstairs. I'll be back in a few moments.'

I left him standing in the middle of our sitting-room gazing, disapprovingly I thought, around him. Peter came in from the sunlight and joined me in the hall.

'What's he doing here? Talk about the bad penny. Remember how he sneaked to your grandfather about that Kinbuck station business? All that sneering about being "wee custards". God, he was a prat, that boy.'

'Sssh. He's waiting in the sitting-room. He says he's come about business. I wonder what on earth that is. Can you get some coffee or tea going? I'll be down in a couple of minutes.'

Five minutes later I was back with Hector. He was still standing in the middle of the room, frowning.

'Do sit down,' I said. He perched on the edge of a chair. Peter came in with a tray. He had made coffee and found a cake. He began to pour.

'Sugar?' said Peter.

'I havena taken it these twenty years,' muttered Hector, bringing into view a folder from his briefcase.

'Ah, you want to get down to business,' said I. 'But have a bit of cake first. And can I get you something a bit stronger than coffee?'

'I don't partake before seven o'clock,' said Hector.

'I can see this isn't a social call. Let's get down to discussing why you came, if you want to.'

Hector opened his folder and spread out the contents on the side table. Among the papers was a map of the area with heavy black lines running through it. Hector picked it up and handed it silently to me. He cleared his throat.

'This is no' easy for me to have to tell you this,' he started. As he began to speak I had a sudden breathtakingly happy mental picture, as in a dream, of three little boys running down a railway embankment among wild flowers to see a streamlined green locomotive under a plume of white smoke beginning to appear round a curve. For a moment or two I was lost in the rapture of that image, and Hector's voice seemed to fade into birdsong. Nothing remained but blue skies, a green slope, white steam and shining boyish faces. I pulled myself together and forced myself to listen. A very odd thing happened. As the vision faded I felt a hot pricking of tears behind my eyes.

'......Aye, no' easy at all, but for old times' sake I felt I couldna just let you get the news in an official letter. It was the least I could do tae put you in the picture.'

I hadn't the faintest idea what he was talking about. Peter, who had taken the map, cried sharply,

'Hey! These black lines run right through Glenturret!'

'I know they do,' said Hector. 'I'll explain.' He held his pale hand out for the map and Peter returned it. Hector placed the map on his knees and went on, 'You'll know, perhaps, that I'm chief planning officer for transport at the Scottish Development Department?'

He paused. Peter and I hadn't known – why should we have done?

'Ma responsibility,' continued Hector sonorously, 'is for overall rail and road planning into the middle of the twenty-first century, and this map is a projection of preferred routes for a major project due to start next year. You'll have been following developments on the High Speed railway plans, of course?'

We nodded. Peter and I each had a natural railway-fancier's interest. I had not, however, thought of the high speed spinal rail line, or HS2, as the problematic idea became known, as affecting me personally. One's interest in something planned for execution many miles away is rather disconnected – like reading a report on the latest Mars explorer.

'You see,' resumed Hector, 'the aim is to join the whole of our rail network up with the continent, but there are problems about running continental rolling-stock past London because, apart from parts of the old Western region, which has spacious loading gauges by virtue of being designed for Brunel's seven-foot broad gauge, the rest of the country is designed to a loading gauge laid down by Stephenson and his fellow engineers at the beginning of the nineteenth century. Every road bridge, footbridge and tunnel on the British system is too small to let continental rolling stock under it. French stock is 4.3 metres high and 2.6 wide, for example. D'you see ma drift? If goods in trans-shipment have to be unloaded at Folkestone or London and transferred to smaller wagons, the whole point of the tunnel as a means of replacing ferry ships is lost.'

'But I thought,' said I, 'that the network was going to begin the rebuilding of bridges and tunnels to allow stock to run through.'

'And I read,' chipped in Peter, ever knowledgeable about what was happening back then in the late '90s, 'That a new type of wagon was going to be designed to our loading gauge for use through to the continent and that imports and exports which involved travel on UK lines would use these special bits of stock.'

'Weel noo,' said Hector, shaking his shiny head. 'It's been realised that there are huge problems of marshalling to be considered. And remodelling every fixed structure on the network.....! It could take fifty years..... Let me come on tae the latest idea noo.'

I was about to ask what all this had to do with me and Glenturret, when Hector produced another sheet of paper from his case.

'Here is the latest plan from the Department of Transport. Its noo firmly agreed, that a spinal high-speed railway to continental loading gauge be built up the centre of the country from West London, via Birmingham, Manchester, Leeds and Carlisle up to Stirling and Aberdeen. It's part of a commitment of the government to bring more work tae the regions. At six points off it will be spurs to take freight. At the end of each spur will be marshalling yards, d'ye see? In fact the first freightliner intermodal terminal built since 1972 was opened a few years back at Grangetown near Middlesbrough, ye know, at the ICI Wilton complex. That is the model for the North-East's European traffic yard. D'ye see the way we're thinking? If no European freight and no businessmen can get quickly beyond

London, the rest of the UK will wither away. Every firm in Britain will want its set-up between Croydon and Folkestone – a nightmare for the folks down there, and appalling unemployment in the north. The other benefit is that it will curtail juggernaut use.'

Hector paused, no doubt for breath. I gazed at him, rather impressed by the rapid, succinct argument. I peered at the map.

'What does "intermodal" mean in this context?' I asked.

'It means one mode of transport links with another; ship to truck to rail to truck – and no handling, except in standard containers by machines. It's all part of thinking beyond oor old position vis-a-vis Europe – more hi-tech, if ye know what I mean.' He adjusted his glasses. 'So. Why am I telling you all this? I expect you're wondering aboot that. Well, let's turn back to the wee map. The termination for the line has got to be in one of the flat parts of Scotland, there must be good road links, it must be on the way to Aberdeen oil and yet not too far from the industrial corridor. In the end it was decided to put the marshalling yard here.'

He pointed to the map with a pen. Under its tip were the words "Glenturret Estate".

I couldn't speak.

'You see,' hurried on Hector, 'the land here is flat and immense, it runs adjacent to the A9, it's in a bowl between hills and the main Granite City line runs through it. It couldna be better placed. We reckon we'll need space for aboot 320 sixty-foot wagons at maximum, so that's near on a hundred and eighty acres of land. The connection with the rail network will be at wee Kinbuck station. Aye, ye remember the fun we had there as boys, I expect. And the central marshalling yard and container depot will be, well, will be *here*.' He gestured round him. 'I mean here – where we're sitting.'

I stared at him as though he alone were visible in an aurora of encircling darkness.

I found my voice.

'Who thought of the idea of putting the yard here?' I asked huskily.

'Och, weel,' said Hector, bridling modestly, 'it was me, actually.'

After the collapse of the studios, Peter and I had been left with just enough of Grandpa's money to prepare Glenturret for public opening, but not much else. Peter had decided to leave London and return home to Startmont. The Balcombe Street flat, which he had eventually bought from his landlords in the early '80s, had shot up so enormously in price, and he had received such a large sum for it when he sold up, that he was able to invest a convincing share into our partnership. It had been largely through his injection of cash that we had been able to put together Glenturret's main attraction – the light railway.

We had been discussing for ages the precise nature of the museum, and the idea of a nostalgia theme coincided with a popular vogue. Glenturret was not a distinguished enough building to be worth visiting in its own right – besides, Perthshire and Stirlingshire already had historical visitor attractions – Glamis Castle among many. I had been inspired by The Weald and Downland Museum at Amberley in Sussex, Peter by the recreation of Victorian life at Beamish and Ironbridge. After many trips to view living museums in other parts of the country, we could see the potential in our own part of the world; people would come to see my huge collection, but then needed something to do when they had finished looking and that something would need to attract children

At the end of weeks of discussion, we had come to the conclusion that what Glenturret needed was a narrow-gauge railway running through it.

What a labour the building of the line turned out to be. It is not until you lay track that you realise how undulating land is that you had thought flat. The firm we employed had to level the attractive slopes of grass which fell from the lawns to the Gothic folly and two ten feet deep cuttings were gouged into them, for the train had to make two return loops in order to lift itself from the stream back to the height of the drive. The bridging of the stream was a huge undertaking and our viaduct was the single most expensive item of the project; nearly a hundred concrete piles go down twenty feet to rock. Peter and I had been determined that the line should start at the house itself. I've always thought that the shiny brass buffer stops with their red crossbeam and sturdy black transoms, just outside the old library windows, were a fine sight. On the ride, we took visitors round to the back of the house, past the old squash courts, to the three sidings for rolling-stock – where Costigan's ill-fated kitchens had stood – and then away over the stream. After the coal bunkers and steel-clad shed for loco maintenance were completed, there came the inspections, health and safety tests, loco certificates, insurance and reams of paperwork. We had slaved to bring a railway to Glenturret. Oh, the irony of it, on that quiet morning which had started so well.

I came back from musing about the effort our great project had cost us to find that Hector and Peter were speaking. Hector's voice seemed to have a new thread of malice in it.

'So ye'll be thinking of trying tae appeal? Mebbe get up a wee petition from your visitors? Weel, I don't think it'll work. I'll tell you that noo. This site is the best we've got, an' I don't suppose an ugly barracks like this, wi' a funfair, or whatever it is, attached, is going to be missed. No one will think it worth preserving. Ah don't myself, I must admit.'

Peter shouted, 'Why the *hell* didn't you put in a word for us, Hector? You lived here as a child, damn it!'

'Mebbe I did. But so what? I didna own any part of it, as you and your friends were only too keen on pointing oot. I was the chauffeur's son, a servant you called me, as I recall. You were all *Master* Anthony and *Master* Peter and *Master* Michael and *Master* David and I was just Hector, the kid wi' the funny accent.'

'Oh, Hector, come on now! Children – well, you know what they're like!' I cried.

'Well, I know what you lot were like. And what have you done since? I might as well be plain. Sherwin-Lemond making arty-farty BBC2 programmes that no one watches. Your brother going off tae America to swindle folk in property deals. What use is that? An' you and your friend, acting like children still, sitting in this daft place playing with your toys and throwing away money that you didna even earn.'

'Look here,' said Peter. 'I don't know about the legal side of this. But it seems odd that a compulsory purchase order can just be slapped on a private estate without there being any leeway for appeal. In China, yes. But surely not in Britain. And, if I can say one more thing, I think you came here give us the bad news in person so you could gloat.'

'Ah'm no bandying words,' said Hector, standing up. 'You forget who I am.'

'Controller of Planning for Road and Rail Development in the devolved Scotland, you mean?' I said.

'McAird's funny wee pointy-headed son from over the garage,' snarled Peter.

There was a silence. Hector walked to the door.

'Ah'm going noo,' he said. 'Any appeal you might make is not going tae get very far. I have the last word on land-use appeals.'

After the frightful shock of Hector's news, Peter and I realised we would have to gear ourselves up to find out how to appeal. Peter plunged into the creation of a petition. The tail-end of autumn wasn't the best time, what with the season coming to an end and the days shortening, but we got a few hundred signatures from our visitors. Peter also enlisted the support of the local MP, Jamie Flynn, a gingery Scottish Nationalist who was evidently torn between a desire to see job creation in the area and a hatred of destruction initiated in Whitehall. Again, oddly, he had not previously heard of the Department of

Transport's far-reaching plans.

So, we continued the slow process of trying to get up a petition to save the museum while letters and phone calls shuttled to and fro. We had had a long discussion about setting up some sort of public appeal, but couldn't agree exactly how to pitch things – and I wondered who would be interested anyway. I really did come, slowly, to take it in that I was going to have to leave my beloved house. With no large sum of money saved, and my once huge inheritance gone, I saw that a compulsory purchase order was all I could look forward to. Peter observed me closely as the days slipped by and autumn drew in the night earlier and earlier. One evening he said, pouring a whisky,

'Tony, I have an idea – a linked idea.'

'What do you mean?'

'How far have we got towards saving the museum? Some signatures.'

'Yes.'

'Some letters sent out.'

'Right.'

'Some encouragement from Jamie – not that anyone has ever heard him utter a word in Parliament since his maiden speech, and he's been there three years.'

'Well, it's something.'

'No. It's sod all, when you think about it,'

growled Peter, ever the pessimist. 'Do you mind if we take a walk round the house while I explain my idea to you?'

'No. if you like.'

I used to like pottering round Glenturret when the crowds had gone. I never tired of my collection.

'Oh, Peter! What's going to happen to all this if we have to sell up?' I cried miserably, as we went upstairs.

'How much do you think we'd get through a compulsory purchase of house and land?' asked Peter, as we paused on the landing. 'It wouldn't be enough to put absolutely everything into storage, to rebuild and re-equip, to recreate all this, would it?'

'I just don't know. And where would we rebuild anyway? I don't want to run *any* old tourist attraction – that was never the point. All this,' and I swept my arm round in a gesture which took in the glassy dark cabinets around us, all the period rooms, all the outhouses, models, cars, lorries and trains, 'all this wouldn't be the same if it wasn't at Glenturret. *That's* the point, isn't it? This house is my *life*. All those years! All this stuff is part of me. I don't *want* it dispersed. I don't *want* it re-assembled somewhere else. I'd rather see it go up in flames than that.'

'*Rem acu tetigisti,* if you remember your Latin,' said Peter. 'You've hit the nail on the head. Few people have tetigistied the rem with a sharper acu'. His eyes were bright, and his head swayed against the dark gleams of the glass-fronted cabinets.

Now, I am going to come clean about exactly what we did. Immediately after it I said not a word, even to Mike. Not a word to anyone, in all these years. Now, of course, it doesn't matter anymore.

Peter and I were ascending the staircase to the "haunted" part of the house.

'Ta-ran-ta-ra!' he cried, whipping out a box of Swan Vestas matches. He took one and struck it. We hadn't put the lights on and the long Scottish evening was turning to night. The match flame flared, reflected in the gloss of many cabinets.

Peter dropped it, lighted, on the floor, where it spluttered and fizzled.

'Whoa! Careful!' I exclaimed, stamping on it.

'Why?' asked Peter.

'Eh?'

'Why be careful?' said Peter, striking another match.

The little yellow flame burned in the orbs of his eyes.

'Go on,' he murmured. 'Tell me about the insurance. All this stuff. What's it insured for?'

The match went out.

'Let's walk on,' cooed Peter.

Without speaking, we found that our footsteps had taken a turn into the strange curved corridor – leading to the haunted rooms of Glenturret, as I still called them, for they had an eerie resonance even into the 21st century.

We sat on the floor, at the spot where, years before, McKechnie and his minions had refused Grandpa's orders to proceed with their work.

'Let's talk about insurance premiums,' came Peter's voice from the blackness.

'Yes, let's.'

I felt my brain recede down a long, long tunnel and I became able to apprehend events only at a huge, spongy distance.

'It's way up there, isn't it? Way, way up.....' crooned Peter, lighting three matches together and throwing them a little way down the curved passage where piles of old magazines and papers were stacked against the wall awaiting sorting and display.

My voice replied, 'The premiums are E...NOR...MOUS.'

I took a match from his box and scratched it along the wall. I put the little flame to the edge of the matting and held it there.

I felt a thick, coiled, perverse excitement thrill me.

The flame caught. Smouldering matting made me cough for a moment.

'My greatest fear, with a collection like this,' I said, 'has been fire. The one thing I've never skimped on is insurance.'

Peter struck another match, and passed the box to me.

'The smoke is getting up my nose,' he said. 'Do you mind if I sit the other side of you?'

He crawled round me.

'You did claim once, didn't you?' he asked after a little while.

'Ah, yes, yes – that one time,' I murmured, 'when the snow melted. All that water.'

I struck a little posy of matches and tossed them up the curved passage. In my head was beating, with loud, plangent insistence, Wagner's funeral music from *Siegfried* – why I did not know. I found that everything – the graceful throw of my arm, the wheeling matches, the slowly eddying smoke and the hard curve of the wall around the circumferential segment of which I could not see – was moving in time to a vast rotating mass of sound in my head. I turned to Peter.

'Can you hear music?' I asked.

'Yes. Oh, yes,' he sighed.

'Can you see a glow?' I asked.

'I can,' he replied. 'I do believe I can. But you were saying....?'

'Um – er – I did claim once. Did claim..... once.

No one came to look at the damage. It was the transformer and generator – all under water, remember? They paid up imm…ed…iate…ly.'

We sat side by side in the haunted corridor with our backs against the convex wall. We could not see round the curve. Precisely this had disturbed me so much as a child: not being able to see what was hidden by it.

We had thrown many matches down there though, and could hear that a crackling was going on, and rolling smoke from burning paper and matting was making our eyes and noses run.

'What a good job they weren't making us install smoke detectors until next year, eh?' Peter laughed.

'There's nothing like a nose for detecting fire,' I replied. 'I can smell burning.'

'I like sitting on the floor,' said Peter. 'I don't often do it these days.'

'The air is fresher near the floor because the smoke and hot air rises. That's what The Boiler used to tell us during fire drill, remember?'

We moved a little way down the passage towards the landing and leant against the wall again. Ahead of us, and round the corner, the haunted corridor began to take hold of its fire. The moving red and orange flare was comforting, like the nursery fireplace, and disturbing, like a dream of Hell.

Some time passed. I realised that most of the short

Scottish night had passed unnoticed across our entranced minds – rotating as the surface of an LP used to rotate, when lit fitfully by candlelight.

Eventually, Peter said, 'I think we ought to leave.'

I couldn't hear him very well because of the booming sound from the other end of the corridor.

'What?'

'We ought to leave!' he shouted in my ear. I nodded and stood up. I was shaky and perspiration made my shirt stick to me. With surprise I discovered that I was dreadfully hot.

We went downstairs. The booming was deafening above us.

'What about documents?' I cried.

'Got 'em,' grinned Peter, patting a bulky briefcase. 'Rescued what we need from the tin box before the night began.'

'Oughtn't we to ring the fire-brigade?'

'Mm. You mean, not as us, but as an anxious wayfarer who spotted smoke? Assuming he had come a long way up the drive to do so.'

'I see what you're getting at.' Insurance claimants need to be absent during their fires.

'Yup. Not much point, is there? And it can't come from this number, now can it? Forget the fire brigade. Now Mike's around I think we should be in London, seeing him, and knowing nothing of the terrible conflagration. Look, why don't you choose something to take as a souvenir? I'm getting the Cresta round to the door – that's what I'd like to keep.'

With the cannoning of fire above and behind me, I opened the railway room door. I tried to switch on the lights, but they didn't work. Some wiring must have got burnt through. I pulled back the heavy velvet drapes which kept sunlight off the layout, and the pale dawn came pinkly in.

There was that perfect, unchanging world over which I had hung enthralled for so many hours. I had expected to feel an agony of indecision when trying to select a single memento of my lifetime's collection. But no, there was no agony, no indecision. Only one item could be chosen. For a second or two I panicked because I couldn't see it anywhere on the running lines, or in the sidings that stretched away into the distance. It seemed intolerable to leave the burning house without it, but then my eye was caught by its bulky green body.

There, at the head of a long train of maroon Hornby-Dublo coaches was *Crepello,* my grandfather's Christmas present from all those years ago.

I had to stretch right over and across a station to get at it, and in doing so I knocked over a model cinema and part of a train of coal wagons. It didn't seem to matter, as it would have mattered yesterday.

I took hold of *Crepello* gingerly and lovingly. I remember my father's words when first we had taken it from its box: "Yes, it's a good weight." What a mileage the little engine had done over the years, and how clean and perfect were its paint and wheels.

I looked round for a box to put it in. There was nothing to hand, so I placed it in the pocket of my leather jacket and went back out into the hall.

God! What a row the fire was making, and how difficult it was to see in the billowing smoke. The daylight led me to the front door which Peter had left open. Fumes rolled through it out into the pearly morning.

'Have you got something?' came Peter's voice. I patted my pocket.

'Yes. *Crepello*. It's in here?'

'What! A diesel locomotive? Not the Trix *Scotsman?*'

'No contest. This was the first thing I ever got from Glenturret.'

'The phone's still working. We had a peculiar voice message from Jamie about ten minutes ago.'

'This early? What, from London? Why? What had he got to say?'

There was a sudden extremely loud bang and a great tongue of fire burst from two upper windows at once, sending glass and stone fragments down near us in a shower. Peter grabbed my arm and we went round the rhododendrons on to the drive. There was the first car in Glenturret's collection, the fragile, flashy, American-looking Vauxhall Cresta. The six cylinder motor was purring.

'Jump in,' said Peter. 'This is our getaway vehicle.'

I got in and took *Crepello* from my pocket and popped it into the glove compartment. Peter sank into the driving-seat and selected 'Drive'. The car moved off down the drive, the tyres scrunching the gravel.

After a hundred yards Peter stopped, and we looked back.

How Glenturret burned!

'Jamie left his message from his London flat. He sounded in rather a state,' muttered Peter. 'He told us to come and see him at the Commons next week if we could. Apparently there isn't a Hector McAird with the Scottish road and rail doo-dah at all.'

'What do you mean?' I said, dragging my eyes away from Glenturret's fiery façade. What a magnificent end had come to the old house! It burned, mournful and imposing in the dawn, larger than the largest funeral pyre, volcanic in its fury, and from its upper windows came huge flames reaching up to the clear sky.

'They've never heard of Hector McAird. They've

not heard of a plan for a spinal high-speed railway up into Scotland either. If you're interested, the motorways are going to handle the bulk of freight and road vehicles are going to have their permitted weights upped to take full-size containers, and while a think-tank *is* in session discussing more high-speed UK lines, it's not expected that anything will come of it until about 2035. Jamie finished his message by saying there was no plan to build a marshalling yard at Kinbuck or here. Funny, isn't it?'

I heard what he said, of course, but there were too many implications behind the information, so I parcelled it away for dealing with later. In the marvellous morning air, in the Scottish autumn, I felt an anaesthetised happiness. What had been done was done.

'Oh, and I've got this,' said Peter, fishing out a pile of paper from his briefcase and dumping it on my lap. He drove on towards the A9 while I flicked through the lined pages. It was the first, hand-written draft of what you have been reading.

'God Almighty! I haven't looked at this stuff for ages! I'd forgotten all about it.'

'Couldn't let it go up in flames.'

'No one will want to read it. I only wrote it for myself.'

And part of my mind murmured to itself: Well, it's all that is left to take on through the 21st century.

'You'd be surprised,' went on Peter. 'I can think of a few people who might find it illuminating.' (He couldn't have imagined that it would sit in a drawer until only last year – but I hope he was right and that you have thought it worth reading.) 'Hang on, I must have a quick slash.'

He scrambled out of the Cresta and disappeared into one of the bushes nearby. I opened the straggly pages of my old journal again. I felt enormously pleased that Peter had thought to rescue it. Taking out a biro, I scribbled the postscript that is now at the beginning of this book. I had framed the question: "What led to my loss?" when there was a fumbling at the door and Peter sank down beside me, his zip not properly done up.

We crunched on down the drive. I looked back in a wing mirror and, as a rolling cloud of smoke cleared, I saw a squat brown shape near the wall of the old squash courts.

'Hey, Peter! Stop a mo. What's that? Can you reverse?'

We peered over our shoulders, and the Vauxhall went back so that I could see the shape.

'It's that brown Nissan that Hector McAird was driving, isn't it?' I said.

'What on *earth* is it doing here? Is Hector here too? Oh Jeez, you don't suppose he knows what we've done?'

Above the old gun-room a large segment of stone-work fell onto the drive, sending up a great plume of dust. Flames roared out from the house. A patter of stone fragments rattled on the Nissan's roof. We moved forward with a jerk and the brown shape vanished under the collapsing facade. With nothing left of my life except a pile of untidy paper on my lap, *Crepello* in the glove-box, and a strange, dull pain in my chest, I looked back no more.

THE END

The insurance company paid up. What we received will be my pension. I have coached A Level English Literature students from my home in London's Little Venice for a time now, and love it. I often wonder if I should have remained in teaching all along. Peter runs a vintage hi-fi shop in Eastbourne. We meet once a month; he comes up to Victoria or I go down and meet him at The Grand not far from his flat. Mike, unlike us two, doesn't have to work – the lucky bum. After his long mental illness, he never went back to America, having sickened of his life there. We now live together.

In case you wonder at the incompetence of the Scottish police and fire investigators, the examination of the building did not rule out deliberate arson at Glenturret, but, astonishingly to us, it was generally believed that Hector McAird, for obscure motives founded in childhood enmity, had torched the place. Peter and I were never suspected. Peter too thinks that Hector, by the oddest of coincidences, might well have been another firebug at work that night. After all, his car was found part-melted and covered in ash when the building had finally burnt to the ground. Peter is sure he died in the conflagration and his remains lay mingled in the ashes, undiscovered. He has never been heard of since.

As for me, I feel I have "risen on the stepping-stones of my dead self to higher things", as Tennyson puts it. The lessons I have taken on into this 21st century are these: do not look back, do not try to preserve the past, do not put emotional trust in possessions, do not lose the opportunity to seize love, do not be surprised by the unexpected, be aware that your early actions may have a long seed-time, relish the humour in as many events as you can, and accept loss as the inevitable consequence of being given life.

Anthony's brother Mike's story of his life in L A, New York and London during the making of a TV docu-drama, and the revenge taken by Mopsa, his concept-artist lover, is told as a framing narrative in the multi-part novel **"Shooting Europe"** *(2019, 692 pp) and on its own in* **"Together Forever?"** *(2020, 370 pp) Available online from Witley Press Bookshop & Amazon as paperbacks and on Kindle.*

Some appreciations of the hardback:

I liked the obvious relish in storytelling, the nostalgia for lost youth, the enthusiasms of the book and the humour of the style.
(Peter Hackett SJ, Editor, 'The Month')

The word that best describes the writing is vibrant. It's pulsating with life and energy; terrific!
(Dr P J Holt, author of 'God – the Case Against' & 'Malden College Tales')

I loved it. So many very funny stories.
(Rosina Dickens)

The book has been very well received in the West Midlands! The sound of hearty laughter shook the '60s tower block in which we are living!
(Denis Barry)

It's the best read I've had for twelve months! Thanks for bringing to life all my boyhood memories.
(Mike Herschel)

This sort of book is one of the better ways of recording recent history.
(Francis Pimentel-Pinto, BBC World Service)